The
Sexuality
Education
Challenge

The Sexuality Education Challenge

Promoting Healthy Sexuality in Young People

Judy C. Drolet, PhD, CHES, FASHA,
and Kay Clark, Editors

ETR ASSOCIATES
Santa Cruz, California
1994

ETR Associates (Education, Training and Research) is a nonprofit organization committed to fostering the health, well-being and cultural diversity of individuals, families, schools and communities. The publishing program of ETR Associates provides books and materials that empower young people and adults with the skills to make positive health choices. We invite health professionals to learn more about our high-quality publishing, training and research programs by contacting us at P.O. Box 1830, Santa Cruz, CA 95061-1830.

Printed in the United States of America
10 9 8 7 6 5 4 3 2 1

Cover design by Ann Smiley
Text design by Cliff Warner
Title No. 564

Library of Congress Cataloging-in-Publication Data

The Sexuality education challenge: promoting healthy sexuality in young people
    / Judy C. Drolet and Kay Clark, eds.
        p. cm.
    Includes bibliographical references.
    ISBN 1-56071-130-2
    1. Sex instruction—United States.   I. Drolet, Judy Catherine, 1951– .
II. Clark, Kay, 1942– .
HQ57.5.A3S4896   1994
613.9'07—dc20   93-43183

Contents

Sexuality Education in School Settings

What Educators Need: Preparation and Presentation

Diversity and Sexuality Education

Community Programs and Partnerships

Evaluation and Research

Appendixes

Preface

Few who work in the area of sexuality education at any level need to be reminded that the subject is sensitive. Providing young people with the information and skills to make careful, healthy choices about sexuality presents enormous and continuing challenges on many fronts. Many of these challenges derive from the fact that, as a society, we still are not entirely at ease with our sexuality. This reality is reflected overtly and covertly in our institutions: in the media, in our political and religious arenas, and in our schools.

Why should we teach young people about sexuality? So they will wait to have sexual intercourse until they are mature enough to make responsible decisions? So they won't become parents too early, with the attendant social and economic consequences to themselves and society? So they won't acquire sexually transmitted diseases that endanger their own health and well-being and that of their sexual partners? So that they will have a healthy understanding of and respect for sexuality in all its dimensions?

Most people who care about youth would answer yes to all of the above reasons. Many people disagree, however, about the best ways to accomplish these goals. How early should sexuality education begin? What should we say, and when and how should we say it? How can families and schools work together? What is "healthy sexuality"? Is giving children the skills to make decisions a disservice in this age when decision making can be a confusing burden even to adults? Disagreement about the answers to these and other basic questions about sexuality education make this an area fraught with frustration and confrontation, even as the consequences to young people of being misinformed, unskilled and uncomfortable about sexuality become ever more serious and severe.

We are a nation of diverse people and communities. The goals and objectives of a successful sexuality education program are strongly linked to community values. So what works in one community may not be practicable in another—even communities separated only by a county line or a city block. To a degree, and not surprisingly, this divergence of perspectives is reflected among sexuality educators.

As we conceptualized a book about sexuality education for young people and spoke with educators across the nation, a picture emerged of a vast, multitiered network of issues. An equally intricate network of people exists whose work is dealing with those issues on a day-to-day basis. In our efforts to provide the best education possible given a context of diverse needs and directives, a lack of consensus as to what "sexuality education" means has emerged in the field. As James J. Neutens notes in Chapter 2, it is ironic that while laypersons have a single perception of what sexuality education should do (namely, reduce negative consequences associated with adolescent sexual behavior), professional educators hold a multiplicity of ideas. This disparity has created an identity crisis of sorts for those in the field, just at a time when the need for educating young people about sexuality has never been clearer or less debatable, and the necessity for strong and consistent messages from adults seems most essential.

To assess this situation as we approach the turn of another century and to provide direction to those who work with young people is the purpose and intent of this book. The issues are broad: Where have we come from, where are we now, and where are we going in the field of educating young people about sexuality? What is sexuality education and who should define it? Who should teach sexuality education? How and where should it be taught? What are its goals? If one goal is to provide young people with healthy attitudes about sexuality, who decides what is sexually healthy? What are the effective strategies to meet the goals? How do we find out and measure what works? What are the barriers and limitations?

To find out, we went to the experts. We asked leading sexuality educators to examine the issues from their perspectives. Authors included theoretical considerations as well as practical implications to address the needs of the wide range of those responsible for educating young people, including educators, administrators, parents and policy-makers.

The contributions to this book represent an incredible amount of expertise. We are pleased and proud to make it available to those who can benefit from it. Because sexuality education is not a single-issue subject, approaches and perspectives sometimes differ. Despite these differences, a real sense emerges, as reflected in the chapters in this book, that a strong community exists in this country, united in the firm belief that not including sexuality as a basic and integral part of the total education of young people is a dangerous exclusion, with consequences that go beyond the individual to permeate the entire society.

This book attests to the fact that progress in the area of

sexuality education is being made, that foundations are being laid on which to build strong programs to benefit young people. Several common themes emerge:

- Positive and healthy sexuality education is essential to the well-being of our children.
- Communication about common goals can be a starting place for resolving differences about strategies.
- As educators we are responsible for attaining the same skills and comfort level about sexuality that we intend to provide to young people.
- Collaboration on all levels to ensure that young people receive similar messages from several different places is an important aspect of building strong programs.

Sexuality educators may be the unsung heroes of our day. There is perhaps no other subject so fraught with peril for those intent on providing young people with information and skills in an area of such import to the health and well-being of a nation. Every day, educators are meeting the challenges as best they can, because they believe that teaching young people about sexuality is an enormously important part of preparing them to lead productive and healthy lives. We hope that this book supports and furthers their efforts.

Sexuality Education: An Overview

Chapter 1

Past, Present and Future Perspectives on Sexuality Education

William L. Yarber, HSD, CHES, FASHA

Educating youth about sexuality has always been a part of the human experience. Until recent times, this education occurred nearly exclusively in the home or through peer interaction. Although perhaps troublesome for parents, sexuality education was not a social issue until it became public.

Changes in American culture, such as industrialization, urbanization and modification of the traditional family, resulted in the need to expand societal educational responsibilities, including the development of sexuality education. Sexuality education thus became a specialized area of study in the last century. It was seen as a solution to the "deterioration" of traditional sexual and family values and the increasing incidence of venereal diseases. These goals of sexuality education continue to be strongly advocated by some in contemporary society.

Sexuality education became a source of contention when social institutions such as schools, the government and health-related agencies began to assume a role in providing such instruction.

Disputes over the content and moral tone of sexuality education have always been present. The polemics continue today.

This chapter briefly examines historical, contemporary and future perspectives on sexuality education for youth within the United States. Particular attention is given to some of the major issues and concerns of sexuality education, particularly within the school setting.

Early Efforts

Undoubtedly there were many important efforts that contributed to the development of the sexuality education field, many of which may not have been recognized or recorded. However, there have been some noteworthy recorded occurrences. A few of the important events often listed by scholars are presented here. Readers desiring a more thorough account of the history of sexuality education should read the articles by Penland (1981), Tebbel (1976), and Trudell (1985).

Sexuality education began to be recognized as a specialized field of study in the early 1900s. Penland (1981) states that the major goal of these early efforts was to counter an emerging "distortion" of the "facts" about sexuality that was occurring at the turn of the century: namely, that pleasure might be an acceptable motivation for sex. Education was designed to reinforce the traditional values of restraint and procreation. Its purpose was to teach young people the "correct" information to prevent them from falling prey to the new immorality (Penland, 1981; Strong, 1972).

In the early 1900s sexuality education began to enter the schools. However, only a few schools offered such instruction and the tone generally reflected the agenda of the purity groups. Since these early efforts, the school has become an increasingly important avenue for sexuality education.

Efforts to expand sexuality education continued in the early part of the twentieth century. For example, in both 1919 and 1930 the U.S. government supported sexuality education as part of the White House Conference on Child Welfare ("Some High Points...," 1938). In 1920 the U.S. Public Health Service published the *Manual on Sex Education in High Schools* (Gruenberg, 1922).

The growth of sexuality education continued, and around the 1940s major national organizations began to call for more efforts in this area. Sexuality education was now expected to contribute to long-term sexual adjustment of individuals (American Association of School Administrators, 1938). This change was largely attributable to an increase in the variation of cultural beliefs about sex and morality. Fewer people now adhered to the absolute puritanical morality of the past.

Even though there were some advances in the 1940s toward a more progressive sexuality education, restrictive messages were still an important component of the curriculum. Masturbation, petting and necking were discouraged because their practice might cause difficulties in subsequent sexual relationships. Penland (1981) describes sexuality education in the 1940s as moralistic, promoting a healthy sexuality for family life, focusing on reproduction, VD, "normal" sexuality and family life, and restricted to same gender classes for most topics. Visual and printed materials supplemented lectures and discussion.

In the early 1950s the American School Health Association began a nationwide program in family life education (Haffner and de Mauro, 1991). This organization also published an important suggested program for schools, *Growth Patterns and Sex Education*, in 1967 (American School Health Association, 1967).

A significant validation of school sexuality education came in 1955 from a joint effort of the American Medical Association and the National Education Association. They published five pamphlets on sexuality for young adults, referred to as the "sex education series." These materials had widespread usage nationally (Haffner and de Mauro, 1991).

The decade of the 1960s brought significant advances. In this decade of the "youth revolution," sexuality education became less focused on preventing sexual degeneracy and began to emphasize factual information, nonjudgmental discussion and values clarification (Strouse and Fabes, 1985). This approach was based on the belief that acquiring factual information about the consequences of sexual behavior would change behavior (McCammon, Knox, and Schacht, 1993).

In 1964, the Sex Information and Education Council of the United States (SIECUS) was chartered with the major purpose of affirming sexuality as a natural and healthy part of life and advocating the right of all persons to sexual information and to make responsible sexual choices. Soon SIECUS began to publish study guides; sex education, masturbation and homosexuality were the topics of the first guides.

However, during the 1960s a concerted effort to stop sexuality education was begun by opposition groups such as the John Birch Society, Parents Opposed to Sex and Sensitivity Education, and Mothers Organized for Moral Stability. Their impact was far-reaching, contributing to numerous state legislatures abolishing or restricting sexuality education, and several local communities experiencing fierce battles over the implementation of sexuality education (Haffner and de Mauro, 1991).

During the 1970s a newer goal for sexuality education emerged: the promotion of sexual health. In 1975 the World Health Organization (WHO) defined sexual health as "the integration of the physical, emotional, intellectual and social aspects of sexual being in ways that are positively enriching and that enhance personality, communication, and love... every person has a right to receive sexual information and to consider accepting sexual relationships for pleasure as well as for procreation" (World Health Organization, 1975).

Sexuality education in the 1980s stressed the development of healthy sexuality to enhance individual growth and fulfillment, utilized a nonjudgmental approach, concentrated on student discussion and values clarification, and included a broader range of topics, including contraception (Penland, 1981). Interest in sexuality education grew during this decade, largely because of the human immunodeficiency virus (HIV) epidemic. Sexuality education was seen as a major means of controlling risky sexual behavior. In 1986, the Surgeon General of the United States declared, "There is now no doubt that we need sex education in schools and that it must include information on heterosexual and homosexual relationships" (Koop, 1986).

However, opposition to sexuality education, particularly in schools, continued to influence the curriculum. Groups such as American Family Association, Focus on the Family, and Eagle Forum mounted major campaigns to discredit comprehensive sexuality education and to promote their "just say no" approach (Kantor, 1993; Sedway, 1992).

Current Issues and Approaches

Sexuality education, particularly in the school setting, remains a subject of controversy in the 1990s. Some of the major issues are briefly discussed here. Currently, most societal groups want sexuality education, whereas previously many groups, particularly the religious and political far right, opposed school sexuality education. Many are now calling for increased efforts, but there are major disagreements on the nature of the educational message.

One argument for sexuality education is that individual development of a healthy sexuality is difficult in contemporary society. Our culture presents conflicting messages about sexuality to our youth. Brick (1989) in her book, *Teaching Safer Sex*, states that:

> ...the young people of this nation
> ...must find their way to sexual health
> In a world of contradictions
> Where media scream, "Always say yes,"
> Where many adults admonish, "Just say no,"
> But the majority,
> Just say...Nothing.

These conflicting messages have costs to our youth; they may have difficulty accepting their sexuality, developing a responsible sexual code of behavior and expressing their sexuality appropriately. Fisher (1990) notes several studies which indicate that youth with negative feelings about their sexuality do not practice pregnancy and sexually transmitted disease prevention as consistently as those with more positive attitudes. Furthermore, negative feelings about sexuality have been found to interfere with acknowledgement of forthcoming sexual activity, learning of sexual information, and communication with others about sexuality. Sexuality education is charged with countering conflicting messages via the presentation of a consistent, unified and positive approach to sexuality.

For many people sexuality education continues to be seen as the solution to the high incidence of adolescent coitus and STD/HIV. The majority of young people have experienced a wide range of sexual behaviors, including coitus. Sexually transmitted diseases, including HIV, cause more serious damage to more teenagers than all other communicable diseases combined. Unwanted pregnancy among teenagers remains a serious problem. Certainly these negative outcomes represent major challenges to sexuality education, although they should not be its sole focus. Actually, for many teenagers, even though many adults may not want to believe it, the coital experience was a positive or at least a neutral experience, although for some coitally experienced youth—particularly young females—the experience has damaged self-esteem. Unfortunately, many American teenagers who participate in coitus do not consistently practice STD/HIV risk reduction or use contraception (Bigler, 1989; Centers for Disease Control, 1992; Ehrhardt and Wasserheit, 1991; Fisher, 1990; Yarber and Parrillo, 1992; Yarber, 1993).

In part because of the disease/pregnancy consequences of adolescent sexual behavior, the public support for school sexuality education is probably at the highest level ever. Nine out of ten parents want their children to receive sexuality education. Most parents want sexuality education in the elementary schools, and almost all want HIV/AIDS education to start by the time children reach pre-adolescence. More than 80 percent of parents want their children to be taught about "safe sex" as a way of preventing HIV/ AIDS (Louis Harris and Associates, 1985, 1988; Gallup and Clark, 1987). The vast majority of states either mandate or recommend school sexuality education and HIV/AIDS education (National Guidelines Task Force, 1991).

A major factor influencing views on sexuality education content is the differing perspectives on whether or not adolescents are sexual beings. The term "adolescent sexuality" is an oxymoron in our culture. Some believe that adolescents *are* sexual beings and need sexuality education to aid them in achieving a healthy sexuality. Whatley (1992) notes that:

Students are sexually active in every way possible, with themselves and with others, feel sexual desires, are sexually exploited, become pregnant, cause pregnancy, have abortions, have babies, catch diseases, explore their own sexuality, explore others' sexuality, are sexually violent, wrestle with issues of power and control.

Others feel that adolescents are *not* sexual beings, that they do not have sexual needs. Therefore, adults should not do anything that would acknowledge or promote adolescent sexuality. Many of this persuasion believe that sexual intercourse before marriage is morally wrong.

The ideological conflict surrounding the question of adolescents' sexuality affects the content of sexuality education. Basically, those who believe adolescents are sexual beings advance a comprehensive approach, while those who deny adolescent sexuality want total abstinence to be promoted by education.

Several emphases or approaches are represented among current school sexuality education, all of which are based on ideological perspectives and historical factors. In some schools, the curriculum might be a combination of approaches, with one emphasis dominating the instructional content. The major emphases are as follows.

Traditional Emphasis

This approach is basically instruction on reproductive biology and STD, with an emphasis on preventing adolescent coitus. It has been and continues to be the predominant form of sexuality education in most schools. In general, the content focuses on the anatomy and physiology of the reproductive systems. Some aspects of pregnancy and childbirth are often presented, as well as medical details of STDs that may include discussion of condoms. Social and psychological issues of adolescent sexuality, such as noncoital sexual expression and sexual response, are rarely discussed, except for the dangers of adolescent coitus. The underlying message supports the traditional family structure and heterosexual sex within marriage (Sears, 1992), with the prevention of unwanted pregnancy and STD/HIV as the major instructional goals.

Abstinence-Only Emphasis

In recent years, sexual abstinence has become a major focus of sexuality education. School curricula that emphasize abstinence have been produced, with many presenting abstinence as the only solution to teenage pregnancy and STD. Other preventive methods, such as condoms, are not discussed. Many of the commercial curricula were developed with federal government support via the Office of Adolescent Pregnancy Program, commonly known as the "chastity bill." This program funds projects that promote abstinence for unmarried adolescents, and has resulted in the development of several prepackaged, abstinence-only, fear-based curricula, including the controversial *Sex Respect: The Option of True Sexual Freedom* and *Teen-Aid* (U.S. Department of Health and Human Services, 1992; Mast, 1986; Potter and Roach, 1989; Roach and Benn, 1987).

Most of the abstinence-only programs are designed to promote the agenda of the political and religious far right and their perspective on sexuality; i.e., sexual behavior should be expressed only in marriage. "Fear-based, abstinence-only" curricula have been utilized widely, although nonadoption or withdrawal of such a curriculum has occurred in several school districts (Huberman, 1993; "Yanking 'Sex Respect'," 1990). A judge in Shreveport, Louisiana, recently ruled that *Sex Respect* and *Facing Reality* violate state law by including religious beliefs, information which is factually inaccurate, and anti-abortion counseling (*Coleman v. Caddo Parish School Board*, 1993).

The abstinence-only curricula have been criticized by leading sexuality educators and professional sexuality groups. Kantor (1993) states:

> There has been a recent proliferation of sexuality education curricula that rely upon fear and shame to discourage students from engaging in sexual behavior. Referred to as abstinence-only curricula, these programs typically omit critical information, contain medical misinformation, include sexist and anti-choice bias and often have a foundation in fundamentalist religious beliefs. These programs are in direct opposition to the goals of comprehensive sexuality education curricula....

SIECUS has developed a listing of far right organizations and fear-based, abstinence-only curricula (SIECUS, 1993).

Abstinence-Based/Delay Coitus Emphasis

Most, if not all, school sexuality education programs present abstinence, but many discuss other disease and pregnancy prevention methods as well. This approach is often called "abstinence-based." The strategy of promoting the delay of coitus has recently emerged, based on the beliefs that coitus in early adolescence is particularly risky and that it is either unrealistic or inappropriate to advocate abstinence by all persons in late adolescence. Programs have been commercially produced that stress abstinence, postponing intercourse and skill building, and discuss contraception without utilizing the scare tactics often present in the abstinence-only programs (Kantor, 1993).

Four important programs in this category are *Postponing Sexual Involvement* (Howard, Mitchell and Pollard, 1984), *Reducing the Risk: Building Skills to Prevent Teen Pregnancy* (Barth, 1993; Kirby et al., 1991), *Will Power/Won't Power* (Wilson and Geboy, 1988), and *Values and Choices* (Search Institute, 1991). These programs have demonstrated positive outcomes, such as reduction of the rates of coitus and unprotected coitus and greater use of contraception (Howard, 1982; Howard and McCabe, 1990; Girls, Inc. 1991; Kirby et al., 1991; Search Institute, 1991).

Comprehensive Emphasis

Some believe that the best way to educate adolescents about their sexuality is by a comprehensive approach involving a broad range of topics and the entire school career, especially as part of a comprehensive school health education program. An important and typical tenet of this approach is that sexuality education should prepare adolescents for the healthy expression of their sexuality instead of focusing only on the prevention of negative consequences. The comprehensive approach not only deals with traditional areas such as reproductive biology and puberty, dating, marriage and STD, but also covers many topics historically considered inappropriate, such as sexual pleasure, noncoital sexual expression, sexuality and society, and homosexuality. This approach affirms the positiveness of sexuality while striving to prevent inappropriate sexual sharing and unprotected coitus.

Two prominent national organizations recently published guides for comprehensive school sexuality education. The American School Health Association produced *Sexuality Education Within Comprehensive School Health Education* (Neutens et al., 1991), and SIECUS sponsored the publication *Guidelines for Comprehensive Sexuality Education: Kindergarten–12th Grade* (National Guidelines Task Force, 1991).

The ASHA book is a guide for those involved in the process of planning and implementing sexuality education in the schools, including teachers, administrators, school board members, parents and students. Among other features, the ASHA guide offers a succinct, eleven-step implementation plan designed to reduce conflict and community distrust; identifies the roles and functions of the advisory committee and offers suggestions about selecting members; and sets forth a guide for evaluation. Two entire chapters outline proactive approaches to avoiding controversy and alert readers to potential problem areas.

The book also includes recommendations to help communities develop appropriate concepts and content education at specific grade levels. The recommendations are written so they can be easily adapted to meet the needs of individual schools, communities and students.

The *Guidelines* represent the first national consensus about what should be taught in a comprehensive sexuality education program. They were developed by the National Guidelines Task Force which included representatives from several sexuality, health and education organizations, as well as nationally recognized school sexuality educators. The *Guidelines,* which provide a framework for communities and states to create new or improve existing programs, have six key concepts broken down into 36 topics that include over 700 messages for four developmental levels within grades K through 12. The key concepts are human development, relationships, personal skills, sexual behavior, sexual health, and society and culture. Specific topics include puberty, sexual identity and orientation, families, marriage and lifetime commitments, decision making, masturbation, shared sexual behavior, human sexual response, contraception, abstinence, STD/HIV, sexual abuse, sexuality and society, and diversity.

Another important feature of the *Guidelines* is the presentation of 15 values related to human sexuality on which the material is based, and which the Task Force contends reflect the beliefs of most communities in a pluralistic society. In recent history, sexuality education's attempts to be nonjudgmental often resulted in its being labeled as value-free. But quality sexuality education is *not* value-free. It teaches universal democratic values such as critical thinking, decision making and clarification of values (Gordon, 1992). Values presented in the *Guidelines* include the beliefs that sexuality is a natural part of living, that all people are sexual, that sexual relationships should never be coercive or exploitative, that people have the right to make responsible sexual choices, that sexuality education is valuable, and that every person has dignity and worth regardless of sexual orientation.

The comprehensive approach can also include school-directed programs that extend beyond instruction. That is, the instructional program is augmented by efforts involving parents and community organizations. An example of one program with a strong school/family/community link is the School/Community Program for Sexual Risk Reduction Among Teens, implemented in a South Carolina community. This comprehensive approach resulted in a sustained decline in the estimated adolescent pregnancy rate two to three years after implementation (Vincent, Clearie and Schluchter, 1987).

Theory-Based Sexuality Education

An important characteristic of current sexuality education is the recent development of newer curricular models. Kirby et al. (1991) state that there have been four generations of sexuality education curricula over the past fifteen years: the reproductive knowledge approach, the decision-making and communication skills approach, the abstinence program, and the newer theoretical and research-based approach. The latter approach is based on several theories, such as social learning theory, social inoculation theory, cognitive-behavioral theory, the health belief model, the value expectancy model, and the theory of reasoned action (Allensworth and Symons, 1989; Boyer, 1990; Flora and Thorensen, 1988; Barth, 1993; Kirby et al., 1991; Yarber, 1993).

Curricula based on these theories are behaviorally based and usually combine selected behaviorally related cognitive messages with the development and practice of social and personal prevention skills. Examples of commercially produced curricula using the theory model are two mentioned earlier, *Postponing Sexual Involvement* (Howard, Mitchell and Pollard, 1984; Howard and McCabe, 1990) and *Reducing the Risk* (Barth, 1989; Kirby et al., 1991), and *STDs and HIV: A Guide for Today's Young Adults* (Yarber, 1993).

Future Perspectives

The ideological conflict between the political and religious far right and more progressive groups remains an important component of contemporary sexuality education. These groups have widely differing perspectives on adolescent sexuality and what young people should be taught about sexuality. Many times, the far right has been very successful in influencing the curricular decisions of school boards, while those who support comprehensive sexuality education have not been sufficiently active to achieve their agenda (Sedway, 1992). Sexuality education programs throughout the country will be compromised as long as this major disparity in ideology exists.

Of all the educational topics addressed by the schools, sexuality education continues to be among the most problematic, resulting in limited effectiveness. Many obstacles, such as lack of consensus on goals and content and inadequate commitment and resources, impede progress. These issues represent current and future challenges. For sexuality education to reach its maximum potential, advocates must strive to accomplish the following actions.

Unify Goals and Purposes

As previously discussed, there are varying opinions as to the goal of sexuality education, ranging from the prevention of all sexual expression in adolescents to preventing the negative outcomes of such expression to affirming and supporting adolescent sexuality. This variety of viewpoints is found among the general public, as well as within the sexuality and health fields. For the advancement of the field, sexuality education professionals must first agree on goals, then be proactive in persuading community members to support these goals.

An important definition of sexuality education was presented in the National Guidelines Task Force *Guidelines* (1991):

> Sexuality education is a lifelong process of acquiring information and forming attitudes, beliefs, and values about identity, relationships, and intimacy. It encompasses sexual development, reproductive health, interpersonal relationships, affection, intimacy, body image, and gender roles. Sexuality education addresses the biological, sociocultural, psychological, and spiritual dimensions of sexuality...including the skills to communicate effectively and make responsible decisions.

Several perspectives concerning the goal of sexuality education are presented here for consideration.

Cassell and Wilson (1989) note that it is a mistake to promote sexuality education by promising to reduce problems. They suggest that the best and most appropriate goals for sexuality education are

- to help prepare people for upcoming stages of development
- to increase comfort with the topic of sexuality
- to increase the attitude that sexuality is a normal and positive part of human existence
- to provide responsible answers to questions and concerns that arise in an age when the media bombards us with sexual messages
- to increase skills that will enable people to live happy, safe and responsible lives as sexual beings

The enhancing of sexual pleasure is often cited as a missing outcome of sexuality education. Selverstone (1989) states that adolescents need help in assessing alternative sexual behaviors and their possible consequences to personal and interpersonal joy and pain. He notes that adolescents need assistance in maximizing their own and their partner's pleasure and safety, while minimizing the risks associated with sexual expression.

Haffner (1993) presents the traits of the sexually healthy adolescent and states that prevention programs will not be successful until sexuality educators accept that young people are sexual beings who have the right to make their own sexual decisions. She continues by noting that:

> Instead of trying to reduce young people's coital experience, efforts would be more effective if they could concentrate on reducing the incidence of *unprotected coitus*. For some young people that will

mean delaying intercourse until they have the cognitive and emotional maturity to obtain and use contraception consistently and effectively. For others, it means helping young people accept that they are sexually involved and helping them develop the skills to protect themselves. Adolescents who are capable of forming healthy sexual relationships must be supported. There is no question that America's young virgins need our support. There is also no question that we have an obligation to support teenagers who are having sexual intercourse, who constitute more than half of the nation's teens.

The real purpose of sexuality education is the development of a healthy sexuality. A healthy sexuality includes the acceptance and celebration of one's sexuality and the integration of sexuality into one's total life in enhancing ways. This approach addresses sexual expression based on ethical principles, validates the importance and role of sexuality in human life, and includes complete disease and pregnancy prevention messages (Yarber, 1992).

Solidify Support
Support for quality sexuality education is widespread. The vast majority of adults and parents support school sexuality education (Louis Harris and Associates, 1985, 1988). Over sixty national organizations have joined together as the National Coalition to Support Sexuality Education, a coalition committed to ensuring that all children receive comprehensive sexuality education by the year 2000 (National Guidelines Task Force, 1991). (See Appendix D.) The judiciary has upheld sexuality education courses against constitutional challenges (First, 1992).

Despite this high level of support, many schools do not have adequate sexuality education programs. Actually, it has been estimated that less than 10 percent of American young people receive comprehensive sexuality education (Kirby, 1984). The number should be much higher. The support is present, but it is often unexpressed or not unified. Opponents thus succeed in limiting programs. As advocates, we must utilize the existing support for our cause. We must form coalitions and join advocacy groups.

Expand Research

Further empirical evidence of the effectiveness of sexuality education programs is needed. Research indicates that sexuality education does not cause sexual behavior and that some programs either delay the onset of coitus, increase the use of protection against pregnancy or STD, and/or reduce the number of sexual partners (Fisher, 1990; Kirby, 1992). Continued confirmation of these findings, as well determining which methodologies are most effective in furthering these goals, would be valuable.

However, advocates need to be cautious about trying to "prove" that sexuality education works and to understand the limitations of research in the area. For example, the broad goal of enhancing a healthy sexuality is hard to measure; it is difficult to acquire young subjects and measure longitudinal effects. Kirby says "sex education classes, like other courses, should be considered successful and effective if they simply increase teenagers' knowledge and information about sexuality" (Reynolds, 1991).

Any evaluation of sexuality education must be realistic and methodologically sound. Kirby (1992) has provided several suggestions for improved research of school-based programs designed to reduce sexual risk-taking behaviors.

Improve Teacher Competency

Inadequate teacher skill is one of the more valid criticisms from opponents of sexuality education. Most often, sexuality education courses are assigned to teachers with little or no professional preparation in the area (Krueger, 1993). An Alan Guttmacher Institute study of sexuality education nationally found that most sexuality education teachers do not identify themselves as sexuality educators, almost none have received graduate training, and most felt ill-prepared to address many of the issues in the area (Alan Guttmacher Institute, 1989; Forrest and Silverman, 1989).

Presenting the numerous solutions to increasing teacher competencies is not the focus of this chapter. However, Krueger (1993) says that sexuality educators, particularly those who are inadequately prepared, often make false assumptions about students. She cites six false assumptions about students, along with supportive evidence and discussion:

- All students come from traditional nuclear families.
- All students are heterosexual.
- All students are sexually involved.
- No students are sexually involved.
- All students' sexual involvements are consensual.
- Students who are "sexually active" are having intercourse.

At the very least, sexuality educators need professional preparation in human sexual behavior and the pedagogy, administration and evaluation of sexuality education. Improved teacher preparation will increase teacher confidence and skill, as well as public trust and acceptance of sexuality education.

Improve Curricula and Instructional Material

Quality instructional guides and materials are needed for the improvement of sexuality education. Most current material minimally accounts for social, health and learning theory, often resulting in inadequate attention to the affective and skill components of sexual learning. Also, many programs do not adequately reflect consumer needs. Too often, students are not asked what important messages about sexuality they need.

Analysis of state sexuality education curricula, mandates, laws, regulations and guidelines reveals that most do not follow the comprehensive approach (de Mauro, 1990). The Alan Guttmacher Institute study found that many teachers wanted better instructional materials and that they often developed their own materials because they found state and district curricula inadequate or inaccessible (Alan Guttmacher Institute, 1989).

Acknowledge Limitations

Advocates for quality sexuality education believe that intervention can achieve desired outcomes, and studies have shown many positive results. However, educators must be realistic about the capability of limited sexuality education. It is probably unreasonable to believe that a one-week or two-week unit in junior or senior high school, for example, will have a major impact on adolescents' sexuality, given that most young people have received unhealthy sexual messages all of their lives. Furthermore, local social and economic conditions affect the receptivity of students to sexuality education. For example, some teens, especially those from disadvantaged backgrounds, do not perceive any reasons to delay intercourse or parenthood (Berlin and Sum, 1988; Wilson, 1987).

Even though we believe that sexuality education can have a valuable affect on students, we must remember that it exists in a social environment and that it is only one solution toward enhancing responsible sexual behavior. Peter Scales, Director of National Initiatives, Center for Early Adolescence, says that "Sex education is not a panacea nor is it a devil. It doesn't solve or create the problem of teen sexual activity. But it's part of the solution" (Sorohan, 1992).

Promote the Comprehensive Approach

The comprehensive approach to sexuality education has been advocated as the best method (SIECUS, 1992). Strategies have been borrowed from approaches utilized for other health areas, such as smoking prevention, STD and family planning (Boyer, 1990; Cates, 1990; Cates, 1991; Coates, 1990; Donovan and Waszak, 1989; Flora and Thorensen, 1988; Fors et al., 1989; Glynn, 1989; Haffner, 1989; Roper, 1991; Rundall and Bruvold, 1988; Stone, Perry and Luepker, 1989).

The comprehensive approach includes several components. For example, the curriculum should address the cognitive, affective and skill domains at all school grade levels and be part of a comprehensive school health education program. A broad range of topics, like those of the National Guidelines Task Force *Guidelines*, should be included. Classroom curricula should be supplemented by other schoolwide programs, such as peer programs, individual counseling, theatrical presentations and media events, and be linked with health and reproductive care services within the school and community (Kirby, 1992). Lastly, parents, youth-serving organizations, religious institutions, health care professionals, the government and media can share in educating youth about sexuality (Haffner, 1990).

Conclusion

Sexuality education continues to evolve. It has not yet reached its full potential. There are numerous barriers to the implementation of quality sexuality education, the major one being disagreements in ideology. Each of us has our own perspective about the role and meaning of sexuality in life, and hence an opinion on how sexuality education should be presented to our youth.

Schools can play a major role in promoting healthy sexuality in our young people. Classroom efforts should be combined with community cooperation. Improved teacher competency and instructional material based on applicable theories and student needs will improve effectiveness.

Differences in ideology will continue, but the advocates for comprehensive sexuality education must be committed to unifying their beliefs, rallying the existing support and gaining further approval. At stake is the sexual health of our young people. Advocates need to continue to fight for adolescents' right to quality sexuality education that will promote the development of a life-enhancing and health-promoting sexuality.

References

Alan Guttmacher Institute. 1989. *Risk and responsibility: Teaching sex education in America's schools today.* New York.

Allensworth, D. D., and C. W. Symons. 1989. A theoretical approach to school-based HIV prevention. *Journal of School Health* 59 (2): 59-65.

American Association of School Administrators. 1938. *Youth education today.* 16th Yearbook. Washington, DC.

American School Health Association. 1967. *Growth patterns and sex education: A suggested program kindergarten through grade twelve.* Kent, OH.

Barth, R. P. 1993. *Reducing the risk: Building skills to prevent pregnancy, STD and HIV.* 2d ed. Santa Cruz, CA: ETR Associates.

Berlin, G., and A. Sum. 1988. *Toward a more perfect union: Basic skills, poor families, and our economic future.* Occasional Paper 3. New York: Ford Foundation.

Bigler, M. O. 1989. Adolescent sexual behavior in the eighties. *SIECUS Report* 18 (1): 6-9.

Boyer, C. B. 1990. Psychological, behavioral, and educational factors in preventing sexually transmitted diseases. *Adolescent Medicine: State of the Art Reviews* 1 (3): 597-613.

Brick, P. 1989. *Teaching safer sex.* Hackensack, NJ: Planned Parenthood of Bergen County, Inc.

Cassell, C., and P. M. Wilson, eds. 1989. *Sexuality education: A resource book.* New York: Garland.

Cates, W., Jr. 1990. The epidemiology and control of sexually transmitted diseases in adolescents. *Adolescent Medicine: State of the Art Reviews* 1 (3): 410-427.

Cates, W., Jr. 1991. Teenagers and sexual risk taking: The best of times and the worst of times. *Journal of Adolescent Health* 12 (2): 84-94.

Centers for Disease Control. 1992. Selected behaviors that increase risk for HIV infection among high school students—United States, 1990. *Morbidity and Mortality Weekly Report* 41:231, 237-240.

Coates, T. J. 1990. Strategies for modifying sexual behavior in primary and secondary prevention of HIV disease. *Journal of Consulting and Clinical Psychology* 58 (1): 57-69.

Coleman et al. v. Caddo Parish School Board. 1993. First Judicial District Court, Caddo Parish, Louisiana, 385, 230, Section C.

de Mauro, D. 1990. Sexuality education 1990: A review of state sexuality and AIDS education curricula. *SIECUS Report* 18 (2): 1-9.

Donovan, P., and C. S. Waszak. 1989. *School-based clinics enter the '90s: Update, evaluation, and future challenges.* Washington, DC: Center for Population Options.

Ehrhardt, A. A., and J. N. Wasserheit. 1991. Age, gender, and sexual risk behaviors for sexually transmitted diseases in the United States. In *Research issues in human behaviors and sexually transmitted diseases in the AIDS era,* ed. J. N. Wasserheit, S. O. Aral and K. K. Holmes, 97-121. Washington, DC: American Society for Microbiology.

First, P. A. 1992. Sex education in the public schools: A clash of religious freedom and the general welfare. *The Educational Forum* 57 (1): 76-83.

Fisher, W. A. 1990. All together now: An integrated approach to preventing adolescent pregnancy and STD/HIV infection. *SIECUS Report* 18 (4): 1-11.

Flora, J. A., and C. E. Thorensen. 1988. Reducing the risk of AIDS in adolescents. *American Psychologists* 43 (11): 965-970.

Forrest, J. D., and J. Silverman. 1989. What public school teachers teach about preventing pregnancy, AIDS, and sexually transmitted diseases. *Family Planning Perspectives* 21 (2): 65-72.

Fors, S. W., S. Owen, W. D. Hall, J. McLaughlin and R. Levinson. 1989. Evaluation of a diffusion strategy for school-based hypertension education. *Health Education Quarterly* 16 (2): 255-265.

Gallup, A. M., and D. L. Clark. 1987. The 19th annual Gallup Poll of the public's attitudes toward the public school. *Gallup Polls* 69 (1).

Girls, Inc. 1991. *Truth, trust, and technology.* New York.

Glynn, T. J. 1989. Essential elements of school-based smoking prevention programs. *Journal of School Health* 59 (5): 181-188.

Gordon, S. 1992. From where I sit. *Family Life Educator* 10 (2): 12-13.

Gruenberg, B. C., ed. 1922. *Manual on sex education in high schools.* Washington, DC: United States Health Service.

Haffner, D. W. 1989. AIDS education: What can be learned from teenage pregnancy prevention programs. *SIECUS Report* 17 (6): 29-32.

Haffner, D. W. 1990. *Sex education 2000: A call for action.* New York: Sex Information and Education Council of the United States.

Haffner, D. W. 1993. Toward a new paradigm on adolescent sexual health. *SIECUS Report* 21 (2): 26-30.

Haffner, D. W., and D. de Mauro. 1991. *Winning the battle: Developing support for sexuality and HIV/AIDS education.* New York: Sex Information and Education Council of the United States.

Howard, M. 1982. Delaying the start of intercourse among adolescents. *Adolescent Medicine* 3 (2): 181-193.

Howard, M., M. E. Mitchell and B. Pollard. 1984. *Postponing sexual involvement.* Atlanta, GA: Grady Memorial Hospital.

Howard, M., and J. B. McCabe. 1990. Helping teenagers postpone sexual involvement. *Family Planning Perspectives* 22 (1): 21-26.

Huberman, B. 1993. Winning one in North Carolina. *SIECUS Report* 21 (2): 9.

Kantor, L. M. 1993. Scared chaste? Fear-based educational curricula. *SIECUS Report* 21 (2): 1-15.

Kirby, D. 1984. *Sexuality education: An evaluation of programs and their effects, an executive summary.* Bethesda, MD: Mathtech, Inc.

Kirby, D., R. P. Barth, N. Leland and J. V. Fetro. 1991. Reducing the risk: Impact of a new curriculum on sexual risk-taking. *Family Planning Perspectives* 23 (6): 253-263.

Kirby, D. 1992. School-based programs to reduce sexual risk-taking behavior. *Journal of School Health* 6 (27): 280-287.

Krueger, M. M. 1993. Everyone is an exception: Assumptions to avoid in the sex education classroom. *Phi Delta Kappan* 74 (7): 569-572.

Koop, C. E. 1986. *The Surgeon General's report on AIDS.* Washington, DC: Department of Health and Human Services.

Louis Harris and Associates. 1985. *Public attitudes about sex education, family planning and abortion in the United States.* New York: Planned Parenthood Federation of America.

Louis Harris and Associates. 1988. *Public attitudes toward teen pregnancy, sex education and birth control.* New York: Planned Parenthood Federation of America.

Mast, C. K. 1986. *Sex respect: The option of true sexual freedom.* Gold, IL: Project Respect.

McCammon, S., D. Knox and C. Schacht. 1993. *Choices in sexuality.* St. Paul, MN: West Publishing Company.

National Guidelines Task Force. 1991. *Guidelines for comprehensive sexuality education: Kindergarten-12th grade.* New York: Sex Information Education Council of the United States.

Neutens, J. J., J. C. Drolet, M. DuShaw and W. H. Jubb, eds. 1991. *Sexuality education within comprehensive school health education.* Kent, OH: American School Health Association.

Penland, L. R. 1981. Sex education in 1900, 1940 and 1980: An historical sketch. *Journal of School Health* 51 (4): 305-309.

Potter, S., and N. Roach. 1989. *Sexuality, commitment and family.* 3d ed. Spokane, WA: Teen-Aid, Inc.

Reynolds, M. 1991. The stubborn paradox of sex education. *The San Diego Union,* 19 December. B-1, B-9.

Roach, N., and L. Benn. 1987. *Me, my world, my future.* Spokane, WA: Teen-Aid, Inc.

Roper, W. L. 1991. Current approaches to prevention of HIV infections. *Public Health Reports* 106 (2): 111-115.

Rundall, T. G., and W. H. Bruvold. 1988. A meta-analysis of school-based smoking and alcohol use prevention programs. *Health Education Quarterly* 15 (3): 317-334.

Search Institute. 1991. *Values and choices.* Minneapolis, MN.

Sears, J. T. 1992. Dilemmas and possibilities of sexuality education. In *Sexuality and the curriculum: The politics and practices of sexuality education,* ed. J. T. Sears, 6-33. New York: Teachers College Press.

Sedway, N. 1992. Far right takes aim at sexuality education. *SIECUS Report* 20 (2): 13-19.

Selverstone, R. 1989. Adolescent sexuality: Developing self-esteem and mastering developmental tasks. *SIECUS Report* 18 (1): 1-3.

Sex Information and Education Council of the United States. 1992. SIECUS fact sheet #3 on comprehensive sexuality education: Sexuality education and schools: Issues and answers. *SIECUS Report* 20 (6): 13-14.

Sex Information and Education Council of the United States. 1993. SIECUS fact sheet #4 on comprehensive sexuality education: The far right and fear-based abstinence-only programs. *SIECUS Report* 21 (2): 16-18.

Some high points in the history of sexuality education in the United States. 1938. *Journal of Social Hygiene* 24:584-585.

Sorohan, E. G. 1992. Are abstinence-only programs effective? *School Board News* 12 (2): 1, 8.

Stone, E. J., C. L. Perry and R. V. Luepker. 1989. Synthesis of cardiovascular behavioral research for youth health promotion. *Health Education Quarterly* 16 (2): 155-169.

Strong, B. 1972. Ideas of the early sex education movement in America, 1890-1920. *History of Education Quarterly* 12 (2): 129-161.

Strouse, J., and R. A. Fabes. 1985. Formal versus informal sources of sex education: Comparing forces in the sexual socialization of adolescents. *Adolescence* 20:251-262.

Tebbel, J. 1976. Sex education: Yesterday, today and tomorrow. *Today's Education* 65 (1): 70-72.

Trudell, B. K. 1985. The first organized campaign for school sex education: A source of critical questions about current efforts. *Journal of Sex Education and Therapy* 11 (1): 10-15.

U.S. Department of Health and Human Services. 1992. Announcement of availability of grants for adolescent family life demonstration projects. *Federal Register*, 29 January, 35-6-3508.

Vincent, M. L., A. F. Clearie and M. D. Schluchter. 1987. Reducing adolescent pregnancy through school and community-based education. *Journal of the American Medical Association* 257:3382-3386.

Whatley, M. H. 1992. Whose sexuality is it anyway? In *Sexuality and the curriculum: The politics and practices of sexuality education*, ed. J. T. Sears, 79-84. New York: Teachers College Press.

Wilson, P., and C. H. Geboy. 1988. *Will power/won't power*. New York: Girls, Inc.

Wilson, W. 1987. *The truly disadvantaged*. Chicago: University of Chicago Press.

World Health Organization. 1975. Education and treatment in human sexuality. Report of a WHO meeting. *Technical Report Series, 572*. Geneva.

Yanking 'Sex Respect' was the right decision. 1990. *Sheboygan Press*, 1 November.

Yarber, W. L., and A. V. Parrillo. 1992. Adolescents and sexually transmitted diseases. *Journal of School Health* 62 (7): 331-338.

Yarber, W. L. 1992. While we stood by...the limiting of sexual information to our youth. *Journal of Health Education* 2 (36): 326-335.

Yarber, W. L. 1993. *STDs and HIV: A guide for today's young adults*. Reston, VA: AAHPERD Publications.

Chapter 2

Sexuality Education:
A Kaleidoscope
of Interpretations

James J. Neutens, PhD, CHES, FASHA

Although sexuality education in the schools has undergone many changes over the years, many of the major issues confronting the discipline remain the same. Outcries from conservative groups, louder in some communities than others, carry the same anti-sexuality-education messages. Polls continue to reflect widespread support from parents, yet administrators may erect barriers to sexuality education out of fear of public reaction. A great many sexuality education teachers still feel woefully unprepared to handle the subject matter adequately. Yet, of all the age-old issues facing today's educators, one of the most perplexing is the kaleidoscope of interpretations given to sexuality education.

Perusal of the several hundred curricula developed over the last two decades reveals that many terms are used as synonyms for sexuality education. These include *family life education, human growth and development, health and human relations, education for human sexuality, family living, reproductive health,* and, of course, *sex education*. A look behind the names uncovers a myriad of objectives, goals, content and methodologies. Even the foundations for programs range from simple cognitive orientations to complex theoretical bases.

This kaleidoscope of interpretations is not surprising for several reasons. First, sexuality education is a hybrid field that draws upon different disciplines—health, psychology, sociology, biology, medicine, home economics, religion and ethics. Second, teacher preparation programs vary by discipline and only a handful of universities offer an actual major or minor in sexuality education.

Third, American society in general is experiencing a "moral smog"—or state of moral confusion (Neutens, 1992) as traditional ethical guidelines are questioned and replaced. For example, the once steadfast policies of organized religion are being debated by both the public and the religious policy-makers. The topics of homosexuality, premarital sex and pregnancy termination are being reviewed and reinterpreted in an effort to incorporate the broader views of the membership. Government agencies are struggling with the issues of abortion, abortion counseling, pornography, publicly funded clinics, and even the development of appropriate sexuality education curricula. Two popular abstinence-only curricula, *Sex Respect* (Mast, 1986) and *Teen Aid* (Benn, 1982) were created through government funding. While the conservative and liberal camps fight over "what's right" and "what's wrong," those in the middle are left in a moral smog that compounds an already difficult decision-making process. As a result of the moral smog, well-founded program objectives may be diluted or distorted at the local level. In other words, rather than meeting community needs, many programs are twisted to meet the whims of a vocal minority.

Finally, there is a lack of consensus as to what "sexuality" means when it comes to sexuality education. This identity crisis is inadvertently supported by sexuality educators themselves. For example, the health educator perceives sexuality education as one of the ten components needed for comprehensive school health education (American School Health Association, 1992). The human growth and development teacher conceptualizes sexuality education as a topic to be integrated into a curriculum that includes self-esteem, interpersonal relations, HIV/AIDS education, family life skills and gender stereotypes (Titus, Gingles and Kanter, 1993). The home economist may have an even broader perspective, adding such content as meal planning, baby care and furnishing the home to the curriculum. Those educators who embrace SIECUS guidelines (National Guidelines Task Force, 1991) view sexuality education as a comprehensive, self-contained package with the general theme being a positive orientation toward human sexuality.

While this kaleidoscope allows for diversity, it perpetuates several dilemmas. One dilemma is accountability. To parents, caregivers and others outside the professional sexuality education realm, all synonyms mean the same thing, and all programs are measured behaviorally. That is, a program by any other name is still "sex education" and as such should reduce the negative consequences associated with adolescent sexual behavior. It is ironic that laypersons have a single perception of sexuality education while the professional educators hold a multiplicity of ideas.

A second dilemma is the formidable task of evaluation, given the myriad of existing programs. These two dilemmas generate a third—the vulnerability of sexuality education programs to attacks from those who oppose them. Teacher training based on this kaleidoscopic framework creates a fourth dilemma: it places educators in an indefensible position because they are required to know "all programs" and "all approaches" when they encounter community opposition. On the political level, state legislators who support mandated sexuality education are often lost as to which sexuality education to support.

Nonetheless, positive strides are being made, mostly as a result of research and program evaluation. As research methods on adolescent sexual behavior become more sophisticated, the under-lying reasons for such behavior are being revealed. These results demonstrate the complexity of behavior, particularly high-risk behavior, and the need for well-designed programs. Program evaluation complements the research findings with more and more evidence indicating the necessity of a theoretical base in sexuality education.

In short, research and evaluation efforts are telling sexuality educators to focus on objectives, content and methodology. Such a focus should facilitate the move away from "disaster" or "crisis" education toward full-blown, comprehensive sexuality education and the elimination of the current identity crisis.

Sexuality Education in Isolation

There is very little debate about the need for sexuality education, but how such education should be delivered is controversial. Should we integrate it with existing curricula or offer it indepen-dently? It may be argued that the stand-alone curriculum empha-sizes sexuality education and the integrated curriculum, through absorption, contributes to the identity crisis. The bottom line decision, however, should be based on the realities of the particular school setting and what will work best in each situation. In some schools the stand-alone curriculum may be the only option. When this is the case, a comprehensive program in human growth and development or a comprehensive program in sexuality education would be in the best interests of the students.

If the school setting allows for either option, stand-alone or integrated, the separation of sexuality education from other curricula may present pragmatic problems of curriculum time and teacher preparation and availability, and may divorce the content from related adolescent concerns. Isolated curricula often fail to integrate adolescent sexual behavior within the context of other adolescent behavior.

Recent epidemiologic data are often used to justify segregating sexuality education from other curricula. Numbers have become the name of the game. Report after report and journal after journal demonstrate the number of adolescents who do or do not engage in intercourse, the number who use and the number who fail to use contraceptives, the number who become pregnant and the number who do not conceive, and so on. These statistics frequently omit history, culture and socioeconomic status as contributors to individual behavior. Based on these data, the apparent solution is to provide a sexuality education program that changes individual personality traits rather than one that addresses larger health, social or economic problems.

Many statistically armed "experts" claim that their views represent those of the public when in fact no such consensus exists. They forge ahead developing programs based on statistics alone. The same numbers are used by others to generate and justify fear-based curricula with an emphasis on "just say no." In both instances, such programs fail to acknowledge the complexity of adolescent sexual behavior and fall far short of recognizing its interplay with other behaviors.

The scope of statistics-based sexuality education programs is far too narrow. Since the questionnaires only investigate selected adolescent sexual behaviors, curricula based on the results tend to be skewed. While the goal of a curriculum may be lofty, e.g., responsible decision making, the content reflects making responsible decisions only about certain aspects of sexuality. For example, most programs insist that reproductive anatomy, physiology, pregnancy and STD/HIV content are a must. Fewer programs deal with contraception and abortion. Very few include homosexuality. And even fewer address what is sexually healthy, leaving students with the impression that pleasure is an unfortunate side-effect of sexuality and is present only to ensure propagation of the species.

Common High-Risk Behaviors

This is not to say that epidemiologic data are faulty in and of themselves, but rather that sexuality educators should be cautious in the use of such data. Adolescent sexual behavior cannot be reduced to mere numbers so that sexuality education becomes an isolated educational endeavor. Instead, the database must be reviewed for all related adolescent behaviors, especially high-risk behaviors. There may be common themes and effective educational methodologies that can be applied to various adolescent behaviors. For example, in reviewing data about adolescent drug use, a teacher may find commonalities with high-risk sexual behaviors, suggesting that methods effective in drug prevention education may be tried in sexuality education.

The need for an overall perspective or frame of reference is borne out by research on adolescents at risk and on the effectiveness of sexuality education programs. Dryfoos (1990) in her investigation of four adolescent behaviors (delinquency, substance use, pregnancy and school failure/dropping out) found six characteristics common to all four behaviors.

The first predictor is age. Early initiation predicts greater involvement in the behavior with a greater incidence of negative consequences. Educational expectations were a second common characteristic. As might be anticipated, low academic expectations are associated with all four problem behaviors. The third predictor for these behaviors was peer influence. Adolescents who possess low resistance to peer influences or have close friends who participate in the negative behavior are much more likely to engage in the behavior themselves. General behavior is a fourth common characteristic. Dryfoos noted that several conduct disorders such as acting out and truancy are related to each of the four behaviors investigated.

A fifth predictor, parental role, showed that insufficient bonding and lack of supervision, guidance and communication are strongly related to the negative behaviors. Similarly, children of very authoritarian and very permissive parents are much more likely to engage in these behaviors. Finally, neighborhood quality, to include socioeconomic status and population density, also serves as a predictor of these problems.

Several studies have demonstrated the link between early onset of sexual activity and drug use, smoking, problem drinking, poor school performance, and delinquent behavior. These relationships hold true for both African-American and White adolescents. Santelli and Beilenson (1992) elaborate on eleven biopsychosocial risk factors for adolescent sexual behavior, pregnancy and STD. There is no doubt that the sexuality education teacher must be cognizant of the intertwining of these adolescent behaviors.

In an overview of programs to reduce sexual risk-taking behaviors, Kirby (1992) points out that the most current sexuality education programs incorporate theoretical bases such as social learning theory, social inoculation theory, or cognitive-behavioral theory which have been shown to be effective in drug and smoking education programs. Given the interrelatedness of adolescent problem behaviors, it appears that such bases should be relatively successful in sexuality education as well, underscoring the fact that sexual behavior and sexuality education are not isolated entities.

A Comprehensive Approach

The changing nature of adolescent health problems as well as the demands to meet them led to an expansion of the concept of a comprehensive school health program in 1987 (Allensworth and Kolbe, 1987). The new concept embraces the belief that multiple approaches are necessary to effectively influence the behavior of adolescents, including their sexual behavior.

The original program components of school health services, school health education and school health environment were retained. However, five additional areas were added: school physical education, school food services, school counseling, schoolsite health promotion and integrated school-community health promotion efforts. Several of these eight components can play an instrumental role in efforts to reinforce or modify adolescent sexual behavior as well as providing avenues for health instruction. For example, school health education programs to increase the use of contraceptives among students may be more effective if school health services offer concurrent information about contraceptives, school counseling programs provide assistance to individuals or couples in the decision-making process, and integrated community efforts make free or reduced-cost contraceptives available at a nearby clinic.

School health education has ten content areas:
- personal health
- community health
- consumer health
- environmental health
- mental health
- nutritional health
- prevention and control of disease and disorders
- safety and accident prevention

- substance use and prevention
- sexuality education

Needless to say, these topic areas address all the major issues confronting adolescents today. This comprehensive approach is exceedingly important since cumulative data reveal the interrelationship among high-risk behaviors.

Using the framework of comprehensive school health education, a teacher should be well prepared to face adolescent risk behaviors. The overlap of topics not only serves to reinforce messages but demonstrates the interrelationship of behaviors to students. For example, the relationship of alcohol use and sexual behavior can be emphasized in both the substance use prevention and the sexuality education content areas. The safety unit can show how alcohol plays a significant role in rape, as well as teach steps to protect oneself from sexual molestation. The effects of advertising on sexual behavior could be discussed in the consumer health unit.

The personal health content area could include information on sexual growth and development, with emphasis on maturity and the ability to make responsible decisions about sexual behaviors. Prevention and control of disease is a natural place to teach about sexually transmitted disease, including HIV/AIDS. The area of mental health could address decision-making skills, emotional intimacy, assertiveness/refusal skills and coping skills for dealing with anxiety and frustration.

As theory-based instruction to prevent unhealthy adolescent behaviors evolves, a teacher may incorporate it into all health content areas. In this fashion, the methodology underlying sexuality education will become consistent with those used in adjacent behavioral areas. Unlike an isolated sexuality education program, theory-based programs are likely to be seen as comprehensive and integrated. Sexuality education teachers' skills are put to better use across all fronts of adolescent behavior. Teachers who prepare for one area can apply many of their methodological skills to other content areas, giving them greater ease in preparation, not to mention an increased likelihood of effectiveness.

Other Issues in Sexuality Education

The identity crisis and integration of sexuality education are major issues, yet other issues also confront those who work in this area. The remainder of this chapter provides a brief synopsis of other issues inherent in sexuality education. Some, such as multicultural challenges, are applicable to all curricula. Others, like the gay/lesbian issue, are unique to sexuality education.

Comprehensive Curriculum

The need for a sequential curriculum is obvious to those in education. However, different opinions are held by many outside the field. In their eyes, sexuality education programs should commence in junior high school at the earliest. The mere mention of sexuality education programs in kindergarten or elementary school can cause blood pressure to rise and tempers to flare. When sexuality education is perceived as crisis education, sequence, scope and comprehensiveness are lost.

In regard to scope, just what should be taught at the various grade levels? How encompassing can the program be? What is acceptable to the community in question? The circumstances surrounding each sexuality education program will mean differences from community to community. The section Sexuality Education in School Settings (Chapters 5 through 10) addresses these issues, including suggested content from pre-kindergarten through post-secondary education.

Teacher Preparation

In the final analysis, the results of all the planning and careful steps taken in implementing a program depend on the classroom teacher. It is the teacher who is most visible to community members, to administrators, and of course to the students. It is the teacher who is asked, or told, to reinforce positive behaviors and to modify or eliminate negative ones. While peripheral players in sexuality education programs may have important roles, "the buck stops with the teacher."

Those who prepare teachers must accept the responsibility of training their charges in the best possible ways. This includes cognitive, affective and skill domains. It implies that educators of teachers will help them to feel at ease with the topic and show them how to communicate with several different audiences. The section What Educators Need: Preparation and Presentation (Chapters 11 through 17) provides detailed information about these issues.

Cultural Relevance

The challenge to sexuality education in this area is to move beyond lip service. Ethnic culture can play a significant role in an adolescent's beliefs, attitudes and behaviors (Abbey et al., 1987; Pittman et al., 1992). This may be especially true when it comes to fertility and sexual decision making. Sexuality educators must discover the best ways to reach their students, including developing an understanding of individual cultures, creating culturally appropriate materials, accentuating cultural pride and providing the skills necessary to resolve conflicting cultural messages. Chapter 18, Cultural Competence and Sexuality Education, expands on this issue.

Gay and Lesbian Issues

One of the most controversial subjects in sexuality education is teaching about gay men, lesbians and bisexuality. More often than not, programs fail to mention anything about these topics unless in the context of HIV/AIDS education. Lack of support and teacher discomfort frequently are given as reasons for this neglect. However, since many gay men and lesbian women become aware of their sexual orientation during their high school years or earlier, educators should accept the challenge to teach about these subjects. Homosexual or bisexual teens may face many crises, including violence directed against them. The sexuality education teacher can help promote tolerance and acceptance by integrating information throughout the curriculum (DeAndrade, 1993). Chapter 19, Gay, Lesbian, Bisexual and Questioning Youth, provides some practical suggestions for dealing with these issues.

Students with Disabilities

Perhaps even more neglected than sexual orientation are the sexual issues confronting students with disabilities. Unfortunately, this is often an area "forgotten" by many parents as well. Disabled students may be left to fend for themselves in a sexual vacuum. The challenge to the special education teacher is obvious but so, too, is the invitation to the sexuality education teacher. Cooperative instruction or team teaching to assist students with disabilities will provide rewards to both students and teachers. Chapter 20, Special Education Students: Issues and Needs, presents information on the needs of disabled students as well as recommendations for the special education classroom.

Coalitions Within the Community

Most sexuality education programs emphasize building community coalitions from the inception of the program through implementation. Yet, examinations of failed programs often show that such coalition building never took place. Instead, the program was isolated until a negative response brought it to the attention of the school board and media. Chapter 21, Sexuality Education Coalitions, offers some solid recommendations regarding community councils, partnerships with existing services, funding, resources and communication.

Youth Service Organizations

While coalitions with community organizations are important for program efficacy, interaction with youth service organizations is paramount. As with all coalitions, the sexuality educator must understand these organizations' goals and how they can support pregnant teens, peer education and school clinics. Chapter 22, Partnerships Through Community Organizations, helps readers understand this issue.

Religious Coalitions

Satisfying the demands of different religious factions is a daunting task for new sexuality educators. However this may be necessary if the program is to remain functioning and intact. Positive thinking is appropriate, however; numerous parochial schools and church programs provide excellent sexuality education to adolescents across the nation. Working with religious organizations is discussed in Chapter 23, The Role of Religious Organizations in Sexuality Education.

Facing Conservative Communities

A conservative community can present significant obstacles to coalition building. But how do we define a "conservative" community? Is it a matter of attitude? geographical location? religious affiliation? Even in extreme instances, is there not room for sexuality education? Chapter 24, Sexuality Education in Conservative Communities, speaks to this issue in some detail.

High-Risk Communities

It seems readily apparent that some communities, towns or cities are at greater risk than others. For example, if asked which community is at greater risk, New York, New York, or Lisbon, North Dakota, most would say New York. Yet how is "high risk" defined? High risk for what? Does a high-risk community require a vastly different sexuality education program? Is coalition building of more importance in a high-risk community? These questions are addressed in Chapter 25, Sexuality Education in High-Risk Populations.

Parents and Caregivers

No matter how sexuality education is approached, the involvement of parents and caregivers will always be an issue. Chapter 26, Parents and Caregivers as Educators, Partners and Advocates in Sexuality Education, explains how to gain the commitment and support of this crucial groups for sexuality education programs. Parents and caregivers' role in setting values is discussed as are their other significant roles. This issue is of the utmost importance since parents and caregivers are secondary consumers of school programs.

School-Based Clinics

From a comprehensive school health program perspective, school-based clinics can play a major role in enhancing sexuality education. However, several issues must be addressed if the clinic is to be a positive force. What are the objectives of such a clinic? Exactly what services will be rendered and by whom? Is there community support for the clinic? What coalitions have been formed with other health services? The connection between classroom services and school-based clinic services needs to be fully delineated. Chapter 27, School-Based Clinics and School Health Care, looks at the many issues surrounding school-based clinics.

Pregnant Minors

School-based programs for pregnant teens run the full gamut—from nothing to full services. Chapter 28, Adolescent Pregnancy and Parenting Programs, discusses this topic, including concerns such as implementation, dealing with controversy, cooperation with other school programs, confidentiality and father involvement. The issues are many and complex. However, if schools are to serve all students and to prevent dropout and its consequential economic burden to society this issue must be confronted.

Student Assistance Programs

These programs fit into the comprehensive school health model very well and can be coordinated with the sexuality education program. However, often such coordination is lacking except for "disaster education," i.e., problems with drug use, high pregnancy rates and the like. Chapter 29, Student Assistance Programs, introduces the concept of student support programs and explains how these can work in the area of sexuality education. If sexuality education teachers accept the responsibility of reinforcing or modifying student behavior, we must understand that no program really stands alone.

The Media and Sexuality

Investigations into the effect of media on adolescents are very revealing. One study of almost 400 junior high students found that those who watched a greater amount of "sexy" television were more likely than lighter viewers to have become sexually active during the prior year. Other studies have found that adolescents view nearly 14,000 instances of sexual material on TV each year and that teenagers rank TV as their third most important source of sexuality and birth control information. This is particularly alarming since 40 percent of teens believe that television gives them a realistic picture about STD, pregnancy and sexual behavior.

The music culture has been shown to have a significant impact on students as well. Although more data need to be collected, it appears that for some students media may be as important an influence on behavior as peers. Chapter 30, The Role of Media in Sexuality Education, examines how the media relate to sexuality education.

Evaluation and Research

Perhaps one of the most important issues confronting sexuality education is that of evaluation and research. The teacher should comprehend the need for such efforts and participate whenever possible. Evaluation and research have been the foundation of many of the strides taken by sexuality education in the recent past. Teachers must become involved in these matters if further advances are to be made. The section, Evaluation and Research (Chapters 31 through 33) provides a comprehensive overview of evaluation and research.

There are a multitude of issues facing sexuality education, many of which extend well beyond the classroom walls. Dealing with these issues may appear to be a grand juggling act; however, accepting the challenge and facing these concerns will enable sexuality education to function as a complex and finely tuned machine capable of producing sexually healthy students.

References

Abbey, N., C. Brindis, M. Casas and S. Schoonmaker. 1987. Family life education for Hispanics: Practical guidelines for schools. *Family Life Educator* 6 (1): 4-10.

Allensworth, D., and L. Kolbe. 1987. The comprehensive school health program: Exploring an expanded concept. *Journal of School Health* 57 (10): 409-412.

American School Health Association. 1992. *Sexuality education within comprehensive school health education.* Kent, OH.

Benn, L. 1982. *Sexuality, commitment and family.* Spokane, WA: Teen Aid, Inc.

DeAndrade, K. 1993. Teaching about gay men and lesbians in the FLE classroom. *Family Life Educator* 11 (2): 8-11.

Dryfoos, J. 1990. *Adolescents at risk: Prevalence and prevention.* New York: Oxford University Press.

Kirby, D. 1992. School-based programs to reduce sexual risk-taking behaviors. *Journal of School Health* 62 (7): 280-287.

Mast, C. 1986. *Sex respect: The option for true sexual freedom.* Gold, IL: Project Respect.

National Guidelines Task Force. 1991. *Guidelines for comprehensive sexuality education: Kindergarten-12th grade.* New York: Sex Information and Education Council of the United States.

Neutens, J. 1992. Sexuality education in comprehensive school health programs: Surviving the "moral smog." *Journal of School Health* 62 (2): 74-75.

Pittman, K., P. Wilson, S. Adams-Taylor and S. Randolph. 1992. Making sexuality education and prevention programs relevant for African-American youth. *Journal of School Health* 62 (7): 339-344.

Santelli, J. S., and P. Beilenson. 1992. Risk factors for adolescent sexual behavior, fertility, and sexually transmitted diseases. *Journal of School Health* 62 (7): 271-279.

Titus, P. M., J. M. Gingles and R. M. Kanter. 1993. Attitudes of teachers and administrators toward human growth and development. *Family Life Educator* 11 (2): 4-7.

Chapter 3

Politics and Policy: Driving Forces Behind Sex Education* in the United States

Cory L. Richards and Daniel Daley

Unrelenting high rates of adolescent unintended pregnancy, abortions, unprepared parenthood, sexually transmitted disease and HIV infection have long since made clear the need to address ignorance in sexual matters. To be sure, American youth face a barrage of messages about sex. Most of their information, however, comes from the advertising industry, the entertainment media or from peers—and much of it is incomplete or inaccurate.

Most parents want to be their children's primary sexuality educators, but they are often unable to fulfill that role because they did not receive sufficient sexuality education themselves. Accordingly, they may be reluctant to initiate discussions about sexual

---

*We make a distinction between the terms "sexuality education" and "sex education" to make the point that, while the goal may be comprehensive *sexuality* education, today's reality—both in terms of curriculum content and certainly in terms of government policy—is by and large very far from that goal and much narrower. For this reason, with only a few exceptions we use the term "sex education" here.

matters—not only out of embarrassment but also for fear of not having enough information to answer their children's questions. This leaves formal, largely school-based, sex education as the major means to provide adolescents—and the adults they will become—with the information and skills they will need to lead sexually healthy lives: at a minimum, lives free of the negative consequences that can arise from sexual activity.

An overwhelming majority of U.S. adults—approaching nine in ten—favors sex education in the schools, and support has steadily increased over time (Louis Harris and Associates, 1985, 1988). Moreover, parents of school-age children are even more likely to support sex education than the public at large (Alan Guttmacher Institute, 1989). Because they believe that information and instruction in the classroom on sexual matters can help reduce the negative consequences of sexual activity, adults not only support education on traditional topics such as reproductive anatomy and pregnancy, but also support education on "sensitive" subjects like birth control and abortion (Alan Guttmacher Institute, 1989). And, despite the high visibility of organized parent groups who protest education on sex-related issues in the schools, very few parents actually exercise their right to opt their children out of such classes (Sex Information and Education Council of the United States, 1992).

Still, public policy on sexuality education lags behind public opinion. As is often the case with controversial issues, pressure from small but vocal and well-organized minorities slows the policy-making process and dilutes its result. Thus, it is not surprising that when the scope and content of sex education in the schools is examined, it is found to be less pervasive, less comprehensive and less age- and content-appropriate than may be generally perceived or desired.

Policy at the Federal Level

Until very recently, the federal government played virtually no role at all in sex education policy. The first federal government body to address the subject was a White House Conference on Child Welfare in 1919. It concluded that the federal government should not play a major role because the "problem of sex instruction…is more properly a task of the school" (Haffner, 1990). But with rising rates of teen pregnancy during the 1970s and the advent of HIV/AIDS in the 1980s, the federal government came under pressure to address these matters as critical public health issues.

Indeed, especially during the Reagan and Bush administrations, Washington seemed caught between conflicting pressures—the need to promote sex education from a public health perspective; a desire to respect the tradition of local autonomy in education policy; and a wish to appease small pockets of vocal, conservative constituencies who either believed that sex education had no place in the classroom at all or that instruction should be limited to abstinence promotion. The effect of these three political imperatives may be seen in the various sex-education-related (but not necessarily sex-education-specific), programs administered by the Department of Health and Human Services (DHHS) and the Department of Education.

Department of Health and Human Services Programs

The federal government's investment in sex education is minuscule—ranging from a total of about $25 million in 1990 to approximately $56 million in 1993. The DHHS Centers for Disease Control and Prevention (CDC) provides most of the federal effort (totaling slightly more than $45 million in fiscal year 1993) through at least eight individual programs or "systems" under its Division of Adolescent and School Health (DASH) (Committee for Education Funding, 1993).

State and Local Departments of Education

In 1987, DASH began working directly with state and local departments of education so that they, in turn, could assist schools and other youth-serving organizations in carrying out core program activities such as developing HIV/AIDS education policies, training teachers and other school personnel, developing and disseminating materials, monitoring the prevalence of student risk behaviors and the status of HIV education in their jurisdictions, and evaluating the impact of programs. State and local education agencies funded by DASH have developed HIV and related school health policies, curriculum guides and teaching materials. Currently, DASH provides fiscal support and technical assistance to every state education agency, the District of Columbia, the Commonwealth of Puerto Rico, American Samoa, Guam, the U.S. Virgin Islands and the 16 local education agencies that serve cities with the highest number of reported AIDS cases (Federal Interagency Ad Hoc Committee on Health Promotion Through the Schools [FIAHCHPTS], 1992).

Information Development and Dissemination

This program supports the development and dissemination of information that can be used to increase the effectiveness of HIV prevention education. To help disseminate HIV education information, CDC includes this information in the U.S. Public Health Services' Combined Health Information Database. The database, which is updated every three months, currently contains abstracts of more than 700 HIV education materials, including HIV education policies, teacher training programs, films and filmstrips, brochures, journal articles and reports.

In 1987, DASH worked with representatives from national, state and local organizations and government agencies to develop its "Guidelines for Effective School Health Education to Prevent the Spread of AIDS." The guidelines provide recommendations for planning HIV prevention programs, preparing education personnel, establishing teacher qualifications, defining the purpose of HIV education, determining essential content for specific grade levels, estimating curriculum time and resources, and assessing progress (FIAHCHPTS, 1992).

Training and Demonstration

DASH established three training and demonstration centers in 1987 to assist state and local agencies responsible for school- or community-based health education in implementing up-to-date HIV prevention education for youth. Two centers focus on state-level training programs, and one center addresses the needs of teams from local jurisdictions. The training sessions also address integrating HIV education into comprehensive school health education and engaging parents and the community in HIV education.

In September 1989, CDC worked with the Education Development Center (EDC) in Newton, Massachusetts, to establish training centers in 13 states to train teachers to implement comprehensive school health education that included education to prevent HIV infection. The centers have trained more than 12,000 teachers from more than 1,000 school districts. In 1990, the U.S. Senate appropriation report directed the CDC to support "a comprehensive approach to health education in the schools including AIDS, IV drug use, sexually transmitted diseases, cancer prevention, and heart health to name a few... [by establishing]... 30 new regional teacher training centers focused on comprehensive school health education." CDC then established a Comprehensive School Health Education Teacher Training Center at 13 additional sites. Currently, there are 24 training centers in 23 states. CDC plans include establishment of a teacher training center in every state (FIAHCHPTS, 1992).

Surveillance System

The DASH surveillance system has two components. The first regularly measures health-risk behaviors, including sexual behaviors that result in HIV infection, STD and unintended pregnancy among adolescents. The secondary surveillance system assesses the extent to which HIV education is being implemented. Each of the 71 state and local agencies supported by the CDC is encouraged to collect information regularly about the percentage of students receiving HIV education, schools providing HIV education, and schools providing HIV education within comprehensive health education. CDC provides technical assistance to state and local education agencies to help improve the quality of the data collected (FIAHCHPTS, 1992).

Evaluation System

This system is designed to help state and local education agencies evaluate and improve the quality of their HIV education programs. Since 1988, CDC has sponsored workshops to help state and local education agencies plan evaluations of their HIV education programs, learn how to apply principles of behavioral epidemiology, collect process and outcome data, measure sensitive behaviors, and select an appropriate evaluation design and report results.

CDC has developed a series of evaluation materials that include evaluation guidelines and measures to assess HIV education policies, teacher training, curricula and student outcomes. CDC also is developing four reports that summarize the literature about specific behaviors that place adolescents at risk for HIV infection; demographic, cognitive, social and environmental determinants of such behaviors; essential elements for effective school-based HIV prevention programs; and a proposed protocol for evaluating such

programs. These reports will serve as the basis for planning efficacy studies of school-based HIV prevention programs for the
next few years (FIAHCHPTS, 1992).

College and University System

In 1990, DASH awarded a cooperative agreement to a university
in each of five states among those with the highest cumulative
incidence of AIDS. A consortium of colleges, universities, trade
schools and other agencies in each of the states was established to
develop and implement education programs that could prevent
the spread of HIV infection and other health problems among
college students in the state and provide training for school administrators and teachers to help implement effective education.
(FIAHCHPTS, 1992).

System of Youth in High-Risk Situations

This DASH initiative, started in 1991, helps local health departments build, strengthen and expand their capacity—and that of
community agencies—for providing effective health education to
prevent HIV infection and other relevant health problems among
youth who engage in high-risk behaviors and youth who are
outside the mainstream of HIV prevention education. Local health
departments receive financial and technical assistance to develop
or expand community coalitions of youth-serving agencies in the
three cities with the highest cumulative incidence of AIDS
(FIAHCHPTS, 1992).

System of National Organizations

Since 1987, DASH has provided financial support and technical
assistance to national organizations in the private sector to enable
them to help schools implement effective HIV education within

more comprehensive school health education programs. Program activities typically include training, helping state and local agencies implement policies, and helping state and local education agencies implement programs and develop materials (FIAHCHPTS, 1992). (The Indian Health Service also receives funds from CDC for similar activities.)

In addition to the DASH programs, CDC's National Center for Prevention Services' Division of STD/HIV Prevention has provided technical assistance in the development of curricula for secondary school youth on prevention of STD and HIV education (FIAHCHPTS, 1992).

Department of Education Programs
At the Department of Education, the Office of Educational Research and Improvement provides minimal funding—a total of only $3 to $4 million—to two programs that could include sex education.

Comprehensive School Health Education Program
This program (authorized under the Secretary's Fund for Innovation in Education) provides funds for assistance to state and local educational agencies for a variety of activities related to improving health education for elementary and secondary school students. Activities may include establishment of programs to provide training for school personnel who will implement health education programs, development of comprehensive school health education programs, assessment of school health education programs, identification and dissemination of model school health education programs, and/or dissemination to schools of information related to nutrition, personal health and fitness, disease prevention, accident prevention, community and environmental health, and other

urgent health problems affecting school age youth (FIAHCHPTS, 1992). While not specific in its focus or intent to cover sex education, sex education is included within the program's broad context.

National Diffusion Network

Schools, colleges and other institutions can use the Department of Education's National Diffusion Network to find exemplary model educational programs for all subjects, including sex education and HIV education. The National Diffusion Network program officers help local schools implement the programs to suit the given school's needs through a series of trainings, site visits, telephone consultations and newsletters. Only Department of Education approved programs can become eligible for inclusion in the network. A program requesting a review must provide evaluation data that prove the program is effective in the school in which it was developed or field tested, and that it could be used successfully in other schools. Over 450 programs had been approved at this writing, with at least 80 receiving federal dissemination funds to help other schools adopt them (FIAHCHPTS, 1992).

One conclusion immediately can be drawn from even the most cursory examination of CDC and Department of Education programs—up to this point, the federal government has not as a matter of policy chosen to support or even specifically address sex education (let alone sexuality education). Congress has appropriated funds in such a way that the federal government's involvement has been either so general ("comprehensive health education") that there is no particular focus on sex or sexuality matters or so specifically aimed at disease prevention (almost always HIV/AIDS) that other sex and sexuality concerns are not addressed.

Moreover, since federal efforts related to sexuality education fall under the rubric of *education* policy (in which the federal government largely defers to local authorities to decide issues of content), the federal government's efforts, and they are extremely modest, revolve around technical assistance, program evaluation, information clearinghouses and personnel training for state and local agencies. The result is that there is no real federal leadership in the area of sexuality education.

Adolescent Family Life Demonstration Grants Program

The one federal program that is openly acknowledged to include sexuality education, the DHHS Office of Population Affairs' Adolescent Family Life Demonstration Grants Program, is largely an "abstinence-only" effort. Enacted in 1981 and often considered the far right's "alternative" to the Title X family planning services program, the Adolescent Family Life Act (AFLA) has two primary purposes: the prevention of teenage pregnancy through the teaching of abstinence, and the promotion of adoption over abortion as the appropriate choice for teenagers who become pregnant.

Grantees may use AFLA prevention funds to support "educational services relating to family life and problems associated with adolescent premarital sexual relations [including] information on adoption; education on the responsibilities of sexuality and parenting; development of materials to support the role of parents as the providers of sexuality education; assistance to parents, schools, youth agencies and health providers to educate adolescents and pre-adolescents concerning self-discipline and responsibility in human sexuality" (Office of Population Affairs, 1992).

AFLA was controversial from the beginning. In 1983, it became the subject of a lawsuit brought by a group of clergy members and other individuals who argued that the program constituted a federal endorsement of a particular religious point of view, and as such was in violation of the "establishment of religion clause" of the First Amendment to the United States Constitution (*Kendrick v. Sullivan*, 1983). Although the Supreme Court ruled in *Kendrick v. Sullivan* that the statute was constitutional on its face, litigation continued for several more years over how the demonstration grants program was actually being implemented. Finally a settlement in the case was reached in January 1993, just as the transition was being made between the administrations of George Bush and Bill Clinton.

The settlement provides that, for length of the agreement (five years), AFLA-funded sexuality education curricula may not include religious references and must be medically accurate, that contraceptive referrals must respect the "principle of self-determination" of teenagers, and that grantees may not use church sanctuaries for their programs or give presentations in parochial schools during school hours. In addition, the plaintiffs' attorneys will be allowed to review sexuality education curricula proposed by grantees and appoint individuals to review requests for grants (Department of Justice Civil Division and the Center for Reproductive Law and Policy, 1993).

AFLA—or the "Chastity Act" as it has come to be called—has never enjoyed broad-based support, due in large part, no doubt, to its attendant controversy. Its appropriation dwindled to less than $8 million in fiscal year 1992, far below the $30 million envisioned in the original 1981 authorizing legislation. Still, the program has had a significant—some would argue disproportionate—impact on sexuality education in this country. Not only does it remain the only explicit federal sexuality education program, but it was also aggressively administered for over a decade in a way that pushed the nation further away from comprehensive sexuality education.

During the Reagan and Bush administrations, the prevention component of AFLA was criticized because funds were used not only to provide services to individuals but also to support and promote "abstinence-only" curricula (what many critics call "fear-based" curricula)—most notably those of Project Respect (*Sex Respect*) and Teen-Aid.

Critics of the "fear-based" curricula developed and supported with AFLA funds have pointed out that these curricula offer no information about contraception or the use of condoms to prevent the spread of STD and HIV, even for those teenagers who are known to be sexually active, and that when contraception is discussed, negative or skewed information, such as claims of high risk of adverse medical consequences or of exaggerated failure rates for birth control methods other than natural family planning is given (Kantor, 1993). Not only were AFLA funds used to sponsor these programs, but, in effect, the AFLA funds were used to support the organizations that developed them, organizations that have become the major opposition to comprehensive sexuality education in the United States.

Policy at the State and Local Level

While the federal government's role in sex education has been limited, the states have taken up the challenge. This is what is known about the extent of the states' involvement:

- All states either require or recommend HIV/AIDS education according to a 1992 Sex Information and Education Council of the United States (SIECUS) study of state HIV/AIDS education programs (SIECUS, 1992).
- Twenty-six states recommend or mandate HIV/AIDS education in grades K through 12 (SIECUS, 1992).
- Forty-six states either recommend or mandate sex education, according to an 1988 survey of states and large school districts on sex and HIV/AIDS education policy by the Alan Guttmacher Institute (AGI, 1989).

- Twenty-three states and the District of Columbia have developed a curriculum (some form of formal suggestion to local school districts on what may or should be taught) on sex education, and 27 states and the District of Columbia have produced one on HIV education as of 1988. Overall, 33 states and the District of Columbia have curricula on one topic or the other and four other states that have not developed their own curricula recommend one or more (usually on HIV/AIDS) produced by a commercial publisher or another state (AGI, 1989).

Besides setting policies and developing curricula, states can support local programs in a number of ways. For example, according to the 1988 AGI study, 15 states recommend or approve specific textbooks or instructional materials for local districts (AGI, 1989). States may also establish minimum standards for teachers and provide training.

Half of the states and the District of Columbia in 1988 required teachers to be either certified or to have had special training (or both) to teach sex or HIV education (AGI, 1989). In 1988, all but three states reported that they had personnel working on the state level on either sex education or HIV education—a total of almost ninety persons nationwide (AGI, 1989). Of these 47 states, all reported DASH-funded personnel working on HIV education and 36 said that they had at least one person working at least part-time on sex education (AGI, 1989).

In the 1988 AGI survey, 27 states and the District of Columbia reported that they spent some money for sex education during the 1987/88 school year, and forty states reported some expenditures on HIV education (AGI, 1989). A 1990 study by the National Association of State Boards of Education (NASBE) and the Council of Chief State School Officers (CCSSO) showed that 12 states that make funds available to state education agencies for HIV education provided more than \$10 million (NASBE and CCSSO, 1990).

This state of affairs is significantly different from what it was only a decade or so earlier; only three states (Kentucky, Maryland and New Jersey) and the District of Columbia required sex education prior to 1980 (AGI, 1991). Still, there are some points of concern regarding how states have and are addressing sexuality education. Among them is the fact that policies among the states are inconsistent; and the problems from sexual activity that adolescents are mostly likely to encounter are not always covered in state mandates or recommendations. The 1989 AGI survey found that, of the forty states and the District of Columbia that required or recommended sex education (at that time):

- Only 19 states and the District of Columbia required instruction on STD.
- Only seven states and the District of Columbia required instruction on pregnancy prevention.
- Two states discouraged or prohibited instruction on contraception.

AGI also found that only eight states and the District of Columbia balanced a discussion of abstinence with a discussion of sexual risk reduction (AGI, 1989).

Moreover, from its 1990 review of state sexuality and HIV education curricula, SIECUS concluded that few address sexual issues directly:

- Although 65 percent of the curricula affirm that sexuality is a natural part of life, few of the curricula provide information on the historical and cultural aspects of human sexuality; sexual values, attitudes, and beliefs; and sexual activities and functioning.

- Only 8 percent include any information on sexual behaviors; and almost one-half of the curricula have limited family planning information (de Mauro, 1990).

Finally, HIV/AIDS receives a much higher priority than other sexual health matters—in part because both states and local school districts receive federal funds for HIV/AIDS education but not for sex education. Indeed, while the AIDS crisis seems to be the driving force behind the expansion of supportive sexuality education policies, sexuality education beyond HIV/AIDS prevention education has often been left behind. Although states have developed up-to-date HIV education curricula, their old sexuality education materials have often not been updated (AGI, 1989). Sexuality education and HIV education often appear to be treated as unrelated subjects, and the curriculum development and training for these programs often are done separately.

Moreover, the 1988 AGI study found that the existence of a state mandate for sexuality education does not necessarily translate into a comprehensive or well-balanced program at the local school district level. Even so, the nation's largest school districts have been strong in their support of sexuality and HIV education and seem to be somewhat more responsive to the needs of adolescents than state-level agencies:

- Nine out of ten large school districts support sexuality education (AGI, 1989).
- According to a 1990 National School Boards Association (NSBA) survey of school districts, 79 percent of responding school districts require HIV education for their students (NSBA, 1990).
- Most of the districts responding to the NSBA survey began requiring HIV education in either the 1987/88 school year (32 percent) or the 1988/89 school year (37 percent) (NSBA, 1990).

- Eighty percent of the responding districts that require HIV prevention for their general education students also require such instruction for their special education students (NSBA, 1990).

Still, data from the 1989 AGI survey indicate that while large school districts are supportive of education to help young people avoid pregnancy and STD, including HIV, they appear to view abstinence from sexual intercourse as the primary means to achieve these goals. Nevertheless, most school districts also cover birth control methods to prevent pregnancy and discuss condoms as a means to prevent transmission of STD and HIV, often as early as the seventh grade. However, they place greater emphasis on the means to avoid STD and HIV than on those to avoid pregnancy (AGI, 1989).

The Impact on Classroom Education

Whether, or to what extent, the existence of a state mandate for sexuality education and/or the specifics of state curricula determine what is actually taught in the classroom has not yet been studied in any detail. However, a 1989 AGI survey of sexuality education teachers across the United States found that most teachers are trying to give their students the information they will need to avoid the negative consequences of undesired or unprotected sexual activity. Specifically:

- The vast majority of sexuality education instructors are teaching their students about abstinence, birth control methods, use of condoms, transmission of sexually transmitted disease, including HIV, and sexual decision making.
- However, almost all teachers think that key subjects such as

birth control, HIV, STD, sexual decision making, abstinence and homosexuality should be taught earlier than they are (Forrest and Silverman, 1989).

Sex education teachers, by their own admission, often are not well informed on many topics they cover. Eighty percent indicate they need more help in teaching about prevention of pregnancy and STD, in the form of more and better factual information, instruction materials and teaching strategies (AGI, 1989). At least one-third say they need additional information about every topic they teach. More than half want more data about STD, sexual transmission of HIV, homosexuality and abortion.

The biggest problem sexuality education teachers believe they face is pressure from parents, the community or school administrators, especially when covering topics such as homosexuality, condom use, abortion and "safer sex" practices. Despite the national polls, one-quarter of sexuality education teachers believe that neither parents nor local community groups support their efforts. About one-third of sexuality educators think their school administration is nervous about possible adverse community reaction, and nearly 20 percent of sexuality educators believe that their school officials do not support them (Forrest and Silverman, 1989).

The Forces for the Future

As the nation looks toward the next century, politics and policy will continue to be driving forces behind sexuality education in the United States, and, for the proponents of comprehensive sexuality education, the challenges are enormous.

Advocates may look to Washington with renewed hope. During the 1980s the opponents of sexuality education found much to cheer about in the administrations of Ronald Reagan and George Bush. The Clinton administration is likely to be much more open in its approach to adolescent sexual matters, and there is a real possibility for leadership on the federal level for sexuality education advocacy. Most notably, the AFLA program, if it survives at all, is certain to discontinue its support of fear-based sexuality education curricula.

But, while administration support may hold promise to advocates, the opponents of sex education have not been disempowered. The politics of sexuality education are playing out at the state and local level with increasing frequency and intensity.

In the decade of the eighties, it was on the state level that the basic mandate for school-based sexuality education was largely realized. But that effort is, for the most part, over, and in some sense only limited gains were made: most states still do not require instruction on STD or contraception. Still, the real question for the future may be how much retrenchment will be suffered. In recent years, to the extent state legislatures have considered sexuality education, the bulk of the action has consisted of attempts to restrict it to abstinence promotion (AGI, 1992). The following examples from 1991 and 1992 alone serve as harbingers of an alarming trend:

- The Georgia legislature passed a sex education bill, later vetoed by the governor, that in effect would have prohibited sexuality education other than abstinence promotion.
- Alabama enacted a law that requires all public school programs or curricula that include sexuality education to emphasize that abstinence from sexual intercourse is the only completely effective protection against pregnancy, STD and HIV, and that abstinence outside of marriage is the expected social standard for unmarried school-age children and youth.
- The Colorado legislature adopted a resolution declaring that

abstinence is the only 100 percent effective protection against pregnancy and STD, and that school boards be encouraged to use curricula and teaching materials that place an emphasis on abstinence.

- The Hawaii legislature, concluding that many schools and communities already "advocate...safe sex" through sexuality education programs and services, admonished its departments of health and education that "it would greatly enhance sexuality education efforts in the state if programs were implemented to encourage adolescents to abstain from sexual intercourse." (HI-HRN 236, 4/30/92).

Similar measures were considered in several other states (AGI, 1992).

At the local level, SIECUS reports that during the 1991/92 and 1992/93 school years, there were as many as 120 controversies over sexuality education in 34 states (SIECUS, 1993b). It is at the local policy level that the opponents of sexuality education—nationally organized but locally focused—have their new stronghold. Sexuality education is being chipped away on the local level as vocal minorities are increasingly successful in challenging comprehensive sexuality education.

Abundant anecdotal evidence indicates that opponents of comprehensive sexuality education are making progress in convincing local school boards to adopt abstinence-only curricula, at times replacing established comprehensive programs. SIECUS and People for the American Way have identified approximately 15 far right national organizations with extensive grassroots networks that focus on instilling sexually conservative policy in the selection of textbooks, curricula and television programming. These groups have focused on local school board elections and have been successful in winning seats on these important and often overlooked policy making bodies. Their mobilization efforts often start with pamphleting and persuasion, beginning within fundamentalist congregations and expanding from that base (SIECUS, 1993a).

At the same time, however, some communities are taking legal actions to fight restrictions on sexuality education or to fight the implementation of sexuality education programs that use fear-based curricula. In Jacksonville, Florida, Planned Parenthood of Northeast Florida and seven families joined together to file a lawsuit against their local county school board. They claim that the school board failed to provide sexuality education that meets the standard of Florida's comprehensive health education laws when it adopted the curriculum *Me, My World, My Future* by Teen-Aid.

In Shreveport, Louisiana, residents were successful in their lawsuit against the Caddo Parish School Board to block the implementation of two curricula, *Sex Respect* and *Facing Reality* by Project Respect, that were deemed in violation of a Louisiana statute that no sex education could include religious beliefs or the subjective moral and ethical judgments of the instructor or other persons (*Bettye Coleman et al. v. Caddo Parish School Board et al.*, 1993).

In East Troy, Wisconsin, the parents of an eighth grade student filed a complaint against the *Sex Respect* curriculum, claiming that it violates Wisconsin's statutory prohibition against discrimination. While their claim was rejected on the local level, the state superintendent of public instruction agreed that the curricula indeed was discriminatory, inaccurate and misleading. However, the superintendent refused to take action, because the Wisconsin statutes in question did not give the department authority to order the school to remove the curriculum—even if it did violate state law.

Meanwhile, New York City students, parents, educators and community-based health education organizations were successful in striking a New York City Board of Education resolution that severely restricted HIV/AIDS education (Planned Parenthood Federation of America, 1993).

In order to not lose the advances made over the last twenty years—and to make further progress—advocates of sexuality education, including sexuality educators themselves, most likely will have to return to the grassroots efforts that originally achieved the gains. With an eye to the federal level, and the increasingly important state and local levels, they will need to harness the grassroots support for sexuality education that is reflected in the national polls. Sexuality educators will have to become better communicators in the public arena, serving as the local experts in defense of sexuality and HIV/AIDS education when the opposition courts their school boards. Moving into the next century, the future of sexuality education will likely be determined by the efforts of those—small or large in number—who are most dedicated to seeing their version of sexuality education, and their vision of the future, in the classroom.

References

Alan Guttmacher Institute. 1989. *Risk and responsibility: Teaching sex education in America's schools today.* New York.

Alan Guttmacher Institute. 1991. *State reproductive health monitor: Legislative proposals and actions.* 2 (4).

Alan Guttmacher Institute. 1992. *State reproductive health monitor: Legislative proposals and actions.* 3 (4): ix, x.

Bettye Coleman et al. v. Caddo Parish School Board et al. 1993. Civil Action No. 385.230, First Judicial Circuit Court, Caddo Parish, Louisiana.

Committee for Education Funding. 1993. *Education budget alert for fiscal year 1994.* Washington, DC.

de Mauro, D. 1990. Sexuality education 1990: A review of state sexuality and AIDS education curricula. *SIECUS Report* 18 (2): 1-9.

Department of Justice Civil Division and the Center for Reproductive Law and Policy. 1993. Settlement agreement: *Kendrick v. Sullivan* (Civil Action No. 83-3175 CRR).

Federal Interagency Ad Hoc Committee on Health Promotion Through the Schools. 1992. *Healthy schools: A directory of federal programs and activities related to health promotion through the schools.* Washington, DC: U.S. Department of Health and Human Services.

Forrest, J. D., and J. Silverman. 1989. What public school teachers teach about preventing pregnancy, AIDS and sexually transmitted disease. *Family Planning Perspectives* 21 (2): 65-71.

Haffner, D. 1990. *Sex education 2000: A call to action.* New York: SIECUS.

Louis Harris and Associates. 1985. *Public attitudes about sex education, family planning and abortion in the United States.* New York: Planned Parenthood Federation of America.

Louis Harris and Associates. 1988. *Public attitudes toward teenage pregnancy, sex education and birth control.* New York: Planned Parenthood Federation of America.

Kantor, L. 1993. Scared chaste? Fear-based educational curricula. *SIECUS Report* 21 (2): 1-15.

Chan Kendrick et al. v. Louis Sullivan et al. 1983. Civil Action No. 83-3175. United States District Court for the District of Columbia.

National Association of State Boards of Education and Council of Chief State School Officers. 1990. *AIDS, HIV and school health education: State policies and programs 1990.* Washington, DC: National Association of State Boards of Education.

National School Boards Association. 1990. *HIV prevention education in the nation's public schools.* Alexandria, VA.

Office of Population Affairs. 1992. Announcement of the availability of grants for Adolescent Family Life Demonstration Projects. *Federal Register* 57 (19): 3506-3509.

Planned Parenthood Federation of America. 1993. Fact sheet on reality-based sexuality education and the law. New York.

Sex Information and Education Council of the United States. 1992. *Future directions: HIV/AIDS education in the nation's schools.* New York.

Sex Information and Education Council of the United States. 1993a. SIECUS fact sheet #4 on comprehensive sexuality education: The far right and fear-based abstinence-only programs. *SIECUS Report* 21 (2): 16-18.

Sex Information and Education Council of the United States. 1993b. Fact sheet on community controversies about sexuality education. *Community Action Kit.* New York.

Chapter 4

Challenges to Sexuality Education in the Schools

Peter C. Scales, PhD, and Martha R. Roper, MA

A ccording to the Sex Information and Education Council of the United States (SIECUS), 17 states require that school districts provide sexuality education at some grade level, and another 30 recommend sexuality education; 38 states require HIV/AIDS education and the rest recommend it (Britton, de Mauro and Gambrell, 1992). Moreover, national opinion polls consistently demonstrate that a substantial majority of parents and other adults favor sexuality education in schools (Scales, 1984; Louis Harris and Associates, 1985, 1988; Alan Guttmacher Institute, 1989; Haffner and de Mauro, 1991).

Despite that support, and despite the research finding that no more than 1 to 3 percent of parents exercise the option to excuse their children from sexuality education (Scales, 1984), researchers estimated in 1979 that no more than 10 percent of U.S. school-children received comprehensive sexuality education (that is, no topics censored out of the curriculum in a full semester devoted to the subject, taken by the ninth grade) (Kirby, Alter and Scales, 1979). Twelve years later, in 1991, SIECUS was estimating the same thing: less than 10 percent of school children participate in sexuality education programs lasting at least forty hours (Haffner and de Mauro, 1991).

So with all the public opinion support, why has so little apparent progress been made? Why is it that numerous examples can be cited of districts accommodating opponents of sexuality education out of proportion to their small numbers—despite studies, recommendations and efforts of advocates? This chapter looks at various movements supporting and opposing sexuality education in schools during the ten years following a major nationwide study of opposition to sexuality education in communities (Scales, 1984) and suggests ways that proponents of sexuality education can confront opposition and further their programs.

Tracking Opponents' Influence

In the very first Gallup Poll on the issue in 1943, 68 percent of American adults favored sexuality education in the public schools ("Left, Right, or Center...," 1978). Despite that support, little sexuality content was included in school courses. It was not until the early 1960s that a few *colleges* began to offer scattered workshops on human sexuality (Kirkendall, 1965). Uncertainty about the effects of sexuality education, administrators' fears about real or imagined opposition and poor preparation of teachers were noted as reasons for the limited offerings in schools (Somerville, 1970). One study of 500 school districts found that most sexuality education programs were started between 1965 and 1968 (Hottois and Milner, 1975). In 1968, the Christian Crusade and the John Birch Society began publishing pamphlets and organizing opposition to sexuality education, charging that sexuality education caused sexual experimentation and undermined the family. These opposition tactics caused the restriction or elimination of numerous programs and a considerable loss of morale among teachers and administrators (Force, 1970).

In 1984, a study of 23 U.S. communities' experiences with sexuality education concluded that the reason for increased censorship and for schools' bowing to opposition pressure was fear of controversy on the part of administrators and teachers, fueled by organized opponents and enabled by disorganized or apathetic supporters (Scales, 1984). In another early study Scales and Kirby (1983) asked 104 leading sexuality educators to rate the importance of 165 possible barriers to sexuality education. They found that administrators' fear of opposition was the single greatest obstacle. The most important cluster of key barriers included the simultaneous organized activity of opponents (and their connection with national "right-wing" groups) and supporters' lack of political activity, such as visibly supporting sexuality education and voting in school board elections, and waiting until being attacked before becoming active.

In 1988, the Alan Guttmacher Institute (AGI) surveyed 4,241 seventh- through twelfth-grade public school teachers in five major disciplines (health, home economics, physical education, biology and nursing) from which the majority of sexuality education teachers are drawn (AGI, 1989). The Guttmacher findings paralleled the earlier research results: One in four teachers believed parents and local community groups did not support sexuality education. One in three thought their school administrators were nervous about possible controversies. And about one in five thought school officials didn't support them. Twenty-two percent of the teachers said pressure from parents, community groups or school administrators was their biggest problem in teaching sexuality education. Another 17 percent said their biggest problem was class materials that were dated, unavailable, difficult or uninteresting for students to read, or difficult to get approved for use (Forrest and Silverman, 1989).

People for the American Way, a group based in Washington, D.C., that monitors right-wing activities, reported in its annual survey that the 1990/91 school year represented the "most severe and widespread outbreak of school censorship" in the last ten years. One in ten challenges to books or programs were about sexuality education, and in one-third of the cases materials were restricted or removed (Sedway, 1992).

Opponents and Supporters, Then and Now

The sexuality education opponents of today represent the same alliance of religious groups and political organizations seen in the late sixties, late seventies and early eighties. The John Birch Society and Christian Crusade gave way to the Moral Majority and Christian Voice, and, most recently, to the Eagle Forum, Focus on the Family, Citizens for Excellence in Education and the Christian Coalition.

Today's groups are more powerful and influential for two primary reasons. First, in the 1960s, there were few causes other than anti-Communism added to the opposition to sexuality education. Today, anti-abortion, anti-gay, anti-school-reform, anti-humanist and pro-school-censorship groups often unite in their opposition to various programs. Second, technology has made it possible for groups such as the Christian Coalition to raise hundreds of millions of dollars from television ministries and sophisticated direct mail efforts to help underwrite activities such as publishing books and pamphlets and financing local school board campaigns. There is scant evidence that sexuality education supporters have learned how to anticipate attack and successfully defend against it (Haffner and de Mauro, 1991).

The arguments for and against sexuality education, and the strategies opponents and supporters use, have changed somewhat from those used from the mid-1960s to the mid-1980s. Opponents formerly argued that schools had no role in sexuality education, and that sexuality education was the sole province of parents and/or religious groups. The new strategy is for opponents of comprehensive sexuality education to define themselves as being in favor of sexuality education, so long as the curriculum exclusively emphasizes abstinence-only, or the "just say no" approach. Abstinence is defined in these curricula to mean that young people should refrain not just from sexual intercourse, but from *any* sexual activity (e.g., masturbation, breast fondling, kissing).

A decade ago, opponents opposed all mention of contraception. Today, the tactic is to argue instead that emphasis be placed on the failure rates of contraceptives. One school district in Missouri deleted references to erections and ejaculation from its health curriculum, but still mentioned condoms in the context of "what can go wrong with birth control devices" (Billingsley, 1992). Mentioning condoms without mentioning erections and ejaculation certainly raises the likelihood that something will indeed "go wrong."

For their part, supporters make fewer exaggerated claims for the positive benefits of sexuality education, e.g., that it will quickly and substantially reduce adolescent pregnancy, prevent HIV/AIDS and other STD, or reduce sexism and sexual violence. Today, supporters seem to be taking a more realistic view of the impact of sexuality education, claiming results to be positive but more modest, i.e., that it can help delay intercourse and lessen the incidence of adolescent pregnancy, but is not likely to eliminate either.

Supporters also point out that even a modest level of impact requires more class time than is usually devoted to sexuality education. For example, a study of more than 30,000 fourth-through seventh-grade students found that between thirty and fifty hours of coverage of various health topics is needed to produce a stable impact on behavior and attitudes (Connell, Turner and Mason, 1985).

Some fundamental dynamics have not changed. For example, the most common arguments opponents continue to use against comprehensive sexuality education is that parents are against it and that it will promote sexual activity.

With regard to parents' wishes, national opinion polls consistently have demonstrated that about 85 percent of parents and other adults favor sexuality education in the schools, including discussion about contraception (Scales, 1984; Louis Harris and Associates, 1985, 1988; Alan Guttmacher Institute, 1989; Haffner and de Mauro, 1991). An August 1992 Gallup Poll reported that seven in ten U.S. parents and other adults want schools to distribute condoms, a development that would have been unthinkable just ten years earlier (Elam, Rose, and Gallup, 1992). Another indication of parental support was reported earlier in a study of 23 U.S. communities: those communities that most significantly involved parents in the development of their sexuality education programs had the most comprehensive and least censored programs (Scales, 1984).

Research shows the claim that sexuality education promotes sexual activity to be as accurate as saying fire stations promote fires. The overwhelming weight of scientific evidence is that sexuality education based on abstinence that includes contraceptive information and practice in decision-making and communication skills can be very effective both in delaying initial intercourse and in increasing the use of contraception among sexually active adolescents (Zabin and Hirsch, 1988; Kirby, et al., 1991; Vincent, Clearie and Schluchter, 1987).

In the first of these studies, the social worker and nurse practitioner from a nearby clinic conducted in-school sexuality presentations and counseling at a junior and senior high school and made clinic appointments for students. Over three years, females in the program delayed sexual intercourse by an average of seven months, and pregnancies among participants dropped 26 percent versus a 59 percent increase among the control group.

In the second study, a 15-session social-learning-based curriculum, *Reducing the Risk*, was used with a large sample of ninth to twelfth graders. Teachers were given three days of training, and parent participation was stimulated through homework assignments. Over 18 months, there was a 24-percent reduction in first intercourse among participants, compared to control students.

The third study trained school teachers, clergy and parents, incorporated a peer counseling component and gained the cooperation of the local media in promoting to adolescents the message to wait, but to protect themselves if they did have sexual intercourse. Over four years, pregnancy rates among 14 to 17 year olds in the program county dropped 36 percent versus an increase of 15 percent in the control counties.

At the same time as supporters have softened their claims about sexuality education's positive effects and have looked increasingly to well-done research studies to buttress their case, opponents have begun to make exaggerated claims for the positive impact of the "just say no" programs. Two such claims are that sexuality education curricula do not lead to any increase in contraceptive use among teenagers and that the abstinence-only programs funded through the Office of Population Affairs' Adolescent Family Life Act do reduce sexual activity (Horn and Archer, 1992).

The studies described earlier demonstrate that, in fact, comprehensive curricula *can* promote the use of contraception. The second claim of opponents is only partly correct. Studies of "just say no" programs show that the only observable impact on sexual behavior is to help maintain for a brief time the virginity of those who have not yet had sexual intercourse; there are no behavioral effects on adolescents who are already sexually active. Mark Roosa and Scott Christopher of Arizona State University reviewed the studies of "just say no" programs and conducted their own evaluation under a grant from the same federal office that funds most of these programs, the Federal Office of Population Affairs. The conclusion from this thorough review was that the abstinence-only approach is an "unsuccessful model" (Roosa and Christopher, 1990). Two years later, the same research team reiterated their conclusions, saying that "after more than a decade of funding and evaluating abstinence-only programs..., [the Federal Office of Population Affairs] has not been able to provide any evidence that such approaches have been successful" (Roosa and Christopher, 1992).

Another example of opponents' exaggerated claims is found in a report published by Focus on the Family Publishing (Colorado Springs, Colorado), an arm of conservative religious leader James Dobson's Focus on the Family organization. It claims that "abstinence education...has effectively reduced the teenage pregnancy rate in many communities" (Richard, 1990). Among the evidence cited was the experience of a junior high school in San Marcos, California, with the Teen-Aid curriculum *Sexuality, Commitment and Family* (Potter and Roach, 1989), a curriculum the Florida Medical Association noted is "fraught with medical inaccuracies and outdated information" (Schild, 1992).

Teen-Aid claimed that the curriculum reduced the number of pregnancies in San Marcos Junior High from 147 in 1984/85 to

20 in 1986/87, an apparently astonishing result frequently cited in opponent literature on political organizing strategies (Wright, 1988). A phone call to San Marcos Junior High School to verify the Teen-Aid statistic revealed no behavioral data to back up the claims. The "data" were obtained by the school guidance counselor, who counted the number of students who voluntarily came in and said they thought they were pregnant.[1] Furthermore, the counselor who originally counted the 147 "pregnancies" in 1984/85 had "no idea" where the district came up with the figure of 20 two years later. District officials also admit that the number has no scientific basis and is inaccurate (National Education Association, 1992).

Opponents' willingness to make unsubstantiated claims means that supporters need to do their own verifications. If supporters read or hear of an unbelievable teen pregnancy reduction supposedly tied to a "just say no" program and unbelievable failure attributed to a comprehensive program, they should contact the schools themselves to ask whether these claims are based on data or just personal impressions, how such data were collected and if the data are available for anyone else to see.

Beyond Sexuality Education

In recent years, attacks on sexuality education have spread to other parts of the school curriculum, most often health education. Opponents in a variety of states from Maine to Washington have attacked classes on stress management, decision making, and critical thinking skills in what some observers have called a new "deluge of complaints" (Sommerfeld, 1992).

---

[1]Conversation 8 October 1992, between Peter Scales and Jerry Harrington, science and Teen-Aid curriculum teacher.

In other communities, activities designed to help students work in groups or teams (cooperative learning) and to promote their self-esteem have been attacked by Citizens for Excellence in Education (CEE). This group is part of the National Association of Christian Educators, based in Santa Ana, California. CEE is a self-described "grassroots Christian ministry" that, ironically, sees "religion" being taught in the promotion of self-esteem. CEE shares its materials with some thirty major politically conservative Christian organizations, such as Focus on the Family, mentioned earlier, and Phyllis Schlafly's Eagle Forum (headquartered in Alton, Illinois), and has such a far-reaching impact that People for the American Way calls it the "most destructive censorship organization active in the schools today" (Bradley, 1992). CEE polled its member ministers to identify the "hot" issues that helped them succeed in the 1992 elections. At the top of the list were self-esteem and sexuality education programs, with drug education likely to be a future target (People for the American Way, 1992a).[2]

Recommendations

Analysis of supporter and opponent tactics over the last thirty years leads to a solid conclusion: Opponents are likely to have a strong impact only when supporters are apathetic and disorganized. If supporters testify at school board meetings and other forums; nurture good relationships with school administrators, board members and media before crises develop; involve parents; and take steps similar to their opponents, the force of opponents' attacks is substantially blunted.

---

[2]Lists of these organizations are available from the Sex Information and Education Council of the United States, Planned Parenthood Federation of America, People for the American Way and the National Education Association.

The following ten steps are recommended to school officials and supporters of sexuality education to help increase the likelihood of a successful comprehensive sexuality education program.

Develop a statement of shared values. Out of the glare of publicity, most "opponents" and "supporters" of sexuality education share many of the same basic values and hopes for children. Unfortunately, too often schools and districts have not identified those common values, and the differences of opinion on a few issues overshadow the agreement on the vast majority. Districts should develop a statement of the values that most adults in the community share that are the foundation for sexuality education programs in the district's schools. A statement of values should be generated by the advisory council a district has established to deal with sexuality or health education. It should be adopted by the district administration and perhaps officially by the school board as a framework for the sexuality education curriculum. A sample statement of values can be found in Appendix E.

Engage in broad-based planning involving parents and representing many points of view. This is an important step for three reasons. First, the more parents are involved, the more comprehensive school sexuality education programs tend to be (Scales, 1984). Second, the statement of values developed by bringing together those who do not all hold the same initial viewpoints strengthens the capacity of the resulting program to withstand criticism because it has invited citizen involvement. Communities using broad-based community task forces are more likely to gradually build consensus and support (Celis, 1993). Third, the resulting program will likely be more effective in helping young people avoid adolescent pregnancy, either through delayed sexual intercourse or increased use of contraception. Murray Vincent and colleagues at the University of South Carolina demonstrated a 36 percent reduction in pregnancy rates among adolescents (compared to a 15 percent rise in the control group) when parents, clergy, school staff and the local media all were providing the same message to young people: Wait to have intercourse, but if you do not wait, protect yourself from pregnancy and disease (Vincent, Clearie and Schluchter, 1987).

Adopt realistic goals. Supporters of sexuality programs are beginning to acknowledge that, although the effects of such programs on young people's behavior can be very positive, significant impact on adolescent pregnancy and other social problems is much more likely when prevention programs are part of a broader, positive youth development agenda that includes steps to reduce poverty, support families, reform schooling more generally, increase young people's access to physical and mental health care, and enhance adolescents' connections to their communities (Scales, 1991; Dryfoos, 1990; Schorr, 1988). The state of Virginia, for example, has adopted a wide-ranging primary prevention plan that recognizes the interconnection among various youth problems and the greater effectiveness of strategies that attend simultaneously to multiple aspects of young people's lives (Virginia Council on Coordinating Prevention, 1992).

Even when embedded in a broader agenda, the likelihood of most sexuality education programs greatly affecting complex problems such as adolescent pregnancy and HIV/AIDS is limited. The U.S. Health Goals for the Year 2000, for example, generally call for improvements in these areas on the order of 1 to 1-1/2 percent per year (Department of Health and Human Services, 1991). The state of Oregon has established "benchmarks" of state progress that are even more modest, calling for reducing adolescent pregnancy by 1/2 of 1 percent per year between now and the year 2010 (Proffer, 1992). More realistic short-term goals include increases in factual knowledge, and, if sufficient hours have been devoted to the program (a rarity), some change in the attitudes or behavioral intentions that support abstinence or use of contraception and the communication and decision-making skills needed to act on those intentions.

Be willing to compromise, but within limits. Sexuality educators and administrators of programs should identify areas in which they are willing and unwilling to compromise. In a given community setting, for example, it might be possible to have a sexuality education program that includes everything but planned discussion of homosexuality. In another community, planned discussion of contraception might be the issue that most opponents wish to be prohibited. It is important to point out that only *planned* discussion of a topic can be limited: one non-negotiable point needs to be that students can raise and teachers can respond to *any* question, whether the topic is prohibited or allowed.

This proviso does not mean teachers are required to answer all questions, merely that they are allowed to. Some teachers in some circumstances might feel that referring a student to parents or to a religious leader for an answer is the best response they can make. They must be free to do so. However, teachers who feel capable of responding to student questions or issues raised must also be free to do so as trained professionals working in an atmosphere committed to academic freedom.

Compromise must occur within the limits set by the district's broad values statement and other policies, as well as the goals of the program. For example, if a goal is that the program will help prevent adolescent pregnancy, prohibiting discussion of contraception will make it less likely to attain that goal. Compromise about the grades in which certain content will be formally introduced is often possible, as is compromise on the materials that might be used in the program. Supporters must have a clear sense, however, of when compromise is ill advised. In some communities, any compromise might be a mistake, because opponents have said or indicated that their real goal is to eliminate the sexuality education program.

Another ill-advised compromise is to grant opponents their request for an alternative "just say no" course. Although a parental excusal option is always advisable, an entire alternative course is not, because it calls into question the whole curriculum, not just sexuality education and the governing process of the schools. If some parents do not like the language arts, science or social studies classes, will they be offered "alternatives" to these too? Enough alternatives, and there would soon be a "private" school set up within the walls of the public one, paid for by the taxpayers.

Use small groups when possible. Large formal meetings bring out the most rigid stances of both supporters and opponents. Often covered by the media, these can become occasions for demonstrating the depth of one's convictions and the breadth of one's support in the community rather than a forum for a rational exchange of views leading to a negotiated compromise. Whenever possible, it is more effective to use smaller groups such as advisory councils to consider various curriculum issues and report back to the board. In these smaller groups (which ideally would include parents, teachers, community resource people, administrators, clergy and students), individuals are less likely to be posturing to their own constituencies and more likely to be open to identifying areas of agreement, the first step in reaching a workable solution to a controversial issue.

Provide teacher, administrator and school board training. Among the biggest errors districts make is failure to invest in training for teachers, administrators and board members. This goes beyond the training teachers need to provide an effective sexuality education program. Teachers, administrators and board members need training on the issues discussed in this chapter.

For example, principals and superintendents often handle sexuality education by issuing vague directions to teachers: "Just don't do anything that embarrasses the school or district." But what specific behaviors does that involve? Are teachers not to talk about their personal opinions? not to share personal experiences? not to talk about contraception? not to be humorous?

Like any other subject, a health and sexuality education curriculum requires a variety of teaching methods and approaches. Well-trained professionals actively involve students in their own learning through activities such as asking questions (Socratic method), roleplays and small group projects. They know when to help students think more deeply about an issue and when to pull back. Occasional use of humor and personal anecdotes to illustrate a point is no less appropriate in sexuality education than it is in history or the sciences. The key to interpreting what is acceptable is of course the context in which it occurs. That is why principals and curriculum coordinators should observe sexuality classes as they do all other subjects to gain a firsthand understanding of how teachers approach the subject matter.

Another common problem arises when administrators expect no controversy about sexuality education. While controversies may be more frequent in sexuality education, they are not unique to that subject. Any curriculum that causes students to grapple with challenging ideas is open to controversy, regardless of the subject being studied.

Administrative support is crucial to effective teaching. Administrators who want effective sexuality education programs must provide adequate inservice training for their teachers, or, when possible, hire teachers who have preservice sexuality education training through teacher preparation programs. Equally as important, administrators must themselves be willing to frequently and publicly discuss sexuality education, even if they are uncomfortable doing so, assertively support their staff, and articulate the reasons for the program and respond to opponents' concerns.

Have a parental excusal option. Most school districts allow parents to excuse their children from part or all of a sexuality education program. The data suggest that no more than 1 to 3 percent of parents elect this option. Some parents complain that excusing their children would cause other students to make fun of him or her. One response might be that this is an appropriate time for parents who do not want their children to participate in a sexuality education class to explain why so that the children can better understand their parents' values.

Have a procedure for responding to complaints. Often, a single parental complaint (sometimes unsigned) causes teachers to be told to change their curriculum or their approach. Teachers should be presumed innocent unless proven guilty, and that presumption should be put in writing, approved by the school board and vigorously practiced by school officials.

One of the best defenses against accusations about teachers is a "walk-around" principal who visits classes and a policy of teachers teaming or observing each other frequently. Sexuality education teachers should invite administrators, school board members and colleagues to observe them firsthand so that they will feel confident when responding to claims about what is supposedly going on in that teacher's classes.

Know the opposition and their concerns. Those truly opposed to sexuality education tend to be few in number in most communities. Many people have reasonable questions about issues such as what content is appropriate at different grades, what the effects of sexuality education are, what the qualifications and training of sexuality education teachers should be, and what role parents will have in curriculum development. An open and broad policy of participation usually satisfies most people that their concerns can be aired and that the school district welcomes their contributions.

Others, however, will be satisfied with no compromise and no reasonable response from school officials, because their agenda involves less the sexuality education program per se than control of the public schools (see recommendation 10). Supporters must know what the research says about various reasonable concerns and practice articulating these responses so they are prepared when under fire in a public setting. An excellent source for advocates is SIECUS's revised *Winning the Battle: Developing Support for Sexuality and HIV/AIDS Education* (Haffner and de Mauro, 1991). But supporters must find out what opponents' real concerns are, and not try to respond with research or logic to opponents whose agenda transcends the surface issue they might raise.

For example, if supporters feel an opponent's real agenda is not sexuality education per se but opposition to school reform in general, the choice of how to respond must be made carefully. It is sometimes better to ignore the larger issue and stick with the specifics, but at other times, it is more advisable to show that the specific sexuality education opposition is just a hint of things to come. The choice often will depend on supporters' assessment of the forum they are in (e.g., school board meeting versus church group discussion), the audience they are trying to convince (e.g., principals versus nurses) and the presence or lack of additional opportunities to influence that audience (e.g., Will there be a vote immediately? Will there be follow-up meetings?).

Be politically active. The Christian Coalition (founded by evangelist Pat Robertson and based in Virginia Beach, Virginia) had sixty chapters in 48 states at election time, running school board candidates who hid their religious agenda (the "stealth technique") which, for many, included abolition of public schools, and who were prepared to run their campaigns through a sophisticated video-based training (NBC Nightly News, 1992). CEE also used the stealth technique, and candidates backed by CEE were predicted to win nearly 3,000 school board seats across the nation in 1992, with vows to restore "Godly morals" to the classroom (Bradley, 1992). According to People for the American Way, the far right did win almost half of the races its candidates entered (People for the American Way, 1992b). In Greenville, South Carolina, one such candidate won a public school board seat by keeping hidden from voters the fact that her children went to a fundamentalist church school and by concealing her opposition to school courses that try to build self-esteem, among other matters ("Parent Who Shuns School…," 1992).

If they do not themselves run for office, supporters must research the full background and positions of every candidate for local offices and help get out the vote for candidates who support a view of democratic, public education in which health education and sexuality education are fundamental components. Especially in school board elections in nonpresidential years, low turnouts of 10 to 20 percent of eligible voters are common, so margins of a few hundred votes or fewer can make the difference in these contests. No amount of community involvement or curriculum committee service by supporters will further their cause if the school board is solidly controlled by those who oppose comprehensive health and sexuality education.

Finally, supporters need to arrange for positive letters to the editor, newspaper articles and electronic media coverage. Too often, supporters are heard from primarily in response to an opponent's attack or negative opinion piece. There has been some debate about whether even to respond to letters, articles, or radio and television programs that make ludicrous or inaccurate claims about sexuality education. The argument is that dignifying the attack with a response hands opponents more forum than they already have. Those who advance this argument hope that "reasonable" people will see and reject the far-right agenda and extreme viewpoints that are often skillfully disguised by moderate-sounding prose.

Choosing not to respond to an occasional attack may be a wise tactic, but what happens when supporters fail to respond to today's persistent and well-organized sexuality education opponents? The strident letters will not stop; the attacks on curriculum and teachers will not abate. Pundits comparing the election of Bill Clinton to the presidency in 1992 with the defeat of Michael Dukakis in the 1988 campaign were unanimous in agreeing that a key ingredient of the Clinton success was a quick and tough response to every charge. Local sexuality education battles are not presidential campaigns, but the politics can get just as nasty. Supporters are silent at their own peril.

Conclusion

Supporters of comprehensive health education and sexuality education, including parents, teachers, school administrators and other citizens, ultimately must have a vision of where health and sexuality education fit within the restructured schooling of the twenty-first century. As battles rage about parental "choice" of schools their children attend, different forms of governance, teacher preparation, expected student outcomes and alternative forms of assessment, it is not enough to justify these areas of study merely as potential prevention against pregnancy, HIV/AIDS, and other sexually transmitted disease.

Ultimately, students' health is intimately related to their readiness to learn. Moreover, health and sexuality education for adolescents represents a crucial area of academic content because of its potential for enhancing the critical thinking skills at the top of most education reform agendas. Studying the collisions of values and technology, of individual belief and social policy, is the training ground for effective citizenship and leadership in a democratic society. That is why health and sexuality education are as important for young people to study as language arts, science, social studies and mathematics. Supporters should follow the steps outlined in this chapter, but they must do so within a framework that has as its foundation a clear and convincing rationale for the centrality of health and sexuality education to the definition of being educated for the twenty-first century.

References

Alan Guttmacher Institute. 1989. *Risk and responsibility: Teaching sex education in America's schools today.* New York.

Billingsly, L. 1992. Revised health class adopted by Board. *St. Louis Post Dispatch*, March 2.

Bradley, A. 1992. Christian activists set their sights on school board seats. *Education Week* 12 (5): 1, 16-17.

Britton, P. O., D. de Mauro and A. F. Gambrell. 1992. HIV/AIDS education: SIECUS study on HIV/AIDS education finds states make progress but work remains. *SIECUS Report* 21 (1): 1-8.

Celis, W., III. 1993. Schools across U.S. cautiously adding lessons on gay life. *New York Times*, January 6.

Connell, D. B., R. R. Turner and E. F. Mason. 1985. Summary of findings of the school health education evaluation: Health promotion effectiveness, implementation, and costs. *Journal of School Health* 55 (8): 316-321.

Department of Health and Human Services. 1991. Healthy people 2000: Objectives related to schools. *Journal of School Health* 61 (7): 298-322.

Dryfoos, J. G. 1990. *Adolescents at risk: Prevalence and prevention.* New York: Oxford.

Elam, S. M., L. C. Rose and A. M. Gallup. 1992. The 24th annual Gallup/Phi Delta Kappa poll of the public's attitudes toward the public schools. *Phi Delta Kappan* 73 (1): 41-53.

Force, E. S. 1970. Family life education 1970: A regional survey. *Family Coordinator* 19 (4): 295-300.

Forrest, J. D., and J. Silverman. 1989. What public school teachers teach about preventing pregnancy, AIDS, and sexually transmitted diseases. *Family Planning Perspectives* 21 (2): 65-72.

Haffner, D. W. 1992. 1992 report card on the states: Sexual rights in America. *SIECUS Report* 20 (3): 1-7.

Haffner, D. W., and D. de Mauro. 1991. *Winning the battle: Developing support for sexuality and HIV/AIDS education.* New York: Sex Information and Education Council of the United States.

Horn, W. F., and W. Archer. 1992. Misguided attack on president's policies. Letter to the editor. *USA Today,* August 14.

Hottois, J., and N. A. Milner. 1975. *The sex education controversy.* Lexington, MA: D. C. Heath.

Kirby, D., J. Alter and P. Scales. 1979. *An analysis of U.S. sexuality education programs and evaluation methods.* Springfield, VA: National Technical Information Service.

Kirby, D., R. P. Barth, N. Leland and J. V. Fetro. 1991. Reducing the risk: Impact of a new curriculum on sexual risk-taking. *Family Planning Perspectives* 23 (6): 253-263.

Kirkendall, L. A. 1965. Evaded problem—Sex on campus. *Family Coordinator* 14 (1): 20-24.

Left, right or center, which way are we going? 1978. *Public Opinion* (October): 33-40.

Louis Harris and Associates. 1985. *Public attitudes about sex education, family planning and abortion in the United States.* New York: Planned Parenthood Federation of America.

Louis Harris and Associates. 1988. *Public attitudes toward teen pregnancy, sex education and birth control.* New York: Planned Parenthood Federation of America.

National Education Association. 1992. Sex abstinence curriculum didn't cause "miracle" drop in pregnancy rate. *Preserving Public Education—Report to the Board of Directors.* Washington, DC: National Education Association.

NBC Nightly News. 1992. November 2.

Parent who shuns school wins board seat. 1992. *New York Times,* 27 December.

People for the American Way. 1992a. And the winner is... *Right-Wing Watch* 3 (3): 2.

People for the American Way. 1992b. Getting Ready for '94 and '96. *Right-Wing Watch* 3 (3): 1-2.

Potter, S., and N. Roach. 1989. *Sexuality, commitment and family.* 3d ed. Spokane, WA: Teen-Aid, Inc.

Proffer, L. 1992. Benchmarks to a better Oregon. *State Legislatures* 18 (7): 33-35.

Richard, D. 1990. *Has sex education failed our teenagers?* Colorado Springs: Focus on the Family Publishing.

Roosa, M. W., and F. S. Christopher. 1990. Evaluation of an abstinence-only adolescent pregnancy prevention program: A replication. *Family Relations* October 39 (4): 363-367.

Roosa, M. W., and F. S. Christopher. 1992. A response to Thiel and McBride: Scientific criticism or obscurantism? *Family Relations* 41 (4): 468-469.

Scales, P. C. 1984. *The front lines of sexuality education: A guide to building and maintaining community support.* Santa Cruz, CA: ETR Associates.

Scales, P. C. 1991. *A portrait of young adolescents in the 1990s: Implications for promoting healthy growth and development.* Carrboro, NC: Center for Early Adolescence, University of North Carolina at Chapel Hill.

Scales, P. C., and D. Kirby. 1983. Perceived barriers to sex education: A survey of professionals. *Journal of Sex Research* 19 (4): 309-326.

Schild, F. 1992. Letter to Betty Castor, Department of Education, Commissioner, Florida State. 29 June.

Schorr, L. 1988. *Within our reach: Breaking the cycle of disadvantage.* New York: Anchor Press.

Sedway, M. 1992. Far right takes aim at sexuality education. *SIECUS Report* 20 (3): 12-19.

Somerville, R. M. 1970. *Family life and sex education in the turbulent sixties.* In *A decade of family research and action,* ed. C. B. Broderick, 215-239. Minneapolis, MN: National Council on Family Relations.

Sommerfeld, M. 1992. Health educators seek help in handling controversy. *Education Week* 12 (1): 8.

Vincent, M. L., A. F. Clearie and M. D. Schluchter. 1987. Reducing adolescent pregnancy through school and community-based education. *Journal of the American Medical Association* 257 (24): 3382-3386.

Virginia Council on Coordinating Prevention. 1992. *1992-2000 comprehensive prevention plan for Virginia.* Richmond, VA.

Wright, L. 1988. *Sex education: How to respond.* Golf, IL: Project Respect.

Zabin, L. S., and M. B. Hirsch. 1988. *Evaluation of pregnancy prevention programs in the school context.* Lexington, MA: D. C. Heath/Lexington Books.

Sexuality Education in School Settings

Chapter 5

Foundations of Teaching: Sexuality Education in the Classroom

Roberta J. Ogletree, HSD, CHES

Formal education about sexuality should begin as soon as a child enters the educational system, whether that be preschool, kindergarten or first grade, and should continue through high school and college. The ideal scenario would be to provide comprehensive sexuality education prekindergarten through twelfth grade and college within a comprehensive health education program (Neutens et al., 1991; National Guidelines Task Force, 1991).

The Sex Information and Education Council of the United States (SIECUS) defines human sexuality as: "the totality of being a person. It includes all of those aspects of the human being that relate specifically to being boy or girl, woman or man, and is an entity subject to lifelong dynamic change. Sexuality reflects our human character, not solely our genital nature" (Hawkins, 1980).

Bruess and Greenberg (1988) further emphasize the broad nature and scope of human sexuality. They describe four dimensions of human sexuality: biological, cultural, ethical and psychological. All elements of the sexuality education program reflect one or more of those dimensions. Reproductive and sexual anatomy and physiology are components of the biological dimension. Gender roles are part of the cultural dimension. Questions and decisions about what is right and what is wrong regarding sexual behavior are elements of the ethical dimension. Emotions and learned responses are part of the psychological dimension. This multidimensional approach, based upon a broad definition of human sexuality, provides a foundation for teaching about sexuality at all levels. Several factors are important to the success of a sexuality education program regardless of the grade level at which the program is being taught.

Principles, Goals and Objectives

What guides a sexuality education program? What provides the foundation upon which the program is based? All sexuality education programs should have a guiding philosophy that reflects the broad definition of human sexuality. All of the knowledge, attitudes and skills that students acquire from a sexuality education program should be related to the basic principles, goals and objectives formulated based on that philosophy.

SIECUS has adopted 19 principles basic to education for sexuality that deserve the attention of sexuality educators (National Guidelines Task Force, 1991). These may serve as a guide to school districts as well as individual sexuality educators.

Goals and objectives of a sexuality education program depend upon the philosophy of the school district, and that philosophy should reflect the values of the community. Many school districts report goals that deal with the following:
• promoting informed decision making about sexuality

- increasing knowledge about reproduction
- reducing sexual activity
- reducing teenage pregnancy

A word of caution about the last two goals: Reduction of sexual activity and teen pregnancy may not be realistic goals for sexuality education programs at the present time. As a sexuality educator or an advocate of sexuality education, do not inflate the goals and potential of sexuality education. It is difficult to change behavior, and promising behavior change may set a program up for failure. Avoid establishing goals that may be unrealistic.

The National Guidelines Task Force (1991) has identified four primary goals for comprehensive sexuality education programs:

1. to provide accurate information about human sexuality
2. to provide an opportunity for young people to develop their values, attitudes and beliefs about sexuality
3. to help young people develop relationships and interpersonal skills
4. to help young people exercise responsibility regarding sexual relationships

The other chapters in this section will discuss specific objectives (knowledge, affective and behavioral) appropriate for different grade levels.

Groundrules

Groundrules serve important functions in the sexuality education classroom at every level, prekindergarten through college. Whenever possible, a class can generate their own groundrules, with the teacher suggesting any that are left out. If possible, groundrules should be posted where they are visible for easy reference.

The two basic purposes of groundrules are to create an atmosphere of trust and comfort that encourages students to participate freely and to clarify language and behavior that is acceptable for use in the classroom.

In addition, groundrules:
- help students know what to expect from the teacher and other students
- reassure administrators, parents and community members that there are boundaries set
- increase teacher effectiveness
- teach students to respect each others' right to express differing opinions
- help avoid situations that could lead to controversy

Here is a list of issues that groundrules should address. Each issue is followed by a sample groundrule.
- Use of language: "Use correct terms instead of slang whenever possible."
- Level of disclosure: "Don't discuss personal matters or ask personal questions."
- Reactions to questions: "There are no 'dumb' questions."
- Acceptance of feelings: "Be sensitive to others' feelings."
- Right to privacy: "It is OK to 'pass' on a question." "Don't discuss comments made in class outside of class."
- Respect for others: "No put-downs allowed."
- Need to involve parents: "Discuss the issues raised in class with parents, but don't exaggerate."

There are many additional groundrules that might be generated by a class, but this list provides a good framework within which to work.

Teacher Training

In order to be effective sexuality educators, teachers need adequate preservice and inservice training, no matter the level at which they will be providing sexuality education. Teacher training is essential because educators must know the subject matter well *and* be able to communicate it effectively. A gap sometimes exists between what teachers know and how effectively they communicate that information. Preservice and inservice training often help to bridge that gap.

A critical issue for those assigned to teach sexuality education is comfort with the role. If a teacher is not comfortable teaching about human sexuality, more knowledge is not going to make that teacher an effective sexuality educator. A teacher who is knowledgeable but is not comfortable with his or her own sexuality is less likely to be an effective sexuality educator.

Professional preparation in sexuality education should provide knowledge regarding sexual growth and development and sexual pressures and concerns affecting different age groups. Equally important, preparation programs must include skills training to help teachers respond to the questions students ask, as well as teach students the skills they need to make decisions about sexuality.

Preparation programs can help teachers understand the values underlying different sexuality issues and become aware of their own feelings, attitudes and values regarding sexuality. This type of educational training can improve educators' understanding of human sexuality and increase their comfort level with it. Unfortunately, relatively few who will be called upon to teach sexuality education in the schools will have had the luxury of professional preparation in human sexuality education. Because of this, continuing education and inservice training are essential.

Teachers as Models

Another very important consideration is that, at every grade level, teachers serve as models to students. Though they may not overtly model sexual behavior, teachers constantly respond and react to sexuality-related issues, sexual innuendos and jokes, and student sexuality-related behavior. Training can help the educator rehearse the skills needed to respond to these situations in a manner that promotes a healthy and positive attitude about sexuality.

Teacher training will prepare educators to successfully deal with issues of sex equity and multiculturalism. Teachers should promote and foster sex equity in the classroom and avoid adopting or using materials that encourage or reinforce sexual stereotypes. In addition, it is important for teachers to recognize cultural differences in beliefs regarding human sexuality. Awareness of cultural differences in sexual attitudes and practices can prevent controversy if the teacher brings such differences to the attention of students. In failing to discuss such cultural differences, teachers may appear to dismiss the concerns and experiences of minority students as unimportant. Educators also must be aware of situations in which students are in the process of acculturation (learning and integrating into a new culture).

Relevant Content

An effective sexuality education program at any grade level should be designed to meet the needs of the individual and the community. Content of sexuality education should be guided by the needs, interests and developmental characteristics of students. In addition, community needs and values are an important source of curriculum content. Community values must be incorporated not only to serve the needs of the community, but also to avoid controversy that could undermine or eliminate the program altogether.

Children need and want information that relates to what they are presently experiencing in their lives. The preschool child may want to know more about how the baby growing inside mommy got there. The early secondary school student may be interested in learning about dating and relationships.

Relevant sexuality education also means taking advantage of teachable moments. When Magic Johnson announced that he was infected with HIV, classrooms all over the United States were buzzing with discussion. Early in President Clinton's administration, the issue of gays in the military was in the news daily. This media coverage provided excellent opportunities for discussing different attitudes toward homosexuality in our society. Current events offer numerous opportunities to discuss sexuality-related issues.

Emphasis should be placed on the positive aspects of human sexuality, rather than dwelling excessively on the negative outcomes of sexual behavior, such as sexually transmitted disease and unplanned pregnancy. Children of all ages need to view sexuality as an important and positive part of their lives and recognize its relation to wellness and good health.

Other Sources of Sexuality Education

There are several sources of sexuality education outside of the school setting. Parents, peers, siblings, media and churches provide children with sexual information. Teachers must recognize that they may be competing with these sources in the provision of accurate information. More important, teachers must devise means by which to help students recognize the value and/or the limitations of information from these sources.

Partnerships with parents and caregivers can be formed so that the school and home can work together to provide students with sexuality education. Parents should always be informed of material and activities carried out in the classroom. Such cooperation helps ensure that students will not be receiving conflicting messages from school and home.

Peers are often cited as a major source of sexuality information for school-age children. However, peers are not always an accurate source of information. Therefore, it is important that the sexuality educator counteract the influence of misinformation given by peers. A perceptive teacher will pick up misinformation that is being passed around among students and strive to provide accurate information.

Sexuality education can encourage evaluation of sexual messages from various sources. For example, students might be required to examine the sexual messages being sent via the media, then encouraged to think about and analyze the potential effects of messages from soap operas, music videos, song lyrics and movies.

Avoiding Controversy

Many communities are experiencing resistance to sexuality education in the schools as a result of pressures exerted by small but vocal community groups. Yet, all major public opinion polls reveal that there is overwhelming parent support for sexuality education in the schools (Louis Harris and Associates, 1985, 1988; Haffner, 1989). The need for community and parental support and involvement cannot be overemphasized. When parents and other community representatives are involved in all phases of curriculum development and delivery, the needs, values and concerns of the community can be voiced and incorporated into the curriculum.

For obvious reasons it is preferable to take an active stance with regard to controversy. Steps to prevent the development of controversy should be taken and policies and procedures should be in place in case controversy should erupt.

Parents can be advocates for sexuality education. The 1989 *Risk and Responsibility* study by the Alan Guttmacher Institute recommended that parents serve as advocates by conveying their support for sex education to teachers and school administrators, meeting with school personnel to review course content and materials, serving on sex education advisory committees and increasing their personal levels of sexuality knowledge to meet their children's needs.

Another common cause of controversy in the schools is improper implementation (Ames et al., 1992). Situations that reflect improper curriculum implementation often revolve around the teacher. For this reason, it remains crucial for the teacher to have adequate background and training. Potential causes of controversy might include inappropriate guest speakers, use of materials without preview, personal bias, and inappropriate use of slang. Adequate teacher preparation and training can help prevent these problems from occurring.

The Role of Parents

Parents should be involved in all phases of the sexuality education program in the schools. This includes the planning, implementation and evaluation stages of the program. A study by the Alan Guttmacher Institute in the early 1980s revealed that only 28 percent of high schools had involved parents in the development of sexuality education curricula (Orr, 1982). The same study revealed that when more parents were involved, more topics were covered in the classes.

At the very least, parents should be notified when a sexuality education unit is approaching so they will have the opportunity to discuss content and objectives with the teacher. In addition, students should be encouraged to discuss class topics with their parents. If possible, parent/child homework assignments to encourage discussion between parent and child should be a part of the curriculum.

Parents can be given the opportunity to participate in the design of the curriculum through parent surveys that determine what the parents want included in a sexuality education program. In addition, parents should be invited to sit on committees charged with the task of determining goals and objectives for the sex education curriculum. Parents should be actively involved in the selection of the curriculum when a prepackaged curriculum is being considered for adoption. If the curriculum is to be developed locally, parents should be key members on the committee to develop curriculum content.

Parents can be involved in the curriculum implementation by allowing them to preview the materials that will be used in the classroom. This can be done through parent preview presentations or by sending a letter to parents encouraging them to come by the school to preview materials.

Parents should also be involved in the evaluation of the curriculum. This can be accomplished through surveys and/or feedback from parent committees regarding the adequacy of the program. Parents should be involved in updating curricula, as well.

This chapter has looked at essential components of the sexuality education program regardless of the level at which it is taught. The remaining chapters in this section deal with issues and concerns related to specific grade levels.

References

Alan Guttmacher Institute. 1989. *Risk and responsibility: Teaching sex education in America's schools today.* New York.

Ames, E. E., L. A. Trucano, J. C. Wan and M. H. Harris. 1992. *Designing school health curricula.* Dubuque, IA: Wm. C. Brown.

Bruess, C. E., and J. S. Greenberg. 1988. *Sexuality education: Theory and practice.* New York: Macmillan.

Haffner, D. W. 1989. Human sexuality education: Whose job is it anyway? *SIECUS Report* 17 (1): 11-12.

Hawkins, R. O. 1980. The Uppsala connection: The development of principles basic to education for sexuality. *SIECUS Report* 8 (3): 1.

National Guidelines Task Force. 1991. *Guidelines for comprehensive sexuality education: Kindergarten–12th grade.* New York: Sex Information and Education Council of the United States.

Neutens, J. J., J. C. Drolet, M. L. Dushaw and W. Jubb. 1991. *Sexuality education within comprehensive school health education.* Kent, OH: American School Health Association.

Orr, M. T. 1982. Sex education and contraceptive education in U.S. public high schools. *Family Planning Perspectives* 14 (6): 304-313.

Chapter 6

Sexuality Education in the Early Elementary Classroom

Peggy Brick, MEd

Young children are alive with curiosity about how their bodies work, why boys and girls are different, how babies are born and grow. Early childhood educators' response to children's curiosity gives them messages—either positive or negative—about themselves as sexual beings. Positive responses lay the foundation for sexual health and self-esteem by helping children feel good about their bodies, good about being male or female, and good about the adults who are willing to help them figure things out.

Every preschool and elementary teacher is a sexuality educator. In every classroom, teachers give messages related to sexuality: children see how the teacher acts as a male or female; responds to sex-related behavior, comments or jokes; sets expectations for boys and girls; and includes, or fails to include, information on sexuality issues. The question is not *whether* children will receive sex education in schools—they will—but whether the learning will be haphazard or thoughtfully designed to lay the foundation for development toward sexually healthy adulthood.

Young children need schools and teachers that will help them overcome the destructive sexual images that pervade today's environment. Children are surrounded by mixed messages. Provocative media idealize perfect bodies, reinforce limiting gender stereotypes, associate sex and violence, and disassociate sexual behavior from its consequences. Children are privy to mysterious adult controversies regarding HIV/AIDS, homosexuality and abortion. They are confronted with changing lifestyles and relationships within their own families. Many are sexually abused—some by inappropriate touch, others by a lack of nurturing touch (Leight, 1988). Yet despite this overwhelming need, schools have been reluctant to initiate planned sexuality education in the early years and to help parents assume a more active partnership role in supporting children's healthy sexual development (Krivacska, 1992).

This reluctance, which leaves the majority of children without adequate adult guidance on sexuality-related matters, seems to be primarily the result of four forces. The first is a vociferous minority that condemns any attempt to formalize sexuality education in the schools. This opposition is particularly effective in discouraging initiatives in elementary schools because most school boards, administrators, teachers and parents are unclear themselves about the meaning and importance of sexual learning for young children. They are not prepared either as educators or individuals to be advocates for children against a well-organized and angry opposition (Haffner and de Mauro, 1991).

A second deterrent is the fact that most early childhood educators have not received training in sexuality education and, therefore, are uncomfortable with the prospect of opening honest discussion on sexuality topics with children. In no other area of the curriculum are teachers more likely to be expected to begin a program without adequate preparation. Untrained teachers, who are likely to be unclear about the meaning of early sexuality education and to lack evidence of adequate administrative and board of education support, are ill prepared and reluctant to take on this role.

A third barrier is that adults in general are confused about the meaning of sexual learning in the early years. Somehow the illusion of childhood "innocence" remains—and with it the belief that a school program would arouse children's curiosity. Sexuality education, which many think of as focused on reproductive anatomy, disease and pregnancy prevention, seems inappropriate for young children.

The fourth barrier, discouraging even to the most dedicated teachers, is the burden of finding time to teach new subjects, especially when these are added to already heavy responsibilities (including alcohol, tobacco and other drug use prevention) when at the same time they are under increasing pressure to raise student test scores in traditional academic subjects.

To address these barriers and to meet the sexuality education needs of young children at the early elementary stage, program planners must set goals for their program and commit to teaching the skills children need to grow up sexually healthy.

Goals for Early Sexuality Education

It is important to demystify the idea of sexuality education in early childhood. An examination of sexual development during childhood (see Figure 1) suggests that four goals are key to laying a healthy foundation for a sexually healthy adulthood (Martinson, 1992; Constantine and Martinson, 1981; Gagnon and Roberts, 1980; Langfeldt, 1990). In a successful sexuality program at the elementary level:

Young children will learn that it's okay to talk about sex and ask questions about it. By the time they are six or seven, most children

---

Figure 1
The Sexual Development of Young Children

Newborn to 18 Months
- Begins to develop gender identity.
- Begins to develop gender role.
- Has sexual responses such as erections and lubrication.
- Discovers genitals and self-pleasuring.
- Learns to value self through nurturing body contact.
- Begins to develop a negative or positive attitude towards own body.

18 Months to 3 Years
- Learns language for genitals and body functions.
- Receives many "messages" from parents and other caregivers.
  — Use of euphemisms for genitals may lead to confusion.
  — Clitoris is often ignored.
  — Masturbation is often discouraged or disapproved of.
- Continues need for body contact.

3 to 4 Years
- Is certain about gender but may not be sure of its permanence.
- Develops sense of "acceptable" behavior.
- Is curious about differences in boys' and girls' bodies.
- Is curious about own origins—where babies come from and how they get out.
- Explores sexuality through play with dolls and peers.
- Mimics adult behavior.
- Tries out bathroom language/"adult" curse words.

5 and 6 Years
- Has strong same-sex friendships.
- Shows strong interest in male/female roles, often stereotypes.
- Often engages in name-calling and teasing.
- Continues sex play and masturbation.
- Is curious about how babies are made.
- Can learn about limits, privacy and manners.
- Can learn to say "no" to unwanted touch.

Figure 1 (continued)

5 and 6 Years (continued)
- Can learn personal responsibility for welfare of own body.
- Explores adult relationships by playing "being" a mother or father.
- Probably has a basic sexual orientation.
- Needs body contact, but usually less than previously.

Adapted from:

P. Wilson. 1991. *When Sex Is the Subject.* Santa Cruz, CA: ETR Associates.

P. Brick, N. Davis, M. Fischel, T. Lupo, A. MacVicar and J. Marshall. 1989. *Bodies, Birth and Babies.* Hackensack, NJ: The Center for Family Life Education, Planned Parenthood of Bergen County.

---

have learned to think of sex topics as forbidden—something to be hidden from adults. This attitude discourages positive communication between children and responsible adults and leaves most children dependent on unreliable, sometimes exploitative sources for their knowledge and, often, for their values. Given the confusion over sexuality in current society, genuine communication about sexual issues is increasingly vital as children reach adolescence. The model for such open discussion must be established in childhood before the dramatic changes and strong emotions of puberty.

Children will develop positive feelings about their own bodies, including the genitals. When children learn the names of all parts of their bodies except the genitals, or when the genitals are given trivializing nicknames, children receive a strong negative message about sexuality. Many girls, whose genitals are less visible and often unnamed, enter adolescence feeling a profound lack of ownership of their own bodies. The foundation for body-esteem includes naming the genitals and understanding that it can feel good to touch them but that such touching is done in private.

Children will feel good about themselves as male or female persons and will be aware of their full human potential regardless of gender. In spite of years of affirmative action, recent research shows that we have not achieved sex equity in most American classrooms. Teacher expectations, often unconscious and even well intentioned, continue to perpetuate traditional gender roles that discourage expression of caring and tenderness in boys and strength and assertiveness in girls (American Association of University Women, 1992). By adolescence, gender role stereotypes impede communication between the sexes and are detrimental to honest, equal and responsible sexuality (Reiss and Reiss, 1990).

Children will understand that each person has the right to determine who will touch his or her body, particularly the sexual parts. Adults typically give children confusing messages about touch. Children's feelings are often discounted; they may be required to be affectionate with an adult even though they have said they do not want to be. Prohibitions about touching other children often provoke guilt ("That's not nice!") rather than teaching self-assertion ("What can you say if you don't want Sari to hug you?") and empathy ("How would you feel if someone kissed you and you didn't want to be kissed?"). Children also need clear messages: "I don't want you to touch Alison if she doesn't want you to touch her." Thoughtful responses to children's behaviors promote respect for one's own body and for others (Brick, Montfort and Blume, 1993).

Such broad and fundamental goals cannot be separated and taught in a few lessons. They must be integrated throughout the curriculum. Schools can take a powerful step in the right direction by committing themselves to teach the skills needed for living with others with the same purposefulness with which traditional academic subjects are taught. Successful programs prepare children to navigate the various challenges of puberty and the teens years by developing social competence through teaching communication, problem-solving, decision-making, assertiveness and conflict-resolution skills (Hawkins and Catalano, 1991).

As children read a book, watch a video or interact with each other, the teacher's questions can promote inquiry, empathy, problem solving and decision making: "What do you think?" "How would you feel if...." "How do you think Annie feels?" "What would you do if...?" "What will happen if...." For trained teachers, the opportunities are constant: correcting an inaccurate term ("The grown-up word for that is buttocks"); encouraging identification of feelings ("How do you feel when Billy puts his arm around you and you don't want him to?"); promoting assertiveness ("Then tell Billy how you feel"); provoking thought about media messages ("Do you think anybody really looks like Barbie? Would you want a Ninja Turtle for a friend?") (Brick, 1991).

Central to such an approach is the deliberate promotion of self-esteem—essential if children are to use any of the lessons they receive regarding healthy living (Bean, 1992). Although effective teachers may already teach such competencies, a curriculum decision can ensure that teachers include rather than exclude sexuality issues.

Twelve Ways to Help Children Grow Up Sexually Healthy

Following are twelve specific ways teachers can promote the healthy sexual development of young children.

Provide equal opportunities for girls and boys; do not impose gender role stereotypes or use sexist language. Although young children, busy establishing their own gender identity, will often exhibit stereotypical behavior, the teacher's role is to encourage learning and responsible behavior that does not discriminate, e.g., "Children should not hurt each other," rather than "Boys don't hurt girls." If behavior is inappropriate, it is inappropriate for either a boy or a girl. When teachers give different "OK" and "Not OK" messages to boys and girls, a pattern is established that discourages equality, understanding and communication between the sexes. Teachers also need to beware of reinforcing images of girls "being" and boys "doing" by complimenting girls on their appearance and boys on their performance.

Teach correct vocabulary. Children gain control of their small world by naming it. With each new word, the child grows in understanding and power. When children are taught the correct words for body parts, "sex talk" moves from being hidden, giggly, naughty and guilt ridden, to being something children can share with adults. Correct vocabulary signals that children have a right to know the answers to their questions and that adults are willing to discuss these things with them. Teachers can use "teachable moments" to put the child's actions into words:

Child: "I see your tush."

Teacher: "Do you know the grown-up name for tush? It's buttocks. Can you say buttocks?"

Be askable. Children are full of sex questions—unless they have learned that most adults prefer not to talk about sexual topics. When adults are "askable," they set the stage for the lifelong process of questioning and learning about sexuality. An askable adult will approve the child's right to ask ("That's an interesting question"); find out what the child is *really* asking ("Where do you think babies come from?"); answer honestly and simply ("This *is* the way dolls are made, but babies grow in a special place inside the mother called the uterus"); check out whether the child has understood ("What do you think about that?"); and be prepared to answer the same question again.

Provide learning opportunities that enable children to learn through their own observations. Schools can invite a mother to class several times during her pregnancy so the children can ask her questions about the growing fetus and about how she cares for the baby even *before* it is born. Baby visitors can be bathed, diapered and fed (breast or bottle) as the children begin to learn "parenting skills." People whose work does not fit gender-role stereotypes—female police officers and carpenters, male nurses and househusbands—can visit and expand the children's awareness of career opportunities.

Provide a variety of resources that encourage children to discover things for themselves. Anatomically correct dolls, a "birthing doll," a chart showing fetal development at different stages, and a variety of books may be gathered in a Family Life Education Center. For younger children this may include a full array of "let's pretend" materials that encourage make-believe and enable teachers to see how the child is dealing with life's pressures.

The very presence of these resources shows that sexuality is a topic that can be discussed. After the first few days of giggles, children accept the naturalness of dolls that include genitals. Many teachers observe that the presence of boy dolls encourages nurturing, "parenting" behavior in boys.

Tell children clearly and directly what is and is not appropriate behavior, without making them feel guilty. Adults often give unclear messages to children about sex-related behaviors. They may prohibit ("Stop that!" "Don't ever let me see you doing that again!" "That's not nice.") rather than instruct ("I know it feels good to touch your (vulva/penis) but your (vulva/penis) is a private part of your body. People don't touch private parts of their bodies in a public place like school. They do that in a private place. Can you remember that?").

Encourage children to tell each other how they feel and to speak up for themselves. Many children learn only passive and aggressive responses to difficult situations. They need assertiveness training that starts early and continues throughout their school years. Teachers may be surprised to find development of assertiveness skills as part of sexuality education, but such skills are crucial to survival in adolescent and adult relationships. These skills can be promoted throughout the day by using teachable moments: "Tell Joan how you feel when she does that to you." "What do you want to say to Robert about that?" In addition, as students discuss and write about how characters in stories feel and how they could respond in particular situations, they learn to generate alternatives and to examine consequences—the first steps in good decision making.

Help children understand the effects of their behavior on others. The absence of empathy is another major problem in human relationships. The sexual abuser commonly lacks understanding of the victim's pain. Alert teachers find endless opportunities to encourage expression of positive feelings ("How could you help Cheryl feel better?") and to help children understand when they help others to feel good as well as when they make them feel bad ("It was thoughtful of you to share your book with Sean." "How does Alicia feel when she's left out of the group?").

Teach children that their bodies belong to them and that each person has the right to decide who can touch her or his body. Here, too, teachers have many opportunities to give clear messages. Both the teacher and the children learn to respect each child's right to say no to unwanted touch. The popular book *It's My Body* (Freeman, 1982) helps children distinguish between the many touches that they like and those they don't like.

Teach children that the sexual parts of their bodies are private. First, of course, the "private parts" need names. "Private" means that these parts are usually covered with clothes and are not shown in public. It feels good to touch the sexual parts of one's body, but people do this in "private places," not in "public places." Once children understand this basic concept, it is much easier to deal with the issue of masturbation: "Sara, I know it feels good to touch your vulva, but remember, your vulva is a 'private part' of your body. Where is it OK to do that?"

Provide nurturing touch that supports children's positive feelings of self and others. Touch is a key sensory experience. From earliest infancy, it soothes and stimulates. Touch is basic to a child's body awareness and sense of self and is a vital part of early childhood programs.

Be a positive role model. When adults demonstrate warmth, affection and support for children or for other adults, they show children how to behave in interpersonal relationships.

Teacher Training

Although much of the effort in initiating sexuality education in schools tends to focus on curriculum development, even carefully developed curriculum will be of little use unless teachers are convinced of the importance of sexuality education, have been trained to do the job, and are confident of the support of the school board and administration.

School administrators should not assume that information at the preschool and elementary level is common knowledge and that teachers need little training. In fact, very few teachers have had any formal sexuality education themselves, and few feel comfortable talking about sensitive topics with children. Ideally, teachers will take a minimum of one college-level course in human sexuality and family life education.

Such a course provides psychological, anthropological, sociological and historical perspectives on human sexual development as well as the theory and practice of sexuality education. Teachers who have had indepth preparation usually implement programs with ease. Confident of their own responses, they can sustain the initiative over the years.

However, whether in a full course or during inservice workshops especially for teaching young children, all teachers need opportunities to do the following:

Examine their own learning, experiences and values regarding sexuality. Since most adults do not have a background that prepares them to promote positive learning about sexuality, it is important for teachers to reflect on their own sexual history and the impact this has on their attitudes and their interactions with children.

Learn about sexual development through the lifespan. A cross-cultural perspective is useful here. Even a brief glimpse of the wide variety of norms controlling human sexual behavior among different peoples demonstrates the important role learning plays in the development of an individual's sexual script and highlights the potential importance of learning in the classroom.

Become comfortable with the language of sexuality. In spite of the omnipresence of sexual images in our lives, most people still have difficulty talking about sexual issues. Several time-honored techniques are effective in helping teachers to confront their own embarrassment with sex words and rehearse using these words in typical classroom situations. In one exercise, sheets of newsprint are hung around the room, each with a word such as *penis, vulva/ vagina* or *masturbation* printed on it. Participants move around the room with magic markers and write slang words under each term. Then they return to their seats and, together, read the slang words aloud. They analyze the lists and discuss their feelings about using both the slang words and the more formal ones. Roleplay in small groups enables each participant to practice using words in typical situations: For example, a child declares, "There's a baby in my Mommy's stomach," or asks, "Why don't I have a 'thing'"? Teachers practice responding and then evaluate their responses.

Analyze the media for messages about sex, masculinity and femininity, and family life. Systematically examining the attitudes and values promoted in the shows their students watch and the printed media they see can result in a raised media-consciousness— a major incentive for responsible sexuality education.

Practice answering difficult questions. Many teachers hesitate to establish an atmosphere where questions are welcomed because they fear certain embarrassing ones: e.g., "Where does the baby come from?" They can learn to respond in ways that validate the question ("That's an interesting question!"), assess the child's meaning ("Where do you think you came from?"), and give a simple answer ("Babies grow in a special place inside the mother called the uterus"). Roleplaying these responses is useful. A school policy and administrative support are also essential before most teachers will feel comfortable answering questions.

Practice using teachable moments. Teachable moments, essential for a meaningful approach to children's sexual learning, are likely to be overlooked or misused unless teachers have had training in recognizing them and significant opportunity to rehearse using them.

Parents and Caregivers as Partners in Sexuality Education

Parents and caregivers as well as teachers need help understanding the dimensions of children's sexual learning. Once they have an opportunity to think about the problematic messages children currently get from a sexual milieu dominated by the media, the overwhelming majority of parents become enthusiastic supporters of sexuality education programs (Brick, 1985; Firestone, 1993).

Workshops enable parents to take a more active and positive role in their children's sexuality education. They also develop parent support for the school program. Almost all parents are eager to learn strategies for answering children's questions and responding to their behavior. A workshop provides a forum where parents can openly and honestly express previously unspoken concerns about masturbation, nontraditional gender-role behaviors, sexual "provocativeness" and even possible abuse. A workshop provides an opportunity for parents and other caregivers to confront such issues openly and honestly and learn how to discriminate between children's normal, healthy curiosity and behaviors that may be cause for concern (Cavanagh-Johnson, 1991). Many will buy books that will help them take a more active and responsible role in helping their children develop positive attitudes about sexuality (Goldman and Goldman, 1988; Leight, 1988; Wilson, 1991). Others buy books for reading with their children (Freeman, 1982; Gordon and Gordon, 1974; Schoen, 1990).

The Curriculum

Until recently there were virtually no resources to guide schools in developing sexuality education programs in the early years (Brick, 1985). This has changed dramatically with the publication of several important resources including *Guidelines for Comprehensive Sexuality Education* developed by a twenty-member national task force (National Guidelines Task Force, 1991). Targeted at developing sexually healthy adults, the guidelines outline age-appropriate developmental messages in six areas: human development, relationships, personal skills, sexual behavior, sexual health, and society and culture. Level 1 addresses middle childhood, ages

5 through 8, and provides a useful framework for developing new curricula or evaluating existing programs.

While school districts initiating sexuality education programs are well advised to utilize a community committee and design curriculum congruent with the values of that community (Haffner and de Mauro, 1991), there are many advantages to utilizing a thoughtfully developed curriculum "package," if the district can find an acceptable one. It demonstrates to teachers that they really are expected to teach the materials and can expect unqualified support should any controversy arise. Such a curriculum can save much research and writing time, provide visuals not easily available elsewhere, and, by including clear teacher instructions, somewhat reduce the need for extensive teacher training.

One such complete package, *Learning About Family Life*, (Sprung, 1992) demonstrates what responsible sexuality education can be at this level. As is appropriate, discussion focuses on the concerns and interests of young children themselves. Most important, the child/teacher interaction modeled in this curriculum illustrates the way sexuality topics can be integrated into the everyday life of the classroom as a normal and natural part of children's total learning experience.

Another set of resources, *Healthy Foundations: Developing Programs and Policies for Young Children's Sexual Learning* (Montfort, Brick and Blume, 1993) is being used to encourage a positive approach in daycare centers and preschools as well as kindergarten through grade three. It includes a manual for school policies regarding children's sexual learning and behaviors which identifies important issues regarding sexual learning:

- What kinds of touch will be encouraged between staff and children?
- How will teachers help boys and girls feel equally valuable and capable?

- How will staff respond to children's questions and comments about sexuality? to "toilet talk" and "street language?"
- How will staff respond to children's public and/or private self-pleasuring? to body exploration and play?
- What criteria will staff use in determining whether a child's behavior is inappropriate and warrants concern?
- What will be the procedures for identification and reporting of suspected sexual abuse?

Advocating Comprehensive Sexuality Education

Guidelines, Learning About Family Life and *Healthy Foundations* articulate with new clarity the appropriate domain of early sexuality education, preschool through grade 3. For the first time, adequate resources exist for schools that are ready to initiate programs. Now the task is to help the public understand the compelling argument for beginning early to develop in children the knowledge, attitudes, values and skills that will enable them to survive in a sexually confused and exploitative society. Adolescence is too late. Puberty is too late. From early childhood a cacophony of voices influences children's sexual development. Children need and deserve an education that will help them sort out the mixed messages, survive the pressures and grow up healthy. From the beginning, such an education will integrate learning about sexuality into other learning about self and society, with the goal that the sexual part of the self be understood, respected and celebrated.

References

American Association of University Women. 1992. *How schools shortchange girls.* Washington, DC.

Bean, R. 1992. *The four conditions of self-esteem.* Santa Cruz, CA: ETR Associates.

Brick, P. 1985. Sexuality education in the elementary school. *SIECUS Report* 13 (3): 1-4.

Brick, P. 1991. Fostering positive sexuality. *Educational Leadership* 29 (1): 51-53.

Brick, P., N. Davis, M. Fischel, T. Lupo, A. MacVicar and J. Marshall. 1989. *Bodies, birth and babies.* Hackensack, NJ: The Center for Family Life Education, Planned Parenthood of Bergen County.

Brick, P., S. Montfort and N. Blume. 1993. *Healthy foundations: Responding to young children's questions and behaviors regarding sexuality.* Hackensack, NJ: The Center for Family Life Education, Planned Parenthood of Greater Northern New Jersey.

Cavanagh-Johnson, T. 1991. Understanding the sexual behaviors of young children. *SIECUS Report* 19 (6): 5-15.

Constantine, L. L., and F. M. Martinson. 1981. *Children and sex: New findings, new perspectives.* Boston: Little, Brown.

Firestone, W. A. 1993. New Jersey teachers evaluate family life education. *Family Life Matters* 18: 1-3, 6-7.

Freeman, L. 1982. *It's my body.* Seattle, WA: Parenting Press.

Gagnon, J. H., and E. J. Roberts. 1980. *Parents' messages to pre-adolescent children about sexuality.* In *Childhood and sexuality: Proceedings of the international symposium,* ed. J. M. Samson. Montreal: Editions Etudes Vivantes.

Goldman, R., and J. Goldman. 1988. *Show me yours: Understanding children's sexuality.* New York: Penguin.

Gordon, S., and J. Gordon. 1974. *Did the sun shine before you were born?* Fayetteville, NY: Ed-U-Press.

Haffner, D., and D. de Mauro. 1991. *Winning the battle for sex education.* New York: Sex Information and Education Council of the United States.

Hawkins, J. D., and R. F. Catalano, Jr. 1991. *Communities that care: Action for drug abuse prevention.* San Francisco: Jossey-Bass.

Krivacska, J. 1992. Sexuality Education in the Primary Grades. *Family Life Matters* 16: 1-3.

Langfeldt, T. 1990. Early childhood and juvenile sexuality development and problems. In *Handbook of sexology, Vol. 7: Childhood and adolescent sexology,* eds. J. Money and H. Musaph, 179-200. Amsterdam: Elsevier Science Publishers.

Leight, L. 1988. *Raising sexually healthy children.* New York: Avon Books.

Martinson, F. 1992. Normal sexual development in infancy and early childhood. In *Juvenile sexual offending: Causes, consequences and correction,* eds. G. Ryan and S. Lane, 57-79. Lexington, MA: Lexington Books.

Montfort, S., P. Brick and N. Blume. 1993. *Healthy foundations: Developing policies and programs regarding young children's learning about sexuality.* Hackensack, NJ: The Center for Family Life Education, Planned Parenthood of Greater Northern New Jersey.

National Guidelines Task Force. 1991. *Guidelines for comprehensive sexuality education: Kindergarten-12th grade.* New York: Sex Information and Education Council of the United States.

Reiss, I., with H. Reiss. 1990. *An end to shame: Shaping our next sexual revolution.* Buffalo, NY: Prometheus Books.

Schoen, M. 1990. *Bellybuttons are navels.* Buffalo, NY: Prometheus Books.

Sprung, B. 1992. *Learning about family life.* New Brunswick, NJ: Rutgers University Press.

Wilson, P. 1991. *When sex is the subject: Attitudes and answers for young children.* Santa Cruz, CA: ETR Associates.

Chapter 7

Sexuality Education in the Upper Elementary Classroom

Pamela M. Wilson, MSW

Students in upper elementary school are at a critical stage in their understanding of themselves as sexual people. Youth at this stage—preadolescence—are still more child than adolescent. But they are internalizing important concepts about themselves and others that will influence them for the rest of their lives: What does it mean to be a girl or a boy? Is a girl who likes "boy" activities a lesbian? What makes somebody gay? Are boys more valuable than girls? Does sexual behavior feel good? What's important in a sexual relationship? When will it be right for me? Are the sexual parts of the body X-rated? Do some people—especially females—say "no" to sexual behavior when they mean "yes"? Do adults want our honest opinions about these issues or should we tell them what they want to hear?

The messages that children receive in response to these questions leave a lasting imprint on their sexual development. While the formal sexuality education program is by no means the only source of sexuality messages, we educators must carefully critique the concepts that come through in the content, process and environment of our programs.

Who Are Preadolescents?

Preadolescence is that period of relative calm before the storm, when children are finishing up childhood and making the transition to adolescence. These children are nine to twelve years old and usually in grades four through seven. Since these ages are intended as guidelines, there might be eight year olds who are functioning as preadolescents and twelve year olds who are more like early adolescents. There is much individuality and variation in the way children develop.

Girls tend to develop one to two years earlier than boys, so there is a marked difference in their physical, psychological and social development. Many girls begin puberty as preadolescents, some having their first period as early as age eight (although the average age is twelve). In a fifth- or sixth-grade classroom, the girls are often taller than the boys and much more physically developed.

At this age, children are intensely curious, constantly teasing and interested in everything, including their own bodies. They notice the obvious differences in development (physical, emotional and social) within their peer group and worry about changes happening too quickly or too slowly. Early developers, more often girls than boys, are sometimes the recipients of hurtful remarks or unwanted attention from friends and classmates.

At the early end of this stage, children are open and direct in their conversations about sexuality. They will ask what they want to know with a forthrightness that tends to disappear with age: How many minutes do you have to stay in sexual intercourse? Can a man have a baby? What causes Siamese twins? Usually, preadolescents are still very open to getting information from adults. For this reason, teaching this age group can be particularly rewarding for educators.

It is true, however, that peer and media pressure to be cool and grown up is starting at much earlier ages than in the past. More and more nine and ten year olds want to wear the latest clothing styles and know the words to all the current music. Eleven- and twelve-year-old boys want to get their ears pierced, and in some communities boys tell us that they begin having intercourse on average at age twelve.

By and large, most preadolescents have not yet begun having intercourse. But they are entering a time in their lives when many will be facing decisions about relationships, sexual behavior, drugs, unchaperoned parties, and many other serious issues. As children enter puberty they become much more aware of the emotions and sexual feelings inside themselves. And, of course, these feelings are fueled by music videos, TV sitcoms, soap operas and movies on cable. Many gay and lesbian adults state that they first became aware of their attractions to members of the same sex at the time of puberty, if not earlier.

Pressures to conform to gender role stereotypes kick in at full force in the latter part of the preadolescent period. Girls especially learn that they can no longer be "rough and tumble" tomboys— that they must start to be concerned about their attractiveness, sex appeal and popularity. Many girls who wanted to be astronauts or scientists in elementary school begin to abandon these dreams in early adolescence.

Boys also have stereotyped gender-role messages reinforced at this age. Many have learned that they must be tough, unemotional, attracted to girls and interested in getting as much sex as possible. Although most twelve-year-old boys have not had sexual intercourse, many are getting the message that they should do it as soon as possible. Once when I was teaching a sexuality education program with a group of fifth graders, a well-developed girl in the group stayed behind to talk with me. She told me that many of the boys (who were all smaller and skinnier than she) propositioned her. They made comments about her breasts and asked if they could have sex with her.

Preadolescence is a time of great discovery, painful comparison, heightened altruism and keen interest in fairness. When adults see youth as resources who can help direct their own learning, preadolescents often live up to expectations. They can also tease each other unmercifully, with "fag" being the number one put-down. This is a critical time to foster an environment of tolerance and to educate children about the impact prejudice and discrimination has on all of us.

Content of Programs

The content of programs for preadolescents must respond to their current stage of development and prepare them for what is coming next. If we want to encourage young people to postpone the time they begin having sexual intercourse, we must provide educational messages before they first initiate this behavior. It should be noted that evaluations of programs designed to help young people postpone sexual intercourse indicate that such programs have only been effective with youth who haven't yet begun having sex with a partner (Kirby, 1992). If we want young people to choose caring, respectful and responsible ways to express their sexuality, we must go beyond the "just say no" message to discuss ways that people can be responsible about sexual behavior. In an Alan Guttmacher Institute survey of 4,200 secondary public school teachers (1989), most believed that their programs provided information too late to be helpful. The vast majority thought that information about birth control, HIV/AIDS, STD, sexual decision making, abstinence and homosexuality should be taught by the end of the seventh grade.

According to the Sex Information and Education Council of the U.S. (SIECUS) *Guidelines for Comprehensive Sexuality Education* (National Guidelines Task Force, 1991), upper elementary programs should concentrate on the following six key areas.

Human Development
- Increase children's knowledge of basic reproduction, clarifying that intercourse can lead to fertilization.
- Increase children's knowledge of the physical, emotional and social changes that accompany puberty.
- Explore attitudes that shape body image—for example, the influence of unrealistic images in the media.
- Introduce the concept of sexual identity and orientation and explain that people are often mistreated because of their sexual orientation.

Relationships
- Help children understand and cope with changes in the family, including separation or divorce of parents.
- Have students explore their feelings and attitudes about friendships, dating and love.
- Identify the myriad ways that adults can become parents and the specific care that children need from parents.

Personal Skills
- Define personal and family values; identify the various sources of values and explain that values among different families and friends often vary.

- Increase students' social skills—listening, starting conversations, making decisions and being assertive.
- Increase children's awareness of sources of help with problems and build skills for finding help.

Sexual Behavior

- Give the message that all people are sexual throughout life and that sexual feelings are normal, and encourage children to talk with their parents and other trusted adults about sexuality.
- Broaden the idea of sexual behavior to include more than sexual intercourse—for example, masturbation, which involves personal choice but does not lead to physical or mental harm.
- Acknowledge that sexual behavior involves pleasure and risk.
- Increase preadolescents' motivation and skills to postpone initiation of sexual intercourse.

Sexual Health

- Provide basic information about pregnancy and birth, including the fact that pregnant women need health care and that certain substances can harm the fetus.
- Introduce basic concepts about contraception—that methods exist to prevent pregnancy and that religious, personal and family values about contraception vary.
- Provide basic information about STDs—how they are transmitted and how they can be prevented.
- Define the basic concept of abortion—that it is legal, that alternatives to abortion exist and that values vary greatly.
- Increase students' awareness of and skills for preventing or getting help with sexual abuse.

Society and Culture

- Increase children's tolerance for (or acceptance of) differences in values, lifestyles, customs and beliefs in their community.

- Identify traditional gender-role messages to girls and boys and the consequences of rigidly accepting these messages.
- Clarify the fact that human diversity exists and that people are treated unfairly on the basis of characteristics such as gender, appearance, sexual orientation, family and living arrangements.
- Increase children's ability to be media critics by helping them critique messages about sexuality in the media.

Programs across the country vary greatly in their content. It is certainly appropriate to tailor individual programs to the specific needs of the community and its families. For instance, a progressive New Jersey school district in a "high-risk" urban area quite appropriately deals with issues of adolescent pregnancy, contraception and sexually transmitted disease with sixth graders. Yet many programs fall short of providing the comprehensive information that children need to be prepared for the life changes they're experiencing now or will experience in the near future.

Coed Versus Single-Gender Format

Many programs are designed for coed groups because educators want to convey the message that males and females can and should be able to discuss sexuality openly with one another. It is believed that such discussions give children practice for a lifetime of healthy male/female communication both in personal relationships and in the workplace.

On the other hand, it is true that by the time they reach preadolescence, boys and girls have had a different set of experiences based on their gender. In childhood, boys and girls spend most of their leisure time in same gender groups where topics of conversation and styles of interaction differ considerably. So when fourth-, fifth- and sixth-grade children are together in a group, boys are more likely to laugh, tease, interrupt and avoid talking about their feelings. Girls are more likely to ask meaningful questions, listen and support each other's feelings. In focus group sessions conducted by the Carnegie Council on Adolescent Development (1992), girls expressed a preference for some separate gender programs, particularly in sports, sexuality education and interpersonal relationships.

It seems most appropriate to have a blending of same gender and coeducational sessions for preadolescents and older youth. This blending can be accomplished in several ways. Agencies committed to coeducational programming might identify a certain number of sessions to be conducted in single-gender groups led by male and female facilitators. Or, within coeducational sessions, youth might carry out some small group tasks in single-gender groupings. Girls and boys can then report to one another on the ideas generated in their groups. Community agencies that serve boys and girls separately provide an important setting for youth to receive sexuality education in a supportive environment. Once youth in these single-gender programs have gained knowledge, skills and comfort on the issue of sexuality, they do need opportunities for dialogue with members of the other gender.

Many programs for preadolescents offer at least one or two single-gender sessions. These sessions should be continued and possibly expanded. Preadolescent girls are often anxious and embarrassed about menstruation and generally feel more comfortable discussing the details of menstrual hygiene without boys present. Boys also welcome the opportunity to air some of their personal concerns in an all-male session.

Providing adult role models who transcend gender-role stereotypes is of critical importance. Since many elementary school teachers are women, it's often necessary to go out into the community to find men—fathers, medical students, counselors, police officers, recreation workers—who can be trained to facilitate sessions with boys.

Answering Questions

One way to allow children to help shape the curriculum is by encouraging them to ask their own questions about sexuality. Preadolescents tend to be quite open and to ask questions that may seem surprisingly sophisticated. They may ask about oral sex, intercourse with multiple partners, or homosexuality. While these questions seem advanced, they are usually focused either on the mechanics or consequences of sexual behaviors (such as genetic abnormalities or miscarriages) and not on attitudes or feelings.

Many questions begin with the phrase, "What happens when...?" A guideline for responding to "what happens" questions about sexual behavior is to cover three issues: pregnancy, disease and feelings. For example, with the question, "What happens when a boy and a girl have sex at a young age?", the leader would discuss the possibility of pregnancy and sexually transmitted disease and the possible feelings of the boy and girl in this situation. When questions are explicit, answer simply and honestly but avoid giving detailed explanations of the mechanics of sexual behavior.

Since most preadolescents have not yet developed the cognitive ability to think abstractly, strive to make abstract concepts as concrete as possible. Use clear, nontechnical language; avoid words such as *sexual activity, body fluids, private parts, family planning* and *abstinence*. These words don't have specific meanings for preadolescents, and even adults have differing ideas about what these words really mean. Give straightforward explanations of any new concept that you present.

Conclusion

Sexuality educators have come to realize that we are offering too little, too late to our nation's children. Many teachers in public schools want to enter into honest discussion with children at earlier ages, but say they need more support from administrators and parents. If our goal is to encourage the development of sexually healthy adults, we must start early to promote positive attitudes and important skills.

Recommended Resources

Carnegie Council on Adolescent Development. 1992. *A Matter of Time: Risk and Opportunity in the Nonschool Hours.* New York: Carnegie Corporation of New York.
An excellent report that identifies programmatic and policy recommendations for promoting positive youth development and for enhancing community programs for young adolescents (ages 10 through 15).

Center for Population Options. 1992. *When I'm Grown: Life Planning Education for Grades 5 and 6.* Washington, DC.
Combines sexuality education and career education with the goal of motivating preadolescents to delay parenthood beyond adolescence. Deals with self-understanding, family, growth and development, friendship, sexuality, life skills, health promotion, STD, careers and optional activities on contraception.

Carolyn Cooperman and Chuck Roades. 1992. *New Methods for Puberty Education: Grades 4-9.* Hackensack, NJ: Center for Family Life Education, Planned Parenthood of Greater Northern New Jersey.

A collection of innovative and progressive activities on sexual anatomy and physiology, puberty, body image and self-esteem.

Louise Derman-Sparks and the A.B.C. Task Force. 1989. *Anti-Bias Curriculum: Tools for Empowering Young Children.* Washington, DC: National Association for the Education of Young Children.
Excellent and inexpensive tool for creating environments and curricula that help children of all backgrounds develop healthy self-identities. Provides activities for confronting and eliminating barriers based on race, gender and/or ability.

Lynne Anne DeSpelder and Albert Strickland. 1982. *Family Life Education Resources for the Elementary Classroom: Grades 4, 5 and 6.* Santa Cruz, CA: ETR Associates.
Over 75 fun and engaging activities dealing with five topic areas: self, family, friends, body and decisions.

Girls Incorporated National Resource Center. 1992. *Past the Pink and Blue Predicament: Freeing the Next Generation from Sex Stereotypes.* Indianapolis, IN.
Identifies real differences in boys and girls; discusses gender-role stereotypes and their impact on girls' interests, skills and opportunities; and offers a set of recommendations to help girls move beyond these stereotypes. Booklet format.

Ann Heron, ed. 1983. *One Teenager in Ten: Writings for Gay and Lesbian Youth.* Boston: Alyson Publications.
Twenty-six people from across the country (ages 15 through 24) talk about the discovery of their homosexual orientation and becoming comfortable with their sexuality. For parents, educators and teens.

Carol Hunter-Geboy and Pamela Wilson. 1987. *Families Talk About Sexuality: A Parent/Child Curriculum.* Alexandria, VA: American Association for Counseling and Development.
A four-session curriculum for parents and their children ages 10 to 13. Unique format encourages parent/child rather than mother/daughter or father/son participation.

Sandy McDaniel and Peggy Bielen. 1986. *Project Self-Esteem: A Parent Involvement Project for Elementary Age Children.* Santa Cruz, CA: ETR Associates.
A practical classroom program designed to be taught by teachers or parent volunteers. Exercises are scripted in detail and divided by grade level, K through 6.

Marcia Quackenbush and Sylvia Villarreal. 1988. Second edition 1992. *Does AIDS Hurt? Educating Young Children about AIDS.* Santa Cruz, CA: ETR Associates.
A guidebook for educating young children about HIV/AIDS. Emphasizes the use of age-appropriate responses to children's questions.

Elizabeth Reis. 1986. *5/6 Flash.* Seattle-King Department of Public Health, Family Planning Program.
Includes 15 lesson plans on family, self-esteem, gender roles, friendship, decision making, abuse, puberty and reproduction.

Pamela M. Wilson. 1991. *When Sex is the Subject: Attitudes and Answers for Young Children.* Santa Cruz, CA: ETR Associates.
Provides practical guidelines to educators and parents for communicating positive attitudes about sexuality to children and preadolescents.

References

Alan Guttmacher Institute. 1989. *Risk and responsibility: Teaching sex education in America's schools today.* New York.

Carnegie Council on Adolescent Development. 1992. *A matter of time: Risk and opportunity in the nonschool hours.* New York: Carnegie Corporation of New York.

Kirby, D. 1992. School-based programs to reduce sexual risk-taking behaviors. *Journal of School Health* 62 (7): 280-287.

National Guidelines Task Force. 1991. *Guidelines for comprehensive sexuality education: Kindergarten-12th grade.* New York: Sex Information and Education Council of the United States.

Chapter 8

Sexuality Education in the Middle and Junior High School Classroom

Selene D. Skonie-Hardin, MPH, CHES

"Wouldn't high school be early enough?"
"How do you address the topic of homosexuality?"
"I know other kids need to learn this, but…"
"How do you explain abortion?"
"Shouldn't the boys and girls be separated?"
"Aren't the students embarrassed to talk about this?"
"Why don't you just teach them to say no?"
"My child isn't even interested in this yet."
"Don't they learn it at church or at home?"

As a sexuality educator you will hear all these questions and more from parents genuinely concerned about protecting their children. Unfortunately, in some cases, parents fail to realize that children cannot be protected forever and that human sexuality teachers are not the enemy.

It can be especially difficult at the middle school level. Children are going through tremendous, sometimes chaotic changes;

their parents are also dealing with these changes. Teachers comment on how different students are from the sixth to the seventh to the eighth grade. Sixth graders appear much like elementary students, while eighth graders are breaking away into adulthood. Trying to find a happy medium—as teacher or parent—in dealing with middle school children is difficult. Adults must allow freedom and responsibility while also providing structure, rules and guidance.

Parents

Parents of children at this stage often do not truly accept the fact that the child is growing up. Some hope to postpone the inevitable; adults know the difficulties that lie ahead. Others bury their heads in the sand and refuse to deal with the complexities of adolescence. These attitudes on the part of parents and caregivers can make it very difficult to teach and prepare children.

If your sexuality education program is to succeed, the majority of the parents must be comfortable with what you are doing in class. Sexuality education courses can be a lightning rod for controversy and school bashing. To avoid such a scenario, parents need to be included in and informed about the program. Establishing a yearly parent information meeting, held at night, sends a strong message that you have nothing to hide. A parent meeting can accomplish several things:

- Materials—handouts, books, models, etc.—can be displayed.
- Parents can sign up to preview videos.
- Questions regarding curriculum can be clarified.
- Parents can be educated.
- Parents can meet the person who will be talking to their children about sexuality.

Parental concerns need to be dealt with as legitimate issues. Most parents have either faulty or inadequate information regarding programs. Like their children's knowledge of sexuality, their views are based only on what they have heard. Honest, forthright explanations that include the reasoning behind particular curricular decisions, can go a long way toward avoiding future controversy.

Students

Children receive continual, unstructured, unmonitored information regarding sexual behavior every day. The question is not whether middle school children should learn about human sexuality, but rather where and from whom they will get their information. We cannot wait until they are "ready." When will that be? How will we know? Will their friends know before we do? Nor can we wait until "they need to know." When will that be? When they are pregnant? When they are engaging in intercourse? When they have contracted HIV? One definition of preparation is "an act or proceeding undertaken in *advance* of some event; a precaution; the state of readiness" (*Funk and Wagnalls*, 1975). Sexuality education is about precaution, preparation and readiness.

At the middle school level, children are beginning to have different feelings toward each other. Physical attractions and more complex emotional relationships are becoming evident. Some students will begin to date and go steady or "go with" someone. We can provide parameters and a framework within which they can make decisions while at the same time teaching them to use all the information available and to analyze what is and is not reliable. For the most part, the parameters of acceptable behavior are established by the family, with subsequent teaching and reinforcement by the school, church and community.

For students to make intelligent choices, they need to develop critical thinking skills. Teachers can help by allowing students to practice these thinking skills in analyzing situations and trying to solve various problems. Sexuality educators seek to develop the following skills in their students (*Health: Choosing Wellness*, 1992):

- introspection—looking at what you believe and think
- abstract thought—thinking about and understanding things you cannot see
- ethical judgment—making judgments based on your own values and other's intentions
- hypothesis testing—approaching problem solving by first predicting an outcome
- decentered thought—understanding situations from someone else's point of view
- deductive logic—developing general ideas and then looking to the real, concrete world for specific examples

At the middle school level, students are just beginning to develop some of these skills; they should not be expected to master these skills in a short period of time. Many middle schoolers still think in very concrete terms; they will only use what information they are able to use. We want to challenge them, to make them think, but at the same time must recognize that there are limitations as to what they can understand.

Students at this age often exhibit a limited understanding of consequences that may occur in the future. They appear to believe that they will always be in control of circumstances, and that they will always be able to protect themselves. It is not uncommon to hear students say, "I would never get in that situation" or, "I would never be that stupid." One way to break through these feelings of infallibility is to have other teens, who have had personal experience with these issues, speak to the class. Teenage parents or young people infected with HIV can influence the students on a level that adults are incapable of reaching.

As students mature and begin to break ties with their families, their peers replace the family as their source for standards of behavior. Many students believe that their situations are unique and that no one has ever before experienced what they are experiencing. If students accept this as true, the only people who are able to give them helpful advice are their friends and peers—the people who are in the same situation.

Children need and want some kind of guidelines. They do not, however, like to be told what to do (Wiles and Bondi, 1986). The varied rates at which people pass through adolescence mean that the middle school teacher may be faced with a wide range of behavior, maturity and intellectual development; a much wider range than at any other grade level. The range may be compounded in some school systems by inclusive education—the inclusion of mentally and physically handicapped special education students into the "regular" classrooms. In some cases, these students will attend with a teacher assistant, which will help both the students and the teacher. If there isn't a teacher assistant, consider pairing these students with others in the class. There are a limited number of materials available for special-needs children, so teachers may find it necessary to develop their own modified handouts and reading materials.

Teacher and Student Comfort Levels

Students take their cues from the teacher and the other students. If the teacher is embarrassed, blushes or stumbles over words, students will think that this subject is something to be embarrassed about. On the other hand, if the teacher acknowledges that sometimes people get embarrassed because they are not used to discussing the topic, and assures the students that their feelings are normal, students will feel more comfortable. It is important to approach sexuality as just another part of the body, a part of all of us, a part of life.

Dealing with student comments and behavior requires a calm demeanor and patience. It can help students to giggle and joke about the topics as long as the teacher monitors the humor so that it is not offensive to other people. Humor becomes offensive when the object of the humor is another student, faculty member, religion, person of the opposite gender, or people with different lifestyle orientations. In monitoring humor in the classroom, teachers should strive to keep the laughter as neutral as possible, laughing at their own feelings or the situation. Humor, when used correctly, can go a long way in helping students deal with new ideas and information.

Questions

Even though some students will feel brave enough to ask questions in class, the majority will not. A question box allows all students the opportunity to ask questions in a nonthreatening manner. Any kind of box can be used; one with a removable cover and small "mail slot" is best. Pass out blank index cards at the beginning of the class period. Students are not to put their names on the cards. They may write any questions that they have on the card. At the end of class all the cards are placed in the box—blank ones, too. The teacher can remove the cards after class is dismissed. It is best to set a time when questions will be answered so that students do not think you are avoiding the issues. It is also important to assure students that all questions will be answered, except for those on your personal life.

Environment

Another factor that contributes to the students' comfort level is the type of room you are in. The room should be pleasant and inviting, and, if at all possible, it should have a door. Some schools have open classrooms which may make some students feel uncomfortable and, therefore, less likely to participate. Students may fear that someone is standing outside listening or that people can overhear their discussions. This can affect how open and honest they are. If you do not have a door, it can help to create the illusion of one by placing the teacher desk, bookcases, plants, curtains, etc., in front of the entrance area.

Instructional Strategies

Students at this age are easily offended and sensitive to criticism. To get them to reach whatever conclusions we wish them to reach, we sometimes must lead them through the back door, making them believe they found the way themselves. Activity-based learning is a good way to accomplish this. In this type of learning students in groups work through a situation together. This gives them the insulation and protection of a group while also allowing them to be verbal and active. Students at this point of development prefer active learning and peer interaction. Working with others helps them clarify their own thoughts and compare their solutions with others' and gives them a chance to argue their points of view (Wiles and Bondi, 1986).

Some of the best learning is unplanned. Flexibility and adaptability are key. Very seldom will middle school students learn at a steady pace for forty or fifty minutes. Their learning is sporadic and unpredictable. Teachers who accomplish the most design lessons to accommodate these idiosyncrasies. Short assignments within the same lesson will match their attention spans. For example, breaking up the lesson into short blocks can help to hold their attention. One method would be 15 minutes of individual, silent reading; 15 minutes of group work to find a problem's solution; 10 minutes for group reports and decisions; 5 minutes for closure activities.

Give students a variety of choices, possibly using several different learning styles for one objective. Use combinations of stories, illustrations, facts, reading, group discussion and written work; allow students to work together or separately as they feel comfortable. For example, for a lesson on fetal development and childbirth you might have a handout to read, questions to answer, and stations with models and illustrations set up around the room. Students could work together or alone to complete the questions by using the information available. Have students involved in decision-making experiences and situational activities. Accommodate individual learning as much as possible by allowing students to lie on the floor while reading, play a radio during certain assignments, or use their artistic talents.

Content

Questions regarding what should be taught at which grade level are always some of the most difficult to answer. Most teachers of human sexuality would like to develop a comprehensive, all-inclusive curriculum. Due to the volume of material available, such a curriculum would be fairly lengthy. Unfortunately, many teachers do not have an unlimited amount of time, nor do they have total control over what is to be taught. Decisions regarding class schedules and curricula have traditionally been made at the administrative level. Teachers are sometimes left to find a way to fit the topics into the available time. When it comes to sexuality education, there are added parental and community concerns. The teacher should be allowed to make professional judgments while collaborating with administrators, parents and community members. In order to have a successful program, the mores of the community need to be taken into account.

Much controversy can be avoided if a formal committee is established for community input. The committee may be comprised of parents, teachers, administrators, ministers, medical personnel and other community members. As a formal committee they can evaluate a variety of curricula and negotiate what the school system's goals, objectives and methods will be. The teacher should be an integral part of this committee, as the person educated and trained to develop and implement sexuality education programs.

When first beginning a program it may be useful to agree to omit or postpone the teaching of some of the more controversial topics in order to *establish* the program. Once credibility and acceptance have been achieved, discussions regarding more controversial topics can take place with the advisory committee. A decision may need to be made on whether to teach many topics briefly or few topics in depth. This will be affected by the length of class sessions and the number of times each class meets, as well as by community input.

In general, early middle school (usually sixth grade) curricula include some or all of the following: puberty, growth and development, families, parenting, fetal development and pregnancy, sexually transmitted disease (including HIV/AIDS), child sexual abuse, friendships and relationships.

In the late middle school years (usually seventh and eighth grades), the following are often included: puberty, reproductive systems, fertilization, pregnancy, childbirth, abstinence, contraception, sexually transmitted disease, sexual assault prevention, relationships, future goals and plans, and decision-making skills.

When making any curricular decisions, it is important for there to be a clearly defined goal. What exactly do you want these students to learn? There is a wide range of programs available, from those with a biological/abstinence-only focus to those that encompass more abstract ideas regarding respect, loyalty, protecting yourself, relationships, parenting and love.

It is possible to provide middle school students with a beneficial human sexuality program without including every possible topic. Various people, experts included, have different viewpoints on how and when certain topics should be introduced to students. Teachers and administrators will find themselves caught between the ideal curriculum and the realities of where they are teaching. All factors need to be weighed, with different teachers in different communities making different choices.

Teachers will find themselves educating parents and other adults as well as their students. They will be asked to justify why certain topics are included at the middle school level and how those topics will be approached in the classroom. The teacher must be knowledgeable and prepared in order to answer inquiries in a professional manner. Educators who are willing to work in a collaborative manner within their communities to establish the best possible program for the children will find acceptance and approval much easier to come by. The advance planning, research and communication is worth the extra effort.

References

Funk and Wagnalls Standard College Dictionary. 1975. Pleasantville, NY: Reader's Digest.
Health: Choosing Wellness. 1992. 2d ed. Needham, MA: Prentice Hall.
Wiles, J., and J. Bondi. 1986. *The Essential Middle School.* Columbus, OH: Merrill Publishing Co.

Chapter 9

Sexuality Education in the High School Classroom

Martha R. Roper, MA, and Peter C. Scales, PhD

What makes teaching sexuality education in high school different from other grade levels? In most cases, differences have to do with the developmental level of the students. Fifteen to eighteen year olds have more independence from their families. They also have more experience, including sexual experience. They have more thinking, research, writing, and speaking skills than younger adolescents, and, therefore, the methodologies to reach these students must include a wide range of activities.

Cognitively, high school students are more capable than middle school students of thinking abstractly, imagining the future, and considering hypothetical situations. They are better able than younger adolescents to understand another person's point of view. This ability is especially important as students begin to understand differences of opinion and to appreciate how their behavior affects others, and has a direct bearing on the teacher's ability to facilitate discussions where a wide range of values and perspectives are aired.

The cognitive and behavioral variations among older adolescents within a classroom can be overwhelming. Some students want opportunities to connect with the outside world and to build bridges into their futures; others want a "free" period. Educators know that people learn differently, but we also know that high school students generally love class discussions. Combining research activities, textbook work, skills training and student presentations with expertly facilitated discussion is important to do with high school students.

Considering that by age eighteen, 72 percent of young people have already had sexual intercourse at least once (Centers for Disease Control and Prevention, 1992), there is an added urgency at this age to make sure students receive the information and skills they need to protect themselves from pregnancy and STD, including HIV. This increases the pressures on and the perceived responsibilities of the high school sexuality education teacher.

Sexuality educators must know what goals the school district has for the program, and work to modify unrealistic ones. For example, some people, including school board members, might believe that information alone—or "abstinence only" programs (simply telling kids not to have sex)—will have an immediate impact on the sexual activity of teenagers. Unfortunately, the causes of and the cures for the problems of youth in the United States extend far beyond the classroom. Yet some sexuality education programs do show promising results. It is important to decide whether to include behavioral change as an objective for the course. There also needs to be a decision about how aggressively to pursue this objective and whether or not to evaluate the program based on the achievement of a potentially unlikely outcome.

Regardless of the choice about goals and evaluation, effective sexuality education programs in high schools will have the following strengths: (1) trained and supported teachers; (2) a clear framework of values on which the course is based; (3) parent involvement; and (4) research-based, appropriate methodology. These factors increase the program's choices of having a positive impact. The rest of this chapter is devoted to discussing these elements of successful high school sexuality education programs.

Trained and Supported Teachers

When it comes to the classroom experience, students' greatest resource is the well-trained, veteran sexuality educator. The high school sexuality education teacher needs skills unique to the age group and the setting. Ideally, the teacher has had formal training in sexuality to prepare her or him to deal with the sensitive, complex and often controversial issues inherent in the teaching of sexuality education. Unfortunately that rarely is the case.

Regardless of his or her academic department, the individual responsible for teaching sexuality education must not only be a professional in the classroom, but a public health advocate for adolescents and a public relations specialist. This multiple role means stepping outside of the isolation of the classroom and into the public health arena.

The following qualities make the contemporary high school sexuality educator a teacher extraordinaire.

In the classroom, he or she:
- is an excellent classroom manager, with few discipline problems
- has a good sense of humor
- is cool under pressure
- is able to refer students to appropriate resources
- communicates with parents and caregivers about the activities of the class
- is trained to teach skills, not just cover the textbook

Within the school, he or she:
- is well-liked by colleagues, students and parents
- is known by administrators as reliable, cooperative and flexible
- volunteers to sponsor after school health-related activities
- is enthusiastic about and supportive of the school in general
- socializes with faculty members both at organized events and informally
- is willing to chat with colleagues who have children in the high school about sexuality education and its effects
- knows and can quote from respected studies
- isn't intimidated by board members, superintendents, principals, supervisors, angry parents, students or other faculty members
- uses a team approach to problem solving and is willing to compromise
- can apologize and move through conflict quickly

Specific to the area of sexuality, he or she:
- is up-to-date with professional journal articles
- belongs to national professional sexuality organizations and attends conferences
- understands the district policies on the media, controversy and sexuality education, and follows them to the letter
- achieves recognition outside the school district
- keeps a list of parents, colleagues, staff members and community professionals who would be willing to provide public support should the opposition question his or her personal integrity
- keeps a diary of prank or obscene phone calls, or calls/questions/letters from unfriendly sources
- knows the board of education, and works to elect members who support sexuality education

Parent Involvement

Even at the high school level, it is advisable to invite parents to spend an evening learning about the curriculum. It is helpful to have this meeting separate from any "open house" event, which provides very limited time for indepth discussion of concerns. A parent night gives teachers the opportunity to spend more time with parents, go over the course outline, explain the effects of sexuality education, answer questions and address sensitive issues.

Parents can be a tremendous source of support. In a community where there is much controversy about the sexuality education program, parents are potentially important allies and advocates. Holding a parent night to meet parents and speak to them about the issues openly and honestly can provide them with needed information, establish credibility, recruit them as advocates, and avoid or minimize trouble later on should the opposition target your school or classroom.

The parent night can be used by teachers as an opportunity to address concerns appropriate to the individual community. Following are some specific issues that might be covered during a parent night.

Sexuality Education Versus Abstinence Education
All good programs are abstinence-based. Parent night is an opportunity to make this point and to explain specific differences between your program and fear- and shame-based programs. One way to explain the difference is that sexuality education is "abstinence" education with a difference: in comprehensive programs, young people are *urged* to say no and given the skills to do so, while in abstinence-only programs, students are simply told to "just say no."

Abstinence-based curricula can include the same topics as fear-based curricula—i.e., consequences of premarital sexual activity and how it may affect one's life, saying no and feeling good about it, how to control pressures, how to protect oneself against unwanted sex—but the approach is positive and includes critical thinking and decision making based on accurate information and a value framework agreed upon by a diverse group of parents.

For example, an effective program might include discussions about the rights and responsibilities associated with various expressions of sexuality and the factors that influence sexual attitudes. Students can learn to communicate clearly about sexuality, and learn to manage the conflicts that normally occur in relationships. This gets to the heart of the difference between positive sexuality education programs and the fear-based, abstinence-only programs: effective programs don't just "let" students think and decide for themselves; they teach them how.

Parents should know that, despite the claims of abstinence-only proponents, studies conclude that the abstinence-only approach is ineffective (Roosa and Christopher, 1990). Good programs based on, but not exclusively limiting their message to abstinence offer honest and open communication with young people about sexuality and sexual decisions—no lies, no medical inaccuracies, no misrepresentations, no hidden religious agendas and no secrets. We know of no "just say no" curriculum that meets these standards.

A Framework of Values

By the time their children are in high school, almost all parents want the school to present a two-fold message about sexuality: abstain from high-risk sexual activity and also know about contraception and disease prevention. Usually a districtwide committee has assembled a curriculum framework and chosen a textbook that has been approved by the local Board of Education. Some school districts invite parent committees to write a values statement (see Appendix E). Other districts collaborate to write a character development curriculum to guide the staff in all disciplines in grades K through 12.

No matter how carefully values statements are developed, some parents will not want their children in the sexuality class. As in the lower grades, policies should be in place that allow any parent to request a transfer of a student from any teacher's class for any reason. The request should be honored graciously and swiftly, with alternatives of independent study, physical education, choice of another teacher, or a correspondence course.

Skills

While we know that information is not enough to get students to abstain or protect themselves, many parents and teachers are still not clear about what to add to the knowledge approach. Teachers end up lecturing, preaching and moralizing to students. Although this is not all bad, and some school boards actually encourage it, there is no evidence that it does anything but make the adults feel better. Training young people to communicate effectively to remain abstinent and to avoid unprotected sexual intercourse, however, actually shows results (Kirby et al., 1991).

The skills students need include refusal and delaying statements and alternative actions. These skills are first explained and demonstrated by the teacher and then practiced by the students in roleplays. A step-by-step guide such as *Reducing the Risk* (Barth, 1993) followed to the letter was found to delay significantly the onset of intercourse and reduce unprotected intercourse among students who had not initiated intercourse at the beginning of the course (Kirby et al., 1991).

Sensitive Topics

Effective high school sexuality educators use images and phrases that engage students; they are open in discussing condoms, masturbation, homosexuality and similar topics. Such openness can backfire if a student later distorts the message to a parent. Since sexuality is a sensitive topic, it is best to simply acknowledge this, and to invite parents to call immediately if they hear something that troubles them. Most parents do want teachers to answer students' questions, and inviting continual communication is usually enough to smooth over any temporary misunderstandings or concerns.

Many parents have concerns about the moral or religious values expressed in a teacher's answers to students' questions. Explaining the importance of critical thinking skills can help allay such fears. "Critical thinkers challenge, test, push, argue, doubt, and question. Teaching students simply to be obedient is incompatible with critical thinking" (Scales, 1993). Teachers need to be clear that far from trying to impose a particular view, they want students to be able to analyze and evaluate a variety of viewpoints.

Everywhere else in the school curriculum we try to develop critical thinkers. Why should it be different when studying human sexuality? Young people want and developmentally need to examine the personal concerns and controversial issues commonly labeled as "sensitive":

> When young adolescents grapple with difficult issues on which there are multiple plausible points of view, and practice their abilities to synthesize, evaluate, debate, determine credible sources, understand research data and positions, they are readying themselves when they become voters, parents, and leaders to create and not just inherit the future. Not coinci-

dentally, their cognitive ability to appreciate the needs of others and what is good for their communities, as well as their social need to make a contribution, are increasing during early adolescence. Encouraging them to think about important personal and public health issues is a learning strategy that fits well with their developmental needs and characteristics. (Scales, 1993)

Inviting Guests to Parent Night

A few final tips on planning the evening with parents. Inviting interested guests to a parent night can be helpful, and, in some cases, is necessary. Administrators, district health coordinators, colleagues, librarians, parents whose children have participated in the teacher's sexuality education classes in the past, and/or district teacher association representatives can provide support, answer questions and serve as resources both at the parent night and later on if controversy becomes an issue in your community. Videotaping the event can serve as a resource for parents who could not attend and administrators who later may need to know the context of a statement should controversy arise.

Methodology

While the school reform debate rages outside the classroom door, the high school sexuality teacher is still assigned a room, thirty students, a curriculum guide and a board policy. Imparting knowledge is what schools do best, but in the case of sexuality education, we want and expect more. It is now commonly known that students who are actively engaged in their learning, through group projects, discussion and roleplaying, and who also view what they are learning as useful, actually learn more (Wheelock and Dorman,

1988). Specialized teacher training with a skills orientation will bring more positive results than traditional lecturing (Kirby et al., 1991).

Coordinating Sexuality Education Within a School

When sexuality education courses or units are offered by departments other than health, the classes usually are not skills oriented but more informational in nature. A ninth-grade biology class might study the human life cycle, including sexuality. A social studies class might study sexuality anthropologically. A sensitive English teacher might discuss gender issues throughout the course. Home economics teachers usually include sexuality issues in their child development and family relations courses. Math teachers might explain to the class what is meant by a contraceptive method being "99.97 percent effective."

Sometimes teachers want to share responsibilities. A biology teacher may want to teach anatomy and physiology but not talk about contraception. Knowing what sexuality education students have received before they get to you, and knowing which teachers include sexuality in their class discussions is helpful in assessing possible gaps in your students' knowledge base.

Getting to Know Students

Begin a class by passing out the course outline and walking students through it. Even in a class students love to attend, grades will be given and all must have clear verbal and written expectations regarding attendance, participation, tests, papers and projects. Sometimes students will balk at doing the work required to get an "A" in sexuality class when other courses are offering honors weight to the grade-point average. These students and some special education students may want to take the course pass/fail.

Spend a week getting to know one another through team-building activities and then put the class into small groups to generate the tough, "essential" questions that will drive the rest of the course or unit: What is a healthy life? and, What is responsible sexuality? Post these questions and refer to them to keep the class on task and focused on the positive.

Personal and Social Skills

By high school, nearly all students will know how conception occurs. At this age they are primarily interested in personal and social skills. Although 54 percent of all high school students have had sexual intercourse at least once (Centers for Disease Control and Prevention, 1992), most still are learning relationship skills and few know how to access the health care system for prevention or dealing with a problem.

Students want to learn personal and social skills, such as how to manage stress, communicate feelings and manage conflict. Refusal skills are particularly important. These are taught mostly by large and small group activities which require a high level of expertise on the part of the teacher.

Skills for remaining abstinent and for avoiding unprotected sexual intercourse are among the most urgent. A curriculum such as *Reducing the Risk* (Barth, 1993) is a good guide for teaching such skills.

Traditional Methods

Traditional methods of teaching sexuality education are still effective if not overused. High school students would prefer to talk with each other than do almost anything else, so it can be very effective to use Socratic seminars (reading the same article and discussing the text), show a videotape to stimulate discussion, use spontaneous question and answer sessions, roleplay, have guest speakers, and even use textbooks with questions at the end of the chapter to spark discussion. Fish bowls, keeping a journal, brain-storming, simulation games, egg/baby projects, poster making, planning a health fair, promoting positive relationships with a series of all-school announcements, passing out "hug strings" (tied around students' fingers to represent hugs), hosting a mock wedding, planning for a baby and going on a field trip all are highly interesting and informative class activities. They serve to reinforce knowledge, values, and the communication/conflict management skills already taught.

Gender and Sexuality Education

Sometimes using same sex groupings for specific discussions is effective, because many females defer to males when males are present and many males don't really hear what females are saying or care to listen when women do speak (Tannen, 1990). Mixed gender classes usually revolve around males because boys create more discipline problems as well as more comments in class discussions. Teachers are so used to giving boys more attention that we are rarely aware we do it.

Gender equity issues often can be explored more easily with single-sex groups. Personal hygiene questions can be answered more fully, and discussions about self-examinations for cancer prevention are more comfortable in same sex groups.

Cooperative Learning in Sexuality Education

As the course develops, students can begin to pick topics and work in small groups to prepare presentations for the class. These activities require students to cooperate and compromise—skills many employers require. Setting up and managing these work groups also demands teacher skill.

These skills are beginning to get national attention since many high schools in America are undergoing reform, or restructuring. Faculties are grouping areas of competencies together, such as communication, decision making, goal setting and so on. They are being asked to narrow down what students need to know and be able to do to be successful in the twenty-first century, and to coach students into performance of expected outcomes.

Independent Projects

Some schools are using the "less is more" approach, where the emphasis is on digging deeply into one topic. Students are required to think critically as they are guided through the creation of a product or performance that requires the skills needed in the world of work.

In a sexuality education classroom, a general process for getting students started on the independent project path might go something like this: In a small group, help students brainstorm essential questions that lead to becoming sexually healthy adults: What affects the quality of life? What is the connection between gender and health? What is responsible sexuality? (National Guidelines Task Force, 1991)

Next, break down these large questions into smaller, compelling, student-generated questions that provide the stimuli for various projects—a video production, a research paper and panel discussion by a small group, or the publication of an informational pamphlet that could be signed and distributed by the student authors at lunch.

Students can also plan assemblies, including media coverage, and organize follow-up sessions for interested persons. Another project might be to produce an educational videotape which can serve as an accurate source of HIV information, using high school students to present the up-to-date information.

Coaching

At the high school level, the sexuality education curriculum comes only partly from the teacher or a textbook; the curiosity and questioning of the students is a driving force. Fostering critical thinking based on accurate information is key to the teaching/learning process. Teachers can coach students, encouraging them to extend their thinking. For example: "Don't forget to add that people who suspect they might have an STD should go to a doctor or clinic promptly and get checked. They should also stop having sexual intercourse and refer sexual partners to a doctor."

Other coaching nudges students to reach farther for better sources of information:

- "Find the most recent *Journal of the American Medical Association*."
- "Check the CD-ROM database of newspapers, and see how the people of Baltimore are reacting to the decision to distribute the Norplant contraceptive in a local high school."
- "Ask the librarian to show you how to ask Washington University Medical School to fax you that journal article."
- "Call your state representative and see what he or she thinks of Amendment 2 in Colorado."*

Contemporary sexuality education teachers are comfortable with technology, with group learning strategies and active student projects, with parent involvement, and with the wide range of values that students bring to the sexuality education class. Effec-

---

* In November 1992, Colorado voters approved Amendment 2, a measure that prohibited the inclusion of Gays and Lesbians as a class not to be discriminated against, similar to civil rights protections by race, religion, and gender. Passage of the measure prompted many groups to boycott their plans to hold conferences in Colorado. In July 1993, the state Supreme Court ruled this amendment to be unconstitutional.

tive teachers know that students are capable of dealing with controversial topics and that students need more than lectures or admonitions to guide their behavior. High school students in the process of becoming young adults need to define for themselves the values that will guide their life-long behavior and to practice the skills that will enable them to live by their values. High school sexuality education teachers challenge their students to pursue this personal journey and provide the structure students need as they move ever closer to adulthood.

Recommended Resources

Resources for teachers and students at the high school level are rich and varied. Some excellent resources include:

Guidelines for Comprehensive Sexuality Education: Kindergarten-12th Grade. 1991. National Guidelines Task Force. New York: SIECUS.

Human Sexuality: A Curriculum Guide. 1983. M. Roper. University City, MO: University City High School.

Reducing the Risk: Building Skills to Prevent Pregnancy, STD and HIV. Second edition. 1993. R. P. Barth. Santa Cruz, CA: ETR Associates.

Sexuality Education: A Curriculum for Adolescents. 1984. P. Wilson and D. Kirby. Santa Cruz, CA: ETR Associates.

STDs and HIV: A Guide for Today's Young Adults. 1993. W. Yarber. Reston, VA: American Alliance for Health, Physical Education, Recreation and Dance.

References

Barth, R. P. 1993. *Reducing the risk: Building skills to prevent pregnancy, STD and HIV.* 2d ed. Santa Cruz, CA: ETR Associates.

Centers for Disease Control and Prevention. 1992. Sexual behavior among high school students—United States, 1990. *Morbidity and Mortality Weekly Report* 40 (51/52): 885-888.

Kirby, D., R. P. Barth, N. Leland and J. V. Fetro. 1991. Reducing the risk: Impact of a new curriculum on sexual risk-taking. *Family Planning Perspectives* 23 (6): 253-263.

National Guidelines Task Force. *Guidelines for comprehensive sexuality education: Kindergarten-12th grade.* 1991. New York: Sex Information and Education Council of the United States.

Roosa, M. W., and F. S. Christopher. 1990. Evaluation of an abstinence-only adolescent pregnancy prevention program: A replication. *Family Relations* 39 (4): 363-367.

Scales, P. C. 1983. Sense and nonsense about sexuality education. *Family Relations* 32 (2): 287-295.

Scales, P. C. 1993. The centrality of health education to developing young adolescents' critical thinking. *Journal of Health Education* 24 (6): 510-514.

Tannen, D. 1990. *You just don't understand: Men and women in conversation.* New York: Ballantine Books.

Wheelock, A., and G. Dorman. 1988. *Before it's too late: Dropout prevention in the middle grades.* Carrboro, NC: Center for Early Adolescence, University of North Carolina at Chapel Hill.

Chapter 10

Sexuality Education in the Post-Secondary Classroom

Deborah A. Miller, PhD, CHES

How does sexuality education differ for secondary students and post-secondary students? Is there a distinct line which separates sexuality education at the secondary and post-secondary levels? This chapter will examine some similarities and differences between secondary and post-secondary sexuality education and discuss issues of concern to educators at the post-secondary level.

The Content of Sexuality Education

The six key concepts that should be part of any comprehensive sexuality education program are human development, personal skills, relationships, sexual behavior, sexual health, and society and culture. The National Guidelines Task Force, composed of representatives from 15 national organizations, schools and universities, expanded these concepts in 1991 and outlined 36 sexuality-related topics which should be taught at age-appropriate levels (National Guidelines Task Force, 1991). These concepts form the framework for any comprehensive sexuality course. However, the depth at which topics are covered may vary considerably from teacher to teacher, state to state or institution to institution.

The purpose of sexuality education at the secondary level is to "protect and promote health and to provide skills needed for loving and responsible relationships" (Meeks and Heit, 1993). Its purpose is not quite as clear at the post-secondary level. Institutions of higher education with teacher preparation programs in health education offer two distinctly different courses related to sexuality. The first course, taken by the largest number of students and comparable to sexuality education at the secondary level, is generally referred to as *human sexuality*. It is usually taken as part of the general education requirements or as an elective and is comprehensive in nature. Figure 1 compares the content of a secondary and a post-secondary course.

In keeping with the recommendation of the National Guidelines Task Force that concepts be taught at developmentally appropriate ages, it is apparent that several topics are more appropriate at the post-secondary than secondary level. In addition, state legislation may prohibit discussing controversial issues such as abortion or alternative lifestyles at the secondary level.

The second course, often called *sexuality education*, is designed primarily for future teachers. It emphasizes curriculum organization; teaching methods and materials; how to work with agencies; policy development; and how to handle controversy in the classroom, community and the media. A comprehensive human sexuality course is usually a prerequisite for this course.

Courses that deal with the human body may be found within a myriad of majors and departments at the post-secondary level, but many of these courses are too narrow in content to be considered

Figure 1
Comparison of Content:
Secondary and Post-Secondary Sexuality Education

Secondary
Introduction to human sexuality
Adolescence: a time of change
The reproductive systems
Parenthood: pregnancy and
  childbirth
Pregnancy prevention (little to no
  information on terminating
  pregnancy)
Relationships and decisions
  about sex
Skill building: communication
  skills, including refusal skills
Common concerns of adolescents:
  masturbation, rape, incest
Little to no information on sexual
  orientation
Sexually transmitted disease,
  including HIV/AIDS
Responsibilities in adulthood

Post-Secondary
Introduction to human sexuality
Childhood and adolescent
  sexuality**
Adult sexuality (including sex
  and aging)*
Reproductive anatomy and
  physiology
Conception, pregnancy and birth
Patterns of sexual response*
Birth control and terminating
  pregnancy**
Sexual communication**
Values and sexual behavior**
Love and intimacy**
Sexual pleasuring*
Gender identity and gender
  roles**
Sexual orientation**
Sexually transmitted disease,
  including HIV/AIDS
Sexuality in disabilities and
  illness*
Sexual problems and therapies*
Sexual research*
Variations in sexual behavior*
Sexual consumerism and the law**
Power and violence in sexuality**
Cultural-historical aspects of
  sexuality*

* Topics typically not covered to any degree at the secondary level
** Topics covered to a lesser degree or not all at the secondary level

valuable, comprehensive sexuality education courses. Biology departments may offer courses in "Human Anatomy," "Human Physiology," or "Human Reproduction and Development," but these courses address only a severely limited aspect of sexuality education. *Information about selected systems of the body and their functions cannot and must not be considered synonymous with sexuality education.* The physical aspects of human sexuality, such as the male and female reproductive systems, are an important part of a comprehensive sexuality education course, but the concepts of personal skills, relationships, sexual behavior, sexual health, and society and culture distinguish a quality sexuality education course from an anatomy and physiology course.

Adding even greater confusion to sexuality education at the post-secondary level is the variety of titles that may be given to sexuality education courses. It is common for sociology departments to offer courses such as "Sociology of the Family" or "Marriage and the Family." The department of psychology may offer a course entitled, "Life Span Human Development" or "Human Sexual Behavior." A combined physical education and health department may have courses entitled, "Social Health" or "Personal Health and Sexuality." Is it possible to determine the precise content of a course and whether or not it is comprehensive from its title?

Unfortunately, the answer to this question is no. Many students select a course at the post-secondary level only to discover that its title was misleading and their needs are not being met. For example, students may enroll in a "Sociology of the Family" course in the hope that it will teach them skills relating to fertility control and improved communication. But the sociology course may analyze courtship, marriage and family relationships and not address birth control or communication skills at all.

Required Versus Elective Courses

Why would a human sexuality course be included as part of the general education requirements at the post-secondary level? How would such a course benefit a business, history or math major? Why would a human sexuality course be selected as an elective by students? There are a variety of answers to these questions, but a few common threads should be pointed out.

First, post-secondary institutions that require a human sexuality course may feel that the content promotes breadth in all students' education. It has the potential to influence sexual knowledge, attitudes and behaviors while contributing to the overall well-being of the students. Second, students at community colleges as well as four-year institutions have the cognitive, affective and social ability to structure their own education in sexuality. For the first time, they can choose courses of personal value to them. Parents, teachers, religious leaders and community members typically are no longer dictating what post-secondary students need to know in sexuality education. Students are seeking information about their own sexuality and the diverse multicultural world in which they live.

Third, HIV/AIDS has been a catalyst for many post-secondary students to re-examine their sexual behavior and lifestyles. Almost 59 percent of them are engaging in consensual sexual activity and are using sexuality to explore meaningful and committed relationships (Kann et al., 1991). Individuals who are engaged or married often enroll in a sexuality course seeking answers to questions they are afraid to ask. Last, but not least, some post-secondary students want to take a course that is interesting, fun and taught using a wide array of teaching techniques and materials rather than the typical lecture format. This does not mean that a human sexuality course requires less academic work on the part of the student. Rather, it implies that students can be internally motivated to spend long hours synthesizing new information that can be applied to their personal lives. In addition, they are fascinated with the latest breakthroughs in research and technology.

At the secondary level, students may have been taught abstinence and the negative consequences associated with early sexual activity: dropping out of high school, poverty, unwed pregnancy, sexually transmitted disease, and loss of freedom (Haffner, 1992; Lavin, Shapiro and Weill, 1992; Meeks and Heit, 1992). For many students, a post-secondary human sexuality course is the last formal education they will receive on sexual issues and may be their first opportunity to explore many sexuality-related topics in a classroom setting.

It is therefore imperative that they have the opportunity to develop responsible and healthful sexual decision-making skills. These skills would include, but are not limited to the use of resistance skills when pressured to be sexually active or engage in inappropriate sexual behavior, assertive communication and active listening skills, and evaluation skills (e.g., being able to recognize sexual violence and respond appropriately when it occurs). These skills are predicated on accurate information about anatomy and physiology, pregnancy and childbirth, birth control and sterilization, sexually transmitted disease, including HIV/AIDS, and numerous other topics. Only with these skills and this knowledge-base can they determine the level of sexual involvement for which they are ready to assume the consequences (Meeks and Heit, 1993; Neutens, 1992; Neutens et al., 1991).

Materials Selection

Textbooks and nontraditional teaching materials (pamphlets, magazines, computer software, etc.) for the secondary level are often screened and selected by committees established by the State Department of Education and local school boards. These committees may be composed of parents, teachers, administrators, religious leaders, health professionals, librarians and curriculum specialists. Their responsibility is to ensure that the state adoption list for materials is consistent with any legislation that has been passed on sexuality education in the schools.

In addition, school districts may have a health advisory board that further screens commercially produced videos or posters as well as speakers and materials from local public health agencies. As part of the larger community, school districts follow the contemporary community standards very closely and try to minimize controversial and sensitive issues.

Community standards are still an issue for sexuality education at the post-secondary level, but to a much lesser degree. It is easier for communities to accept teaching controversial and sensitive issues to adults than teenagers. Consequently, post-secondary sexuality education can be a bridge for communities to grow and change.

Faculty members at community colleges, technical colleges, and four-year institutions have the academic freedom to select any and all materials that they use in the classroom. Departments that offer multiple sections of the same course may adopt a policy that all sections will use the same textbook. In this case, a committee composed of the faculty members teaching the course will screen textbooks and vote on the adopted text for the next academic year. Most faculty members, however, wish to retain their autonomy and select textbooks that meet their own individual needs and teaching style.

An important criteria for textbook selection is the number of credit hours received for the course. A two-hour course does not have enough time to delve into the same issues that a three-hour course does. Therefore, the textbooks may vary considerably in content and length.

Post-secondary institutions have seen their student body gradually age over the years. According to recent statistics, *nontraditional students* (those who have been out of high school for at least three years before they began their college education or those who are age 25 or older) make up almost one-third of the student population. These changing demographics have forced faculty members to focus on issues such as infertility, birth defects, sterilization, divorce, domestic violence, menopause, estrogen replacement therapy, sexual dysfunctions and therapies, sexual disabilities and illness, and sexuality throughout the life cycle. Consequently, post-secondary textbooks are more explicit in nature, address a wider range of sexuality topics, and focus on sexuality through older adulthood.

Team teaching is another factor that may influence textbook selection and/or course content at the post-secondary level. It is common for disciplines such as biology and psychology, health and psychology, or biology and anthropology to offer innovative courses. Post-secondary teachers have greater flexibility in their schedules and are encouraged to develop interdisciplinary courses. In addition, post-secondary teachers have the opportunity to collaborate with personnel from student health services, the counseling center or campus security. These program enhancing options are not available to the vast majority of secondary school teachers.

Teaching Strategies

At the secondary level, it is common for school districts to follow state guidelines and set teacher/pupil classroom ratios. In most instances, a teacher is responsible for no more than thirty students at a time. A class this small enables the teacher to utilize a wide variety of teaching strategies to help a student understand a particular concept and/or practice a specific life skill (Majer, Santelli and Coyle, 1992; Meeks and Heit, 1992; Pollack, 1992; Williams et al., 1992).

Class sizes at post-secondary institutions, on the other hand, vary from less than ten in a seminar setting to up to 250 students in a large lecture hall. Post-secondary teachers may be severely limited in their teaching strategies, assignments and exam material due to the sheer number of students enrolled in a single course. In addition, the layout of the room, which might include tiered seating or immovable chairs, may restrict interaction between the students.

The ideal class size at the post-secondary level would also be thirty, but forty is typical and manageable. This size or smaller allows the greatest variety of teaching strategies to be used and lends itself to high student interaction.

How does the teacher determine which teaching strategy should be used? Is it possible to address students' different learning styles? What happens if the teaching strategy doesn't work? All teachers have to answer these questions daily and make adjustments. Roleplaying, small group discussions, cooperative learning, decision making, debates and student presentations are just a few teaching strategies which can be used for skill building. Communication skills and refusal skills must be taught and practiced in a safe classroom setting before a student can incorporate them into his or her lifestyle. The strategy used depends on the desired outcome, the students' response, the class size, and both the comfort and the maturity level of the students in the class. Older students will respond differently than younger students, and the teacher will have to adapt accordingly.

The following roleplay situation demonstrates the potential difference in maturity level and subsequent responses:

> Julio, Jon and Brad have been best friends for over ten years. They were inseparable in high school and decided to attend the same college and be roommates until graduation. In less than two months, they will all graduate with degrees in business and have planned to open a restaurant together. On a dare, all three of them went to the health department to be tested for HIV. Jon tested positive and must decide if he will tell his best friends. Brad and Julio have to decide how they will deal with Jon if he tells them he is HIV positive.

If an older student plays Jon, he usually will tell his friends he is HIV positive. Developmentally, he has the maturity to know that his friends are at risk too and believes they have a right to know. He also cares about and trusts his best friends enough to tell them. A younger student, on the other hand, usually will decide not to risk the alienation of his best friends. He has not had the same bonding experiences with his roommates and does not yet have the emotional maturity to make a decision that takes others' potential risk into account.

Learning Styles

How do different students learn new material? Auditory learners rely predominantly on their hearing. Visual learners need to see pictures or words before the new information has any meaning to them. Kinesthetic learners are tactile and need to feel or manipulate something before they can internalize its meaning. Based on these three learning styles, teachers often have to adapt their teaching strategies to meet everyone's needs.

Teaching relies heavily on the spoken word and few, if any, special accommodations have to be made for auditory learners. They will usually acquire the information they need from lectures, discussions, buzz groups or brainstorming techniques. Almost every teaching strategy will accommodate the needs of the auditory learner.

Advanced preparation by the teacher is needed for the visual learner. Overhead transparencies, slides, models, charts, videos and computer video disks enable the material to become real for this individual. The adage, "A picture is worth a thousand words," describes the visual learner aptly. In addition to the above strategies, demonstrations and field trips are also appropriate.

The kinesthetic learner is somewhat at a disadvantage in a sexuality education course. Some post-secondary institutions do not have manipulatives or models that students can use for reinforcing information. The societal taboos associated with touching sexual genitalia, including models, may be difficult to overcome in the classroom. Every effort must be made to address the needs and comfort level of the kinesthetic learner.

Peer Education

Peer education on sexuality issues at the post-secondary level may be undertaken as service projects by fraternities and sororities or individual volunteers. In addition, peer education may be written into grants that are submitted by the Office of Student Affairs, Departments of Health Education or Student Health Services. Topics may range from discussions on positive and healthy relationships to telling your parents and friends that you have tested HIV-positive.

Peer educators should be screened and trained so they may present appropriate and accurate information to their peers in a nonthreatening manner. Students may feel more comfortable with a peer educator rather than a teacher. Discussions may be more open and honest and peer educators may be able to address the emotional/social aspects of sexuality which may not be brought out in the classroom. No matter what the setting is, peer education complements the academic component.

Future Challenges

As the twenty-first century approaches, men and women must learn to embrace and respect the differences among human beings and learn from each other. Young adults at the post-secondary level must be exposed to a wide variety of sexual topics if they are to be prepared for the next century. As Socrates said, "There is only one good, knowledge—and one evil, ignorance" (Yarber, 1992). Consequently, post-secondary sexuality educators, not legislators, should be the decision makers in the area of sexuality education content.

Legislation mandating or recommending sexuality education in grades nine through twelve should be applauded. Although many students at this age level need more information than is currently being taught, at least they are exposed to some form of sexuality education (Kirby, 1992; Pollack, 1992; Williams et al., 1992). This same claim cannot always be made at the post-secondary level where student may select the course as an elective or avoid it entirely. Unless a sexuality education course is required, a student may graduate from both a secondary and post-secondary institution never having received any formal sexuality education. It is time for post-secondary institutions to require sexuality education as part of everyone's undergraduate degree program.

The information explosion that has occurred in the twentieth century has left most post-secondary institutions scrambling to adapt their academic programs to fit the needs of the future. Post-secondary institutions have not been willing to grant sexuality education an importance equal to that of computer technology, science or mathematics. If we are to reach any of the *Healthy People 2000* objectives on family planning, violent and abusive behavior, maternal and infant health, HIV infection, or sexually transmitted disease, then greater emphasis must be placed on sexuality education through the life cycle. Ultimately, this may mean a mandated course at the post-secondary level. We must not let poverty, over-population, and sexually transmitted disease become even greater threats to our society than they are today.

Until then, however, sexuality education must also take place in the community setting. Hospitals, clinics, churches and related organizations must fill the gap in providing formal sexuality education. Mini-series, lectures and panel discussions given by licensed sex therapists, doctors, psychologists, social workers, qualified church leaders and other health care professionals will enable us to provide continuous and accurate sexuality information to anyone who wants it.

References

Haffner, D. W. 1992. Report card on the states: Sexual rights in America. *SIECUS Report* 20 (3): 1-7.

Kann, L., N. E. Anderson, D. Holtzman, J. Ross, B. I. Truman, J. Collins and L. J. Kolbe. 1991. HIV-related knowledge, beliefs, and behaviors among high school students in the United States: Results from a national survey. *Journal of School Health* 61 (9): 397-401.

Kirby, D. 1992. School-based programs to reduce sexual risk-taking behaviors. *Journal of School Health* 62 (7): 280-287.

Lavin, A. T., G. R. Shapiro and K. S. Weill. 1992. Creating an agenda for school-based health promotion: A review of selected reports. *Journal of School Health* 62 (6): 167-174.

Majer, L. S., J. S. Santelli and K. Coyle. 1992. Adolescent reproductive health: Roles for school personnel in prevention and early intervention. *Journal of School Health* 62 (7): 294-297.

Meeks, L., and P. Heit. 1992. *Comprehensive school health education: Totally awesome strategies for teaching health.* Blacklick, OH: Meeks Heit Publishing.

Meeks, L., and P. Heit. 1993. *Education for sexuality and HIV/AIDS.* Blacklick, OH: Meeks Heit Publishing.

National Guidelines Task Force. 1991. *Guidelines for comprehensive sexuality education: Kindergarten–12th grade.* New York, NY: Sex Information and Education Council of the United States.

Neutens, J. J., J. C. Drolet, M. L. Dushaw and W. Jubb. 1991. *Sexuality education within comprehensive school health education.* Kent, OH: American School Health Association.

Neutens, J. J. 1992. Sexuality education in comprehensive school health programs: Surviving the "moral smog." *Journal of School Health* 62 (2): 74-75.

Pollack, A. E. 1992. Teen contraception in the 1990s. *Journal of School Health* 62 (7): 288-293.

Williams, K. L., M. S. Doyle, B. A. Taylor and G. Ferguson. 1992. Addressing sexual orientation in a public high school. *Journal of School Health* 62 (4): 154-156.

Yarber, W. L. 1992. While we stood by... The limiting of sexual information to our youth. *Journal of Health Education* 23 (6): 326-335.

What Educators Need: Preparation and Presentation

Chapter 11

Sexuality Education at the Elementary Level: Preparing Teachers

Warren L. McNab, PhD, FASHA, and Charles E. W. Regin, PhD

Perhaps one of the greatest fears the elementary teacher initially encounters in teaching health education is the planning and presentation of material pertaining to sexuality education. Yet the competent teacher has the unique ability and interpersonal skills to effectively reach elementary students with any academic topic, including human sexuality. With support from the community and administration, adequate preparation on content and teaching methodologies, and a positive philosophy of sexuality education, elementary teachers can experience success and comfort in teaching this topic.

Sexuality education at the elementary level helps lay the foundation for healthy attitudes about sexuality that can help children who may be at risk. If factual material is presented in a positive manner in the elementary grades, negative attitudes, apprehensions and fears regarding sexuality may be reduced and replaced by a positive understanding that each person, regardless of age, lives part of his or her sexuality every day. Sexuality education increases elementary students' knowledge, communication skills, self-concept and social skills and helps young children feel good about themselves.

Sexuality education is justified at the elementary level because it allows children to use learned skills to feel good about and cope with predictable aspects of their physical and emotional development. The overall goal is to enhance the attitudes, knowledge and skills that will improve students' quality of life.

What Do We Mean by Sexuality Education?

Understanding one's own sexuality is basic to physical, mental/emotional and social health. Sexuality is the ability to feel and give warmth and love, to develop a positive self-concept, and to make responsible decisions regarding the physical, mental/emotional and social aspects of one's sexual health (McNab, 1981). In accepting and knowing the positive aspects of sexuality, children will come to believe in themselves and will be able to deal with their own sexual health in a positive way. Children at the elementary level will be interested in feelings about self-concept, fitting in with peers, and understanding changes pertaining to physical growth and development. Unfortunately, teachers may have to address the negative aspects of sexuality as well: issues related to sexual abuse, neglect, lack of love, not being accepted, and poor self-concept which may result in behavioral problems, poor grades and rebellion or seclusion.

Sexuality education in the elementary grades makes sexuality more understandable to young people and helps lay a factual foundation which can also incorporate parental feelings and values. Sexuality education involves teaching students to recognize and accept sexuality in themselves and others, in hopes of their using this knowledge toward the greatest creativity and fulfillment in their lives (McNab, 1981).

Teachers of sexuality education at every level should be able to explain to parents, administrators and students what sexuality education is, its goals and objectives and what topics it encompasses, and to justify why it is needed in the comprehensive health education program. Our entire education system is based on the belief that knowledge will help individuals make decisions which will better their lives. Teachers must believe in themselves as sexuality educators and be positive advocates of their programs. It is important that sexuality educators develop a philosophy of sexuality education.

The Teacher and the Community

The elementary teacher's professional philosophy should fit within the parameters or guidelines established within the community as reflected in the elementary sexuality education curriculum and district policy. Ideally, an advisory committee consisting of community members, administrators and teachers will have established a curriculum which reflects the needs of elementary students and complies with state and local mandates pertaining to sexuality and HIV education. The *National Guidelines for Comprehensive Sexuality Education* provides a good basic K through 12 framework for the development of sexuality education curricula (National Guidelines Task Force, 1991). The positive philosophy and enthusiasm of a good elementary school sexuality educator will provide a clear role model for students. Students will emulate this teacher's behavior when they experience the warm, caring approach the teacher uses to address their developmental needs.

The school can be a partner with the family, church and community in helping young children understand themselves as sexual beings. What is needed is a comprehensive program involving school administrators, teachers, and parents and caregivers in a collective effort that emphasizes the positive and rewarding aspects of sexuality throughout the elementary school years. It is important that administration and community leaders support elementary teachers' efforts. If the administration and community do not support the sexuality education program, it will not be successful. Community leaders and the school board serve as planners and advisors to the development of the sexuality curriculum. They are in a position to anticipate potential problems, and should communicate to parents the positive objectives and accomplishments of an effective elementary sexuality education program.

A sexuality education advisory committee made up of a variety of community leaders, parents, teachers and school officials can provide parents with the opportunity to examine educational materials and curricula before instruction begins. Elementary teachers can encourage administrative personnel and parents to observe a sexuality education class, so they will be aware of the types of objectives and lessons that are presented to students. An informed administration serves as a support system to the elementary teacher and can explain the curriculum to apprehensive parents. Parents should be kept informed of what is taught in the curriculum and encouraged to continue the sexuality education of their children in the home.

What Will They Ask—What Will You Say?

Perhaps the most important skill for effectively teaching sexuality education is the ability to communicate. True communication occurs when students interpret the meaning of the words and feelings in the same way as the teacher who sent the message. Student discussions with teachers, the questions they ask parents, and their interaction with peers all require the ability to speak, listen, comprehend and communicate. Communication skills learned at this young age enhance or inhibit a child's ability to make responsible decisions related to sexuality later in life.

Questions asked by children at this level usually relate to anatomical differences, names of body parts, how babies are made and how one can get along with friends and family. The conversation should be kept positive and nonthreatening. Students need to be reassured that wherever they are in their sexual development they are "OK," "normal," and accepted.

The bottom line is to be askable. The elementary teacher needs to be prepared to talk accurately and honestly about any topic pertaining to sexuality. The teacher must create for students a friendly, comfortable environment that allows questions under any conditions. Silence concerning topics of sexuality may foster guilt, fear, ignorance, apprehension and an overall negative attitude towards sexuality. Teachers who believe in the need for sexuality education at this level will find a variety of teaching techniques to facilitate discussions, questions and participation by the students. Inservice programs, courses, conferences and method books related to sexuality education can help the elementary teacher design methodologies for effective sexuality education.

Mastering the Vocabulary

One problem beginning teachers often face is mastering the appropriate vocabulary to facilitate open communication with students. For example, in the elementary grades "peter," "dink," "dong," "tool" and "dick" are all slang terms meaning penis. Young people quickly learn that four-letter "power words" get attention.

The teacher should be alert to language choices but model and encourage proper use of sexuality terms. Providing the appropriate terminology can enhance discussions about the various aspects of sexuality. Use proper vocabulary from the start. This means the teacher must be familiar with appropriate terminology relating to sexuality and the cultural setting in which instruction takes place.

A simple way for a prospective teacher to become familiar with terms related to sexuality before entering the classroom is to say the anatomical terms as well as the slang terms out loud. Pronounce the term correctly and then use the appropriate term in a sentence. By practicing this over and over, one becomes familiar with the terms, pronounces them correctly and realizes that there isn't anything that cannot be discussed about sexuality if you know and are comfortable with the vocabulary. All educators of sexuality will be surprised or possibly embarrassed at some time. If embarrassed, be flexible; let the students know you are human and these feelings are normal. Students can also practice saying vocabulary terms to reduce their anxiety and raise their comfort level.

Answering Questions

One of the most important tasks a sexuality educator has is to anticipate and answer spontaneous questions related to a variety of topics covered in a sexuality class. Answer the questions when they are asked; don't postpone them. Be honest. Overshoot—tell students a little more than they want to know. Initially, be aware that there will be giggles and laughter until a comfort level is reached between the teacher and students.

What are the interests of elementary school children pertaining to sexuality? What types of questions do they ask? How should one answer these questions? Always expect the unexpected. Lucille Trucano (1984) in her book, *Students Speak,* which surveyed health interests and concerns of students in kindergarten through grade 12, identified the following as example questions asked by elementary students about sexuality and growth and development:*

Kindergarten

- How do you get babies?
- How do babies come out?
- Why are families important?

First Grade

- How do you get twins?
- How do babies get fed in Mom's stomach?
- What do babies really do for you?

Second Grade

- Why do families break up?
- Why do you have to be grown up to have a baby?

Third Grade

- Why do some parents abuse their children?
- Why do people fall in love?
- Why don't we get along with brothers and sisters?

Fourth Grade

- How can babies get handicapped in the mother's tummy?
- How do you keep your family happy?
- How can you tell if your family loves you?

---

*Permission to include information from *Students Speak*, copyright 1984, Comprehensive Health Education Foundation (CHEF)® was granted from CHEF®, Seattle, Washington. Additional use or duplication prohibited without written permission from CHEF® All rights reserved.

Fifth Grade

- What do you do when your mom and dad fight a lot, and you can't do anything about it?
- What are some ways to get along with parents?
- What is a true family?

Sixth Grade

- How come boys can't have babies?
- How does a divorce affect kids?
- How do you relate to girls/boys you like a lot?

Questions usually relate to the physical, mental/emotional and social aspects of sexuality. Students often use slang terms for shock value to test the teacher to see if he or she will be embarrassed. Let students know that only appropriate anatomical terms will be used in the classroom. Here are some basic guidelines for teaching sexuality education at this level:

- All questions are valid and should be answered.
- Raise your shock level.
- Work to keep out personal bias.
- Believe in what you are teaching.
- Know the administration's philosophy.
- Encourage students to also talk to their parents.

Teaching really takes place when students ask questions pertaining to the material presented. Always provide an anonymous question box that everyone can contribute to for all health topics, especially sexuality education. Create hypothetical activities that require problem solving, decision making and thinking based on "gut level" feelings as to what is right or wrong behavior. When students can address questions collectively, they won't feel they are "wrong" or "stupid" when they answer or ask a question. A groundrule for the class should always be "There are no dumb questions." The use of literature to reflect examples of situations pertaining to sexuality also facilitates questions and student participation. Anyone can teach about the anatomical aspects of sexuality; it takes a unique individual to address sexuality education and deal with students' feelings associated with this subject.

As evidenced by the previous questions asked by students, sexuality education is most appropriate at the elementary level. The topics of families, friendship, growth and development, self-concept, relationships, personal skills and sexual behavior are all relevant to the elementary student.

Preparing to Teach Sexuality Education

The teacher should become familiar with and use reliable sexuality content materials, but there is more to being successful in this area than just knowing a lot. A sense of preparedness goes beyond knowledge.

Readiness is not just preparation of and proficiency in the content. It even goes beyond methodology selection or the strategy of setting up the teachable moment. It includes willingness on the part of the *teacher* to plan, present and evaluate the information, and the willingness of the *student* to accept, ponder and discuss that which is presented.

Teacher Readiness

Teacher readiness can be divided into two areas: professional readiness and personal readiness.

Professional Readiness

Professional readiness includes knowledge of information, perceived local support and having a clear picture of local mores and history. Reliable and updated information concerning human sexuality can be obtained from state curriculum guides, federal agencies such as the Centers for Disease Control and Prevention and national professional organizations which promote comprehensive sexuality education materials (see Appendix D). Each of these resources can be used to establish a foundation for the program. It has also been shown with other health-related areas that the more a teacher knows about a subject, the more that instructor is willing to teach that subject (Paulsen, 1987).

Support for the topic area can be found from many sources including parents and caregivers, the administration, community groups and clergy. It is important to know the local "power structure" that will have an interest in the area of sexuality education, and to what degree their opinions will influence others. It is prudent to acknowledge the power structure, keep them informed of what is being done, and even to involve them in an advisory role, if possible.

The local power structure is often a result of the community's makeup. Understanding the religious, ethnic, socioeconomic and political makeup of the community through involvement with local issues can give the educator insight and direction as to curriculum content. Being doomed before you start can be minimized by knowing the history of sexuality education in the community, the district, the school and even in a specific classroom. "What/who succeeded and why?" and "What/who failed and why?" are only two of the questions to ask colleagues and others regarding sexuality education. Educators need to know what was tried before and should talk to those who made the successful attempts.

A teacher's professional readiness can be enhanced by a number of different strategies. It may be possible to attend, take part, or even organize local forums concerning issues related to sexuality. Teachers can also participate in workshops that provide knowledge and strategy updates and allow for the exchange of ideas among peers. Each of these strategies is useful in its own way.

Personal Readiness

All these strategies can give the teacher the opportunity to examine his or her own beliefs and potential biases. Subtle, unacknowledged preferences can send strong, and perhaps unwanted, messages to students. To check for biases, teachers can reexamine the materials they've chosen for discussion in class. These choices can then be compared to those recommended in reliable resources. This comparison may point out previously undetected patterns (e.g., Are the materials unbalanced regarding information about birth, family structure or the emotions?) that illuminate personal preferences. If biases are discovered, a teacher has many options. If the bias is one of content imbalance, a restructuring of the time allotted to each area can be easily managed. If the bias runs deeper and may not be easily changed, the teacher must not be the "messenger" in that area. Alternative sources that can be used to present a balanced picture of all sides include recommended videotapes, screened guest speakers and self-guided handout materials.

Student Readiness

Student readiness for education about sexuality at the elementary level is often affected by the manner in which the teacher addresses the topic. An open and supportive environment in the classroom should be well established before a topic such as sexuality education is introduced. This open and supportive environment is created through careful planning throughout the school year. Some examples include allowing the students increasing self-governance responsibilities if they demonstrate competence; introducing class discussions about sensitive issues (not necessarily sexuality related) gleaned from the local newspaper, television, or the school. It is important to establish acceptable and unacceptable behavioral rules when discussing these issues. None of these strategies will work unless openness and supportiveness is demonstrated first by the teacher on a daily basis. The strategies used to create an honest, trusting and impartial atmosphere should be maintained throughout the year.

More than anything, the teaching of human sexuality issues should flow as smoothly as other curriculum topic areas. Introductory information can be effectively integrated into other content areas such as math, science or English. For example, in a science class in which genetics is being discussed, family trees that identify various genetic traits can lead into a discussion of various family structures in our culture—single-parent homes, unknown biological parents, and multiple parent and child families. In English class, an assignment to write about a "home" issue and then discuss it in a small group setting would allow the teacher to monitor students' ability to interact. These integration activities can offer feedback regarding students' readiness for the topic.

The Process of Sexuality Education

To successfully present materials, information and skills in the classroom that will be understood by students, the teacher must comprehend the *process* of sexuality education. The number of content variables may seem limitless, but there are general guidelines that will help the teacher move from the planning stages to successful implementation. Here are some guidelines to follow:

- Identify your strengths as a sexuality educator—acknowledge strong points, work on enhancing weaker ones.
- Secure appropriate administrative support—make sure that the team leader/coordinator/principal is aware of the program plans.
- Assess the current status of sexuality education in the classroom, the building, the district—balance what you would like to do (the ideal) with what can be done (the real).
- Write clearly the goals of the program which include measurable objectives—make allowances for both short- and long-term expectations.
- Select the appropriate scope and sequence of the topic—this includes what content should be known by students before you begin.
- Determine how to best implement the material—identify the strategies that will give the greatest likelihood of success. Reflect on what has succeeded in the past. How do most of the students learn? Is this a visual learning group? If so, choose strategies such as pictures and videotapes. Do they learn more by doing? Then roleplaying and debates can be expected to be successful.
- Screen all available resources—become familiar with local and national materials that will supplement the scope of the program content.
- Evaluate the program—obtain appropriate input from strategies used both before and after the content has been presented to the class.
- Practice damage control responses—despite a teacher's best efforts, something may not go as well as desired. Keep in mind that the teacher is responsible for what he or she says but cannot be responsible for what the students hear. If a student

misrepresents information given in class to a parent, teachers should be prepared to present both the content and the process used to the parent at an adult's level. Be prepared to work on a compromise; however, as the professional, the teacher must keep the integrity of the program in mind when discussing alternatives.

Unifying Goals

Regardless of what is eventually formulated through the process, a set of unifying goals that act as the foundation for the program is necessary. These goals should delineate the overriding theme for all activities, both in the classroom and in lesson plan preparation. Each district needs to develop goals that are sensitive to community needs, while maintaining professional integrity. The following are offered as a starting point.

The individual who partakes in a structured sexuality education program should be working toward:

- respecting the rights and privileges of children and family members
- adjusting appropriately to changing physical, mental, emotional and social roles, responsibilities and privileges as they occur throughout the life cycle
- dealing comfortably and appropriately with the demands of his or her own gender
- communicating effectively as a member of a family and of society
- making informed choices pertaining to sexuality

In addition to the above guidelines, resources are available that suggest behavioral objectives, content for each grade level, scope and sequence between grades and even suggested number of lessons in the unit. *Students Speak* (Trucano, 1984) is an excellent starting point as is any issue of the national publication *Family Life Educator.*

Selecting Methods

The criteria used to select appropriate learning activities in sexuality education should be no different from the criteria used to select strategies for other topic areas. Methodology choices range from bulletin boards to worksheets, from panel discussions to video tapes and from problem solving to roleplaying. The choice should be based on the teacher's determination of what will best facilitate learning for the students.

The selection of learning activities should be driven by the teacher's knowledge of the students' ability to communicate with peers, the students' level of self-esteem and self-confidence, and the ways the students best learn. Anspaugh and Ezell (1990) have examined the process of selecting learning activities. The following suggestions can be applied to selecting sexuality education methods.

Select strategies that contribute to total learning. Some activities lend themselves to acquiring knowledge, while others are better suited to attitude assessment and decision making. Ideally, the strategies selected should help the student develop the ability to reason and assess the information being presented.

The more complex the concept, the more activities are needed to develop the concept. As a general rule, for each concept, two strategies or activities should be employed. If the material being studied is difficult, more than two strategies or activities should be used.

Begin with the simple and move to the complex. Once the class has been prepared for the activity through proper introduction, the students should become part of the learning activity.

Use audiovisual aids whenever possible. Audiovisual aids add another dimension to teaching concepts and are excellent for reinforcing learning.

These suggestions are a reasonable starting point for method selection in sexuality education. When combined with the teacher's delivery skills and understanding of the students and the community, they lay a foundation for successfully imparting the selected information and skills to students. Whichever strategies are finally chosen, they should challenge children to think and to make decisions. The activities used should incorporate a cooperative process between the student, the teacher and those at home. Again, it is important to remember that strategies for teaching sexuality education can be drawn from the same method pool used for other content areas.

Summary

Elementary school teachers already have the ability to present lessons in an informative, creative and enthusiastic manner. These same abilities will enable them to learn about and teach the many established content areas of sexuality education. Through their dedicated efforts in a comprehensive school health program, teachers can help elementary school children learn about and feel good about one of the most positive and unique aspects of their lives—their sexuality.

References

Anspaugh, D. J., and G. O. Ezell. 1990. *Teaching Today's Health.* 3d ed. Columbus, OH: Merrill.

McNab, W. L. 1981. Advocating elementary sex education. *Health Education* 12 (5): 22-5.

National Guidelines Task Force. 1991. *Guidelines for comprehensive sexuality education: Kindergarten–12th grade.* New York: Sex Information and Educational Council of the United States.

Paulsen, B. K. 1987. *Final report needs assessment for nutrition education in Nevada's public and private schools: A teacher survey.* Report submitted to the Nevada Department of Education.

Trucano, L. 1984. *Students speak—a survey of health interests and concerns: Kindergarten through twelfth grade.* Seattle: Comprehensive Health Education Foundation.

Chapter 12

Professional Preparation of Middle and Secondary School Teachers

Judy C. Drolet, PhD, CHES, FASHA

"The great difficulty in education is to get experience out of ideas."

—George Santayana

HELP WANTED: Classroom teachers who are knowledgeable about curriculum development and the basic facts of sexuality; comfortable with their own sexuality and that of others; familiar with appropriate language; aware of current social issues; able to write grants and evaluate student outcomes; and capable of advocating with parents, school boards and the media.

For decades, sexuality education has received proportionally more scrutiny than any subject in the curriculum. Along with the subject matter, people who offer "sex ed" also are critiqued as they encounter myriad and frequently conflicting expectations. The connection between quality sexuality education programs and the caliber of teachers working within them has been reiterated by both theoreticians and practitioners. Most "experts" agree that the key ingredient in a worthwhile and acceptable educational experience is the skill of the teacher.

With sexuality education, the individual teacher may indeed embody the entire program. One teacher may be responsible for offerings in a single classroom or an entire district. Depending on availability of other staff and district size, teachers offering sexuality education may find that their responsibilities extend beyond the classroom to dealing with funding agencies, opposition groups and public health clinics. Yet, more often than not, courses are assigned to school staff who have little, if any, professional preparation. Among the many issues and apprehensions surrounding sexuality education, concern about qualifications of individuals assigned to do the teaching is perhaps the most valid (Bruess and Greenberg, 1988; McDermott and Marty, 1983).

At the elementary level, classroom teachers usually are responsible for all subjects. Therefore, inclusion of sexuality education in preservice preparation of elementary teachers is essential; but it is rare. At the middle and high school levels, a teacher is more likely to be specifically assigned to teach sexuality education. The focus of this chapter, therefore, will be issues of concern at these upper levels.

In middle and high school grades, teachers are expected to pay greater attention to the diverse personal issues of their students (Lieberman and Miller, 1984). Most school systems tend to introduce sexuality topics in ninth or tenth grade (Committee on School Health, 1993). Ideally, a certified health educator would teach this material. Realistically, however, middle or high school staff who may be assigned this duty are coaches, home economists, nurses, counselors, physical educators, science or other teachers who "got stuck with sex ed." In rural or smaller districts, an individual may be responsible for all sexuality education offerings at all levels.

Unfortunately, teachers from all levels are likely to share a common background. "Few teachers...have received training in sexuality education as part of their formal professional preparation" (Haffner, 1990). "Most elementary school teachers and some middle, junior high, and secondary school teachers have had little preservice preparation or experience in teaching sexuality education" (Bensley, 1991). This lack of formal instruction often leaves teachers stranded, needing to teach themselves before they can teach their students.

State legislation produce policies that complicate the problem further. Forty-six states either mandate or recommend sexuality education (Alan Guttmacher Institute, 1989). However, setting requirements and providing funding for necessary training of those who will teach this subject have *not* occurred. Lack of money, time and response to requests for training and guidance are not acceptable excuses. When discomfort paralyzes teachers, mandates alone cannot make sexuality education work.

Setting the Standards: Where Are We Now?

As early as 1912 the National Education Association supported special training for sexuality education teachers. In 1983, even the Vatican warned that the sensitive nature of sexuality education should be entrusted to "mature teachers" within the school community (Euchner, 1983). The Sex Information and Education Council of the United States (SIECUS) supports minimum standards for sexuality educators and recommends that all health educators must receive such training (Haffner, 1990). American Association of Sex Educators, Counselors and Therapists

(AASECT) offers requirements such as passing a knowledge test, participation in a two-day workshop to explore attitudes and values, and basic training in counseling skills, among others.

Ultimately, however, college/university professional preparation programs have determined and continue to determine the nature of content and process available to train teachers in sexuality education. The changing and complex nature of this area mandates that training of at least 40 to 45 hours of "content" as well as "methods and issues" should be a prerequisite, complemented with periodic inservice experience.

As we approach the millennium, we are faced with the challenge of defining a complex array of roles for sexuality educators. Today's sexuality teachers encounter large heterogeneous classes and a vastly expanded curriculum. The sensitive nature of most topics demands that they create a safe classroom environment with respect, trust and caring as fundamental groundrules. Perhaps more important, they may find themselves facing a myriad of student questions about sexual harassment and coercion, HIV/AIDS, abortion, safer sex and acquaintance rape. They will compete as credible resources on a multitude of topics absorbed from the nightly news, television talk shows that debate sexuality-related subjects, various magazines, and, unfortunately, weekly "rags." Even when local agency speakers come to the classroom, the teacher still has to respond to the questions, conflicts and fears elicited by the presentation. Teachers must learn the essential skill of recognizing "the question behind the question."

Then there are the facts:
- For teens in the United States, the average age of first intercourse is 16.2 for girls and 15.7 for boys. (Hechinger, 1992)
- Seventy-five percent of all unintended teenage pregnancies happen to adolescents who do not use contraception (Hechinger, 1992).

- The existence of child abuse, especially sexual abuse, has been denied on both the professional and societal level (Committee on School Health, 1993).
- Of all STDs reported, 86 percent occur among youth ages 15 to 29 years (CDC, 1991).
- Among sexually active teenage girls, the number who have had multiple partners has risen to 61 percent, up from 38 percent in 1971 (Gibbs, 1993).

So what have we accomplished since 1912? Some leaders in the field would answer "not very much." Estimates are that less than 10 percent of U.S. school children are exposed to "reasonably good" sexuality education (Gordon, 1990). Many teachers report such gaps in their own knowledge that the best they can offer their classes is incomplete or inaccurate information (Alan Guttmacher Institute, 1989).

Among incoming sexuality education teachers, fear of being ill-prepared surpasses concern about attacks from the opposition. These concerns are coupled with the continued reluctance of administrators and school boards to let teachers address controversial issues. Compounding this situation is the gap between what needs to be done and what teachers actually can do. How do you prepare students to make decisions in the world when you are told to teach about HIV but cannot mention "sex"? How do you lower teen pregnancy rates without talking about communicating with a partner about condoms or adoption?

Another dilemma faced by future teachers and those who prepare them is the perceived opposition to sexuality education. Yet national Gallup, Roper and *New York Times* polls reveal that at least 83 percent of U.S. adults favor such instruction (Gordon, 1990). How then can we prepare individuals to feel secure and confident as sexuality educators?

What Do Teachers Need to Know?

The "good news" is that teachers have state credentials, and, presumably, the best interests of the young people with whom they interact at heart, especially if they assume responsibility for teaching sexuality education voluntarily. Depending on school location, resources, funding and other variables, sexuality educators need preparation in:

- information
- self-knowledge
- classroom skills
- interpersonal skills
- comfort
- language

Information

Minimally, sexuality education teachers need the same background as other teachers. But the special nature of sexuality education presents unique challenges. Knowledge that includes facts about biological, psychological, ethical and sociological development is assumed to be the foundation of sound information on human sexuality. Lectures on this material alone, however, no longer equip teachers for their classroom experiences. How can we motivate new teachers and nurture the creativity and energy that helps define the "art" of teaching? How do we create environments where at least one teacher really *knows* each student?

Contemporary teacher training is expected to help an instructor become knowledgeable, sensitive, enthusiastic and able to instill a value for individual differences. The most ideal training would be offered by academically trained professionals, preferably with credentials in human sexuality, in a time frame adequate for synthesizing cognitively rich materials and modeling and practicing personal and social skills (Moglia, 1990).

Self-Knowledge

Opportunities for enhancing self-knowledge are equally (if not more) essential, so that prospective teachers can recognize and clarify their own understanding, attitudes, biases and responses to the myriad values and views of our society and cultures. Greater emphasis on and preparation and opportunities for affective education are critical if teachers and their students are to develop needed personal and social skills to meet the challenges of a complex world (Fetro, 1992; Gordon, 1990; Vincent, 1991).

Classroom and Interpersonal Skills

Sexuality teachers must be able to conduct discussions that keep students involved; encourage expression of feelings, beliefs and attitudes; allow practice in developing communication and listening skills; facilitate tolerance for ambiguity when "answers" are complex and individually defined; and provide a forum to explore dilemmas and conflicting perspectives. Additionally, with sexuality education perhaps more than any other subject, when a teacher says "I don't know, but I'll find out," a response must be conveyed back to the student within a reasonable length of time.

More specifically, we need to teach future teachers the skills themselves—what they are and how to use them—so that they, in turn, eventually can teach their students. For example: "The anatomy lesson must come in a larger context of building relationships based on dignity and respect" (Gibbs, 1993). A focus on promoting positive self-esteem will offer opportunities to address questions such as: How do we communicate? How do we make decisions? How do we set goals? How do we resolve conflicts?

Comfort

Being totally comfortable with all aspects of sexuality education is unlikely. Yet future teachers, and ultimately their students, need to practice and increase their comfort levels to know how they feel and what they will do when faced with certain situations and pressures. Teachers' credibility is bolstered when honesty, respect and self-acceptance evolve from their interaction with students. Teachers should refrain from making assumptions about their students and interact with them in ways that help them feel special and unique (Krueger, 1993). This approach may help to diffuse controversy, while providing a message that having choices and being in control are options.

Language

One critical factor in increasing comfort is exploring the power of language—especially sexual language—when preparing middle and high school sexuality teachers. Future educators must understand the importance of using accurate terminology versus euphemisms, the emotional intensity of meaning associated with sexuality-related words, and the potential barriers to and means of improving interpersonal communication given the context and connotation of sexual language.

What Should Teachers Be Able to Do?

Increasingly the roles and responsibilities of teachers responsible for sexuality education have extended to reflect those for school health educators delineated by the National Task Force on the Practice and Preparation of Health Educators (1985). Depending on need, financing, resources, locale and other issues, teachers of sexuality education could be expected to:
• assess individual and community needs

- plan effective programs
- implement programs
- evaluate effectiveness of programs
- coordinate provision of services
- act as a resource person
- communicate needs, concerns and resources to others

Needs Assessment

The mosaic of a typical classroom clearly reflects ranges in growth and development as well as a continuum of risk behaviors. Yet "sexuality education teachers are more likely to teach about abstinence than almost any other topic" (Alan Guttmacher Institute, 1989). Recognizing the importance of knowing about each unique group of students is essential. In teacher preparation, future sexuality educators can learn how baseline data on knowledge, feelings, attitudes and practices can be a foundation for curriculum development, selection and placement. Considering the personal nature of sexuality topics, providing an anonymous means of acquiring information is important. A "question box" will encourage direct student input about their needs. We cannot assume that any group or individual sexuality education needs will be identical.

Future sexuality teachers can learn to use qualitative methods such as focus group interviews to identify sexual interests and concerns and guide emphases among curriculum topics. A survey could be distributed as a pretest of knowledge. Information about students also can be found unexpectedly in class assignments. For example, a student might complete the sentence stem "Homosexuals are _____" with "just like me."

Preparation courses can offer roleplay practice in interviewing parents or other school staff who provide support services to adolescents and can suggest areas of need. Overall, sexuality educators must determine the difference between "what is"—

current knowledge, attitudes and behaviors—and "what should be"—the changes needed if students are to learn to function as sexually healthy and responsible adults. If prepared to conduct needs assessments, future sexuality educators will be more likely to offer educational experiences that are developmentally appropriate and culturally sensitive.

We also need to identify strategies for establishing meaningful connections between teachers and the universities that prepare them. Prescriptions for reform should be complemented by efforts to identify, support, disseminate and enhance outstanding model programs currently in use in our nation's schools.

Planning Effective Programs

The first step in planning to offer (or not offer!) sexuality-related instruction generally will be taken by school administrators. They will need to consult state guidelines so that local offerings are consistent for age and developmental level. Community advisory groups (including parents and representatives from community agencies, medical professions, law enforcement and service groups, the religious community and others) may provide input and oppose or support sexuality education offerings.

Even though they may not have the power to make this decision, future teachers should know that planning sexuality education as part of a comprehensive school health program is highly recommended (Neutens et al., 1991). Connections among health-related issues (including sexuality issues), risks and practices are more easily identified in a comprehensive context. A comprehensive program includes "an organized set of policies, procedures and activities designed to protect and promote the health and well-being of students and staff..." (Joint Committee on Health Education Terminology, 1990). This comprehensive approach can provide a planned scope and sequence for a prekindergarten through grade 12 curriculum that helps ensure that students acquire necessary knowledge, attitudes and skills.

As part of training for program planning, preparation courses should offer practice in writing overall program goals, or what is to be achieved. These goals should reflect the school district's philosophy (e.g., "healthy sexuality is an essential part of growth and development") and specific measurable objectives that reflect information acquired about needs (e.g., "a peer support group will be established for students engaging in high-risk sexual behaviors"). Planned activities should be designed to meet these objectives.

Future sexuality educators can learn to plan instruction as part of an overall prevention program. Prevention programs target students, peer groups, families and the community. A variety of methods and activities are included to reduce risk factors and strengthen personal and social skills. Over twenty years of research have revealed that planners need to consider the following key elements:

- accurate information
- activities to enhance self-esteem
- communication skills (including refusal and assertiveness)
- decision-making skills
- refusal/resistance skills
- coping skills
- goal-setting activities
- use of peer helpers
- parent involvement

When preparing teachers, faculty should include discussion and practice of these elements essential for planning successful programs (Fetro, 1991).

In their preparation courses, future sexuality educators also can be trained in how to use local needs assessment results as well as national surveys and other research in planning programs. For example, citing frequencies of sexual behaviors, or data on perceptions about risk for transmission of STD can strengthen the effectiveness of sexuality education. Identified needs can guide the selection of textbook supplements, the planning of subject matter of current interest, and the integration of a variety of homework and extension activities, including multi-media. Information about needs can help in establishing mechanisms to link the sexuality education teacher with other school resources and/or school staff (e.g., counselors, nurses) with available community resources (e.g., an adolescent health center or county health department).

Overall, preparation faculty can design assignments that will allow future sexuality teachers to systematically examine program plans for deficiencies, gaps and alternatives. A well-planned program will more likely experience greater success and ease in implementation.

Implementing Programs

After prospective teachers learn to identify needs and plan programs, preparation in implementing programs can begin. Future teachers must be made aware of the necessity of school administrators and policy makers endorsing sexuality education. Lessons should include specific ways to present a clear rationale for sexuality education to parents and other school staff. In some settings, professional preparation programs may need to demonstrate how future sexuality teachers can link their programs with those offered by community agencies and health departments to offer complementary learning experiences (e.g., guest speakers on HIV/AIDS).

Preparing for implementation requires a strong emphasis on communication skills. Class activities that highlight verbal skills and nonverbal body language, as well as ways to respond to sensitive questions are critical. A variety of instructional strategies (e.g., small group discussion, games, videos, bulletin board displays) should be identified and mastered. Group projects presented in class can be particularly useful, as they offer practice in building consensus on subject matter and methods, delegating manageable tasks and being responsible to those with whom one is implementing a project.

Evaluating Programs

Once sexuality education is in place, future teachers will be responsible for determining if the program is doing what it is designed to accomplish. Determining if implementation is occurring as planned and what impact the program is having is accomplished through evaluation. Evaluation can be used to strengthen the sexuality program.

Although a tremendous phobia about "evaluation" often exists among school staff, all teachers really are evaluators. They prepare exams and quizzes and observe their students at work. Preparation courses should prepare future teachers to evaluate personal and social skill development (e.g., through roleplay situations requiring refusal to engage in sexuality activity).

Training also should include interpreting other evaluation findings. For example, a school board member might request interpretation of findings about sexual behaviors from the Centers for Disease Control and Prevention *Youth Risk Behavior Survey.* Overall, preparation in evaluation should focus on evaluation's role in improving (as opposed to "proving") programs and providing future direction.

Coordinating Services

Training that fosters leadership, organization and communication will best facilitate future sexuality educators' acquisition of coordination skills. Whether it deals with team-teaching, working with student associations, or determining how high school seniors can offer peer education presentations, training should enable future teachers to see how collaborative involvement can help ensure a supportive environment and successful programs. Teachers also need to learn how to identify community resources (e.g., agencies that provide testing information, support groups) so they can refer students as necessary.

In the training classroom, future educators can roleplay and practice models for diffusing confrontational situations that might place the program in jeopardy. Training can assist educators in identifying potential duplication of services or gaps in services. Well-developed coordination skills will better enable future sexuality educators to reduce conflict and increase cooperation in the delivery of programs and services.

Acting as a Resource Person

Considering the sensitive nature of the topic, the likelihood of a sexuality educator serving as a resource on sexuality-related information and processes is almost guaranteed. Requests may come in a variety of forms on an almost daily basis. Preparing for this role again requires considerable emphasis on communication skills. Various settings may require specific types of responses. In addition to participating in school district programs (e.g., a panel discussion on adolescent pregnancy), future sexuality educators may be called upon to have training in computer skills and the ability to interpret reports and select print materials. Teachers may be asked to sponsor a schoolwide peer helper program or serve as a respondent to media coverage of a new condom distribution program.

Preparation faculty can introduce future sexuality educators to the reciprocal benefits of active participation in professional activities. While serving as important resources for state, regional and national associations, future sexuality educators can learn the benefits of affiliation. Journals often include teaching strategies, useful evaluation and research findings and a variety of resources, while association conferences provide opportunities for networking. Preparation should foster an awareness of key leaders and organizations such as the Sex Information and Education Council of the United States (SIECUS) and its 1991 guidelines for comprehensive K-12 sexuality education and the national coalition of over sixty organizations joined together to ensure that children and youth receive comprehensive sexuality education (see Appendix D).

Communicating Needs, Concerns and Resources

Once sexuality education needs, concerns and resources are identified, they can be conveyed to a variety of people using diverse methods. Target group and setting will guide selection of the appropriate means to accomplish this. Future sexuality educators need preparation in making presentations, writing summary reports, lobbying and understanding the processes that influence passage of state and federal bills. Class activities might include developing tables and figures, roleplaying a panel discussion for union representatives, or rehearsing an interview with school board members. Preparation in responding to letters to the editor or appropriate participation in local town meetings or decision-making bodies will complement learning on how to initiate discussions of controversial sexuality education issues with community groups and organizations. Future teachers should be prepared to take advantage of every opportunity to facilitate communication about sexuality education.

Personal Attributes of Teachers

In preparation for inservice programs, "values-free" teaching of sexuality education may be espoused. This is a goal that is impossible to attain. The inclusion or exclusion of topics and the choice of printed and audiovisual materials reflect the teacher's values. In fact we do prepare teachers to transmit values—for example, that sexual behavior should be responsible behavior; that sexism, exploitation and violence are not acceptable; and that positive self-esteem is critical to healthy sexuality.

Certain characteristics can better enable an instructor to provide worthwhile experiences that will be valued by students, parents, administrators and the community. Over the past twenty years, sexuality educators have suggested various attributes that remain relevant (Greenberg, 1989; Johnson and Belzer, 1973; Manley, 1986; Wagner, 1985):

- enthusiasm and a high comfort level with human sexuality
- awareness of evolving social changes
- sensitivity to and respect for views of others
- mastery of facts and skills to provide diverse educational experiences
- a sense of humor
- tolerance of ambiguity

Future Challenges, Barriers and Opportunities

As if preparing for all the responsibilities discussed earlier weren't enough, teachers of the nineties and beyond the year 2000 face other challenges as well: Pressure for multicultural education and the Americans with Disabilities Act will affect how sexuality education deals with ethnic differences, special needs students, gender-role issues and sexual orientation. How can sexuality education foster and preserve respect for diversity and uniqueness?

Comprehensive training must extend our vision to the "world community." In our country, the challenges of the nineties afford a never-before-identified opportunity to address the year 2000 health objectives for our nation. More than 100 objectives can be attained directly or influenced indirectly by school health programs. Family life education and sexuality education will play a prominent role in this process. HIV/AIDS education, for example, can be a catalyst for more comprehensive health education programs. Preparation that emphasizes the integration of sexuality education into a comprehensive health education program will best promote achievement of individual, local, state and national goals, such as those identified in *Healthy People 2000* (U.S. Department of Health and Human Services, 1992). Furthermore, the need to address global objectives is becoming more urgent. In recent years we have witnessed incredible and far-reaching changes in world government structures and are reminded *again* that population policies are not defined solely by hometown teen pregnancy rates but extend to the Middle East, China and Russia.

In many areas, teachers interact with children in poverty, children from families on public aid, foster homes or institutions, and the unemployed. Beyond urban settings, we must address the needs of low-income children in "rural ghettos." Are future sexuality educators adequately prepared to respond to these students?

Teachers cannot tackle these challenges alone. Future educators must learn about the importance of partnerships among school staff and between schools and the community and how to participate in and build these coalitions. Such alliances hold the most promise of helping children and youth become informed and skilled in making choices that will decrease their sexual health risks and increase their quality of life.

Teacher training can emphasize how parents and guardians can become advocates and allies when positive teacher/parent interactions and effective programming occur. Future sexuality educators can learn how youth service groups, community health agencies, and local, regional and state networks can continue to pursue collaborative efforts via the coalitions and cooperative agreements espoused by sexuality and health education leaders. Such alliances ultimately may enable sexuality education to reach its full potential and can bridge the gaps typically created by controversy, territoriality and well-intentioned but burdensome mandates. Such efforts may even benefit some of the often overlooked out-of-school youth.

A clear connection exists between quality teacher preparation experiences and knowledgeable, competent, skilled teachers. Future teachers will be models and mentors for the school-age youth entrusted to them. Contrary to the assertions of opponents, well-trained teachers *can* help students understand their worth as well as the consequences of their choices. Sexuality teachers of the year 2000 and beyond can be highly trained individuals who value, respect and understand themselves and their students' attitudes, feelings, needs and changes. The challenge to teacher preparation programs is to provide them with the learning opportunities and skills they need.

> The pertinent question is not how to do things right
> but how to find the right things to do, and to concen-
> trate resources and efforts on them.
> —Peter F. Drucher

References

Alan Guttmacher Institute. 1989. *Risk and responsibility: Teaching sex education in America's schools today.* New York.

Bensley, L. 1991. Steps for implementation. In *Sexuality education within comprehensive school health education,* ed. J. J. Neutens, J. C. Drolet, M. L. Dushaw and W. Jubb, 1-11. Kent, OH: American School Health Association.

Bruess, C. E., and J. S. Greenberg. 1994. *Sexuality education: Theory and practice.* 3d ed. Dubuque, IA: W. C. Brown and Benchmark.

Centers for Disease Control and Prevention. 1991. *Division of STD/HIV Prevention annual report, 1990.* Atlanta: U.S. Department of Health and Human Services, Public Health Service.

Committee on School Health. 1993. *School health: Policy and practice.* 5th ed. Elk Grove Village, IL: American Academy of Pediatrics.

Euchner, C. 1983. The Vatican endorses sex education in schools. *Education Week,* December 14.

Fetro, J. V. 1992. *Personal and social skills: Understanding and integrating competencies across health content.* Santa Cruz, CA: ETR Associates.

Fetro, J. V. 1991. *Step by step to substance use prevention: The planning guide to substance use prevention.* Santa Cruz, CA: ETR Associates.

Gibbs, N. 1993. How should we teach our children about sex? *Time* 141 (21): 60-66.

Gordon, S. 1990. Sexuality education in the 1990s. *Journal of Health Education* 21 (1): 4-5.

Greenberg, J. S. 1989. Preparing teachers for sexuality education. *Theory into Practice* 28 (3): 227-232.

Haffner, D. W. 1990. *Sex education 2000: A call to action.* New York: Sex Information and Education Council of the United States.

Hechinger, F. M. 1992. *Fateful choices: Healthy youth for the 21st century.* New York: Carnegie Council on Adolescent Development.

Johnson, W. R., and E. G. Belzer, Jr. 1973. *Human sexual behavior and sex education.* 3d ed. Philadelphia, PA: Lea and Febiger.

Joint Committee on Health Education Terminology. 1990. Report of the Joint Committee on Health Education Terminology. *Journal of Health Education* 22 (2): 97-108.

Krueger, M. M. 1993. Everyone is an exception: Assumptions to avoid in the sex education classroom. *Phi Delta Kappan* 74 (7): 569-572.

Lieberman, A., and Miller, L., eds. 1984. *Teachers, their world and their work: Implications for school improvement: The 1984 ASCD Yearbook.* Alexandria, VA: Association for Supervision and Curriculum Development.

Manley, J. 1986. Teacher selection for sex education. *SIECUS Report* 15 (2): 10-11.

McDermott, R. J., and P. J. Marty. 1983. Teacher education in human sexuality: Design for improvement. *The Teacher Educator* 18 (4): 2-10.

Moglia, R. 1990. The professional preparation of sexuality educators: A pivotal factor for sexuality education. *SIECUS Report* 18 (2): 13-15.

National Task Force on the Preparation and Practice of Health Educators. 1985. *A framework for the development of competency-based curricula for entry-level health educators.* New York.

Neutens, J. J., J. C. Drolet, M. Dushaw and W. J. Jubb. 1991. *Sexuality education within comprehensive school health education.* Kent, OH: American School Health Association.

U.S. Department of Health and Human Services, Public Health Service. 1992. *Healthy People 2000: National health promotion and disease prevention objectives, summary report.* Boston, MA: Jones and Bartlett.

Vincent, M. L. 1991. With high tech, are we losing touch: The time to re-emphasize affective health education. *Journal of Health Education* 22 (5): 272-282.

Wagner, N. N. 1985. Sex education in schools. In *Sex education: Some guidelines for teachers,* ed. D. Went. London: Bell and Hyman.

Chapter 13

Teacher Training for Sexuality Education: A Model

Nancy Abbey

Training educators for successful implementation of any new teaching approach is a process, not a single, one-shot event. This is because any new approach—whether it introduces new curricula or creative approaches to existing sexuality education, or proposes an entirely new sexuality education program for a school community—involves change.

Changing is a formidable task. We have all experienced in our own lives the struggle of changing a long-term behavior—even one that no longer serves us well. Changing teaching behaviors is a no less difficult task.

The challenge is complicated by the nature of sexuality education. Sexuality education differs from other areas of the school curriculum in several important ways. First, there is the challenge of teaching an emotionally and politically charged subject. Teachers must handle the topic with sensitivity and awareness of the myriad of parental and community concerns. Many very accomplished educators approach teaching sexuality education with well-founded concern and apprehension.

Second, if sexuality education is new to the school or district, introducing it into the curriculum will require change at the school, district and community level as well as change at the personal teacher level, compounding the complexity of the task.

Finally, since we seem no closer now to the ideal goal of preservice preparation for all sexuality education teachers than we were years ago, few teachers understand the rationale for teaching sexuality education in the schools and even fewer are prepared in any way to teach it. All these issues combined present a training challenge far larger in scope than the challenges facing a trainer in other subject areas.

With this in mind, the goal of an effective training for sexuality educators is to acknowledge and guide the process of change in teaching behavior. Such training should promote a supportive environment; provide the knowledge, attitudes and skills to effectively teach sexuality education; and foster a sense of self-efficacy in the teacher.

It is the sense of self-efficacy—the teacher's confidence in his or her ability to effectively integrate new materials and innovative teaching strategies into the classroom—that has proven the most critical to the transfer of learning from teachers' training to their performance in the classroom.

This chapter will present one approach to meeting the challenge of training teachers for effective implementation of sexuality education in the classroom. It will introduce a paradigm that describes the process of change educators undergo as they develop the sense of self-efficacy needed to integrate skills and innovations into their teaching. This paradigm forms the basis for training interventions that meet the needs of sexuality educators at each phase in the change process.

A Model for Change

To understand how change relates to initiating and implementing sexuality education in the classroom, the Change Based Adoption Model (CBAM) developed by the Research and Development Center for Teacher Education at the University of Texas in Austin was studied. In the center's efforts to help schools implement sex equity programs, they saw many failures resulting from a lack of understanding about how school communities adopt change. From their own experience, the work of Rogers (1971), and the results of a study done by Crandall (1982), the center developed the Change Based Adoption Model (CBAM), which describes the process individuals go through as they adopt a new idea or innovation (Hall and Loucks, 1979).

A basic premise of the CBAM model is that an individual experiencing change goes through a series of perceptions about the change, ranging from personal views to the overall effect of the change. These perceptions, or concerns, must be acknowledged and addressed before the individual can successfully begin acting differently. And the individual must be the focus of any intervention to effect change at the institutional level (Crandall et. al., 1982).

There are many correlations between this description of the change process and the concerns and questions of educators being prepared to teach sexuality education. Beginning sexuality education teachers are often so concerned about the effect teaching sexuality education will have on themselves and their students that they are unable to focus on developing the skills they need to successfully implement a program. Using CBAM in sexuality education trainings heightens the trainers' awareness of these needs, and helps organize the training process and content.

The Change Based Adoption Model describes individual change

in terms of stages of personal concern about the change. The stages represent a developmental process from lack of awareness of the need for change, to full integration of the innovation into one's present system. For example, sexuality educators' first concern after becoming aware of a proposed change might be a desire for information about the change: What will the sexuality education program look like? After learning about program content, the next stage of concern will probably focus on the demands the program would place on them as teachers: "How will teaching sexuality education affect me?"

The focus of concern continues to change as the individual progresses through each stage, touching on management issues, improving teaching skills to make a program better, collaborating with colleagues, and, finally, using experience, knowledge and skills to refine the program on a continuing basis. Following is a brief description of the stages of concern experienced by a potential sexuality education teacher.

- At *Stage 1*, educators may have little awareness, and basically no concerns, about the need for sexuality education. A program development workshop to train a core group of parents and staff in the steps necessary to initiate or improve the sexuality education program is the appropriate intervention at this first level.

- As the core group talks with people about the need for sexuality education in the school, *Stage 2* is reached: team members want more information about the sexuality education program.

- *Stage 3* is the personal concern stage. At this stage individual educators begin considering what sexuality education will "look like" in their classrooms, and how teaching the subject will affect them personally.

- At *Stage 4*, educators are concerned with the management issues involved in teaching the curriculum. These might center on how to find the time to implement a program within an existing course, how to obtain the necessary materials to implement a program, and how to adapt the program to meet community standards and the needs of individual students. More advanced, experienced sexuality education teachers can act as mentors at this point, helping newer educators resolve problems and move through this stage of concern.

- *Stage 5* is the concern about consequences stage. Here educators are asking the question, How is my teaching affecting students and what can I do to refine my techniques so I can have more impact. At this stage, teachers are ready to focus on increasing their skills level.
- Once skills (and confidence) are increased by skills training, educators want to share and learn from others. This is *Stage 6,* the collaborative stage, when educators are ready for coaching from colleagues and support groups.
- *Stage 7* is ongoing attention to maintain the change. The need for booster sessions, inservice training, conferences and refresher courses to renew enthusiasm and refocus on content and process continues as long as an educator is teaching.

By looking at training as a developmental change process, interventions and trainings can be organized to correlate with the stages of concern of the CBAM model (see Figure 1). The interventions include both formal trainings and on-site activities that facilitate progress through the levels of concern.

The remainder of this chapter will describe how the seven teacher interventions adapted from CBAM can be used in training sexuality education teachers. Four interventions involve formal trainings; three address concerns of teachers to facilitate readiness for the next level of training.

The Program Development Workshop

The program development workshop prepares a team or core group of staff and parents at Stage 1 to implement the necessary

---

Figure 1
Levels of Concern and Intervention

Stage of Concern	Expression of Concern	Intervention
awareness	Not concerned.	program development workshop
informational	I would like to know more about sexuality education. What would a program look like?	staff orientation
personal	How will teaching sexuality education affect me?	basic educator training
management	I seem to be spending all my time getting ready.	mentor assistance
consequence	How is my teaching affecting students? How can I refine it to have more impact?	skills advancement training
collaboration	How can I relate what I am doing to what others are doing?	collegial coaching and support
refocusing	I have some ideas about something that would work even better.	booster sessions

---

steps to initiate sexuality education in a school district or improve an existing program. This training focuses on how to develop involvement and support among administration, governing board members, teachers, parents and the community. The program development workshop should provide teachers with:

- information about the need for sexuality education that can provide the basis for developing a district rationale for sexuality education
- an understanding of the process of change in a school.
- strategies for developing administrative and school board approval and support
- a recognition of the need to involve parents and community to the fullest extent
- knowledge of available state-of-the-art curricula
- a plan for developing involvement and support of decision markers, parents, community and teachers

During the program development workshop, the team develops an action plan that proposes how to accomplish these tasks. There are several components to the ideal action plan.

Generate interest and support. This first step involves informal conversations with administrators, teachers and key community members. The primary purpose is to arouse interest in sexuality education and foster a desire for more information. A second goal is to uncover concerns that can be addressed later in the staff orientation.

Identify key decision makers and opinion setters. Depending on the size of a school district, the superintendent may be an important person for an initial conversation. That conversation should indicate a next-in-command who will keep the superintendent informed and who will become more involved. This person is often an assistant superintendent in charge of instruction or curriculum. Be prepared to have several conversations with this person.

Identify site principals. Principals are critical to the success of any effort to enlist teachers in trainings. Because of their position as arbiters between school policy and concerned parents, principals are very sensitive to the issues surrounding sexuality education. Principals are at great disadvantage when they lack information with which to respond to parents' and caregivers' concerns. They need to be informed early in the process of implementation and be kept informed. A well-informed principal backed by clear district policy can be a program's greatest support in a school district.

Identify key teachers. This can be a delicate process. The most enthusiastic, innovative teachers are not necessarily leaders who influence other teachers. According to a study by Rogers (1971) of how people react to change, there are five adopter types.

"Innovators" are outgoing and highly motivated to try original concepts. They are generally not accepted as one of the crowd and are sometimes thought of as peculiar. "Leaders" are influential and open to trying innovations, but are more grounded than innovators. They are often responsible for encouraging others to change (Mundry and Hergert, 1988).

Others are classified into the "early majority," the "late majority" and "resisters." The early majority is careful about adopting innovations. They need more information and persuasion than leaders. The late majority is cautious about change and slower to adopt. They will watch the leaders and follow if results of their innovations are positive. Resisters challenge any change but are usually not influential.

In this first stage, the focus needs to be on building the interest and support of the leaders. Innovators will need little urging to join the effort and the early majority will be influenced by the direction taken by the leaders.

Assuming this process is taking place after or in conjunction with the adoption of policy and curriculum for a sexuality education program, talking to parents and community members is not critical at this stage. Key people will have been oriented to sexuality education issues during the process of adoption and will already have a high level of interest. If the district has *not* initiated the process for program adoption, this step must involve parents and the community in the process. Advocates must also broaden their purpose to include focusing the district's attention on the need for formal policy concerning sexuality education (Wagman and Ludlow, 1988).

Staff Orientation

Involving the community, administration and staff in the effort to implement sexuality education triggers stage two, the informational stage. With interest piqued, educators want to know, "What does a sexuality education program look like?" Intervention at this level does not need to take the form of a formal meeting. It can consist of a series of interventions that include brief presentations at faculty meetings or to the governing board, a handout describing the framework for the program, a notice on the faculty bulletin board on the status of sexuality education in the school district, a pamphlet that frames the need for sexuality education in the district, or a display of sexuality education materials.

The informational stage focuses on the need for understanding what sexuality education "looks like" and the rationale for teaching it. The "picture" of the program can be created by providing a paper describing the district's adopted curriculum, a copy of the state health framework, and/or a display of materials. Those educators who will be teaching sexuality education in the classroom will be anxious for more information and ready for training to prepare them for implementation.

The objective for this stage is to satisfy the staff and administration's need for information about sexuality education and to move those teachers who will teach the subject to a readiness for basic teacher training. When educators' questions take on a personal tone they are being propelled into Stage 3, the personal concern stage: Will parents complain? Will I be teaching sexuality education? Will the administration support teachers? How will the community standards and my personal standards of sexual conduct be reflected in the curriculum? Teachers at this stage are ready for the basic educator training.

Basic Educator Training

The basic educator training must address the question, "How will teaching sexuality education affect me?" This question reflects some primary concerns of entry level teachers: (1) What are the limits of what I can say and do? Will my principal support me if a parent gets upset? (2) What demands will teaching place on me? and, most crucial, (3) How will I teach it? What lessons plans will I use? How will I answer questions from the students?

These questions need to be addressed sufficiently to relieve fear and doubt before teachers can feel confident about using the teaching strategies in their classroom. The greatest mistake made at this level is to initiate practice of classroom lessons and strategies before satisfying educators' primary concerns.

Addressing these concerns can be done in three separate trainings or combined in a three- or four-day training. Separate trainings done at intervals over a short period of time have the advantage of allowing participants to absorb the concepts before moving from, "What are the limits of what I can say?" to, "How do I teach it?" They can try the strategies with their students between sessions and share the results at the next training meeting. Short, periodic trainings may also be more acceptable to school districts because they place less strain on the district budget and teacher substitute pool.

The drawback to short trainings is the lack of intensity, and the time needed at each session to bring the participants' focus to the training and to establish continuity of learning. When a single basic training addresses all three concerns, it has the advantage of integrating the three functions into a more holistic approach. For instance, in observing modeling of classroom strategies, educators get a more practical picture of what is expected of them and at the same time see how they may have to consider the sensitivity of the topic. The longer training can be more intensive, because teachers are able to shed sidetracking concerns on the first day and then give their undivided attention to the rest of the training.

The drawback to the longer training is that teachers do not have the opportunity to try new strategies with students and then share the results. Also, the difficulty of getting teachers released for three or four consecutive days is often a major obstacle.

Essentially, each training format has enough advantages to be viable. Budget considerations and teacher substitute pools are often the strongest determinants of which format is chosen for training.

Content of Training

Basic training should provide teachers the opportunity to:
- Discuss political issues surrounding sexuality education; parental concerns; how to build parental involvement and support; district and state codes regarding the conduct of sexuality education programs.

- Explore personal values and biases regarding human sexuality and sexual behavior; identify guidelines for teaching about controversial, sensitive topics.
- Observe a suggested family life course framework and examine a theoretical basis for effective sexuality education; consider how these can be applied to their setting.
- Learn factual information about reproductive anatomy and physiology, adolescent sexual development, birth control, sexually transmitted disease, HIV/AIDS and related health issues.
- Participate in model classroom strategies for educating adolescents to make healthy decisions about their sexual behavior, including encouraging postponing initiation of sexual intercourse.
- Practice responding to difficult questions asked by students.

Absorbing these six essentials is a formidable task. Educators need adequate time to observe, participate in teaching strategies, and become comfortable with the content. It is critical that trainers model effective lesson structure and skillful use of strategies that educators can integrate into their own practice. The main objective of training at this stage is to satisfy the need to understand, "How will teaching sexuality education affect me? and "How will I teach it?"

Unless teachers are experienced sexuality educators, it is a mistake at this stage to have teachers practice delivering lessons. Time for absorbing the material and practice in the classroom is needed to complete this stage and move to the next.

Mentor Assistance

The fourth stage is about management issues of teaching sexuality education. At this stage, the educator may struggle with implementing the teaching strategies modeled in the training and feel burdened by daily preparation for teaching. This is a critical point where many teachers fail to incorporate the learning from the training unless there is direct support to make the changes in their teaching.

The ultimate training program would provide an expert family life educator as a mentor for each classroom teacher trained. This optimal mentoring would include individual coaching of the teacher or regular group meetings with the teachers to discuss concerns and facilitate problem solving.

If staff from the training agency are not available to do intensive follow-up, one-on-one mentoring from an experienced family life educator can offer this support—and make the difference between growth and frustration. The mentor may co-teach difficult lessons, observe and coach the teacher through more complex strategies or simply meet with the teacher to share materials, offer suggestions for improved performance and discuss classroom management issues.

This process will foster the growth necessary to move teachers through initial frustration to feelings of success, which in turn moves them to the next stage, that of wanting to improve their skills.

Skills Advancement Training

At Stage 5, educators are ready to enhance their skills and to focus on increasing the effectiveness of the classroom strategies they are using. They ask, "How is my teaching affecting students?" and, "How can I refine it to have more impact?" They have moved from concern about content to the need to make better use of their resources. Educators at this stage are ready for training that stresses practice of skills.

Current educational research indicates that skills-based training for teachers of core subjects has resulted in more effective implementation of innovations. Skills-based training has become a popular term used for any training that involves some practice of teaching skills. The term is used here to describe training that concentrates on (1) explicitly defining a skill, (2) modeling the skill, (3) supervising practice of the skill, and (4) providing ongoing coaching as teachers integrate the skill into their daily teaching.

The success of skills-based training seems to result from its ability to increase a participant's sense of self-efficacy—the belief in one's ability to implement a skill successfully. The application of these principles to sexuality educator training can be a particularly valuable component of the training process.

An effective skills advancement training should provide teachers with knowledge and practice in how to:

- Analyze and/or design an effective lesson and teach it.
- Implement basic teaching strategies (guiding discussions, managing small groups, leading roleplay and/or behavioral rehearsal).
- Keep updated on critical areas of sexuality education (HIV/AIDS, STD, educational codes, etc.).
- Explore options for performing modes outcome and impact evaluations in the classroom.
- Prepare for collegial coaching and support (group trust building exercises, guidelines for giving and receiving feedback).

The success of a skills training depends upon follow-up and maintenance of skills. Therefore, participants must attend the training as part of a two- to four-member team who can meet on a regular basis in a collegial support group.

Collegial Coaching and Support

Educators who have participated in advanced skills training and entered into routine use of the innovations learned will continue to assess the impact of sexuality education on their students and refine their strategies to increase effectiveness. At this point educators may be interested in collaborating with others to learn more, increase their skills and expand their resources. This is stage six of the CBAM model: they are ready to form collegial support groups.

Collegial support groups provide the ongoing reinforcement and maintenance of skills critical to sustaining the sense of self-efficacy fostered by the skills advancement training.

The success of a group depends upon its members establishing an environment of trust and mutual support. To allow others to observe and critique skill performance requires a high degree of safety within the group. The foundation for this trust is laid during the skills advancement training but it must continue to be fostered once the group gets back to the school setting. For this reason, it is best if the training provider participates in the initial meetings to facilitate group-building processes. If this is not feasible, a district staff person skilled in group process should assist in the meetings until the group feels secure in their rapport.

Effective collegial support groups meet on a periodic basis to address the following:

- Evaluate the success or failure of classroom activities and teaching strategies.
- View and analyze videos of each others' classroom performance or organize practice sessions to reinforce teaching skills.
- Share new teaching activities and materials.
- Share frustrations, successes and concerns.

Booster Sessions

The last stage of the change process, stage seven, is ongoing. Regular, periodic booster sessions provide an opportunity for renewal and refocusing. Sessions should introduce new information, offer a forum for stimulating discussion of curriculum innovations, and provide opportunities to share ideas and expertise.

Focus of the booster sessions can be guided by a periodic needs assessment. The coordinator of the sessions should augment the results of the assessment with her or his own observation of educator needs to develop an agenda. Booster sessions might include the following:

- presentations on educational research that relates to teaching family life/sex education
- previews of the latest print and audiovisual materials; sharing of classroom resources
- demonstrations of new classroom activities
- practice sessions for building teaching skills conducted by expert trainers
- updates on contraceptive technology, sexually transmitted disease, HIV/AIDS and other technical topics
- discussion of the status of sexuality education in the district and state

Given the great demands on teachers' time and the perpetual shortage of funding for staff inservice, booster sessions frequently fall victim to neglect. It requires determination on the part of the administrator managing sexuality education and commitment by the district to ensure that they happen. This final intervention pays great dividends in terms of teacher enthusiasm and performance.

Conclusion

Sexuality education has made great strides in the past decade. The ability of many programs to have a positive impact on students' decisions about their sexual behavior has been demonstrated. It is equally important to prepare educators to present these sexuality education curricula with sensitivity and skill.

The Change Based Adoption Model offers a key to meeting the training needs of teachers by understanding their concerns as they move from initial awareness of the need for sexuality education to its integration into their classroom teaching to the need for renewal of their enthusiasm and skills.

References

Crandall, D. 1982. *A study of dissemination efforts supporting school improvement.* Andover, MA: The Network, Inc.

Hall, G. and S. Loucks. 1979. *Implementing innovations in schools: A concerns-based approach.* Austin, TX: Research and Development Center for Teacher Education, University of Texas.

Mundry, S., and L. Hergert. 1988. *Making change for school improvement: Leader's manual.* Andover, MA: The Network, Inc.

Rogers, E. 1971. *Diffusion of innovations.* New York, NY: The Free Press.

Wagman, E., and S. O. Ludlow. 1988. Teacher training for AIDS education. In *The AIDS challenge: Prevention education for young people*, ed. M. Quackenbush, M. Nelson and K. Clark, 111-125. Santa Cruz, CA: ETR Associates.

Chapter 14

The Affective Dimension: A Prerequisite for Effective Sexuality Education

Murray L. Vincent, EdD, CHES, and
Laura B. Pfefferkorn, MAT

Sexuality education as it exists today often, regrettably, consists mostly of those matters pertaining to plumbing, or, as Sol Gordon has written, "a relentless pursuit of the Fallopian Tubes" (Gordon, 1990). This is extremely disconcerting to members of our profession who recognize the importance of providing today's youth with a strong foundation in sexuality education.

Quality sexuality education programs enable students to learn not only about issues related to sex and sexuality, but about themselves and their roles in the larger society. Sexuality education must, by its very nature, deal with the whole person and the context in which individuals' lives unfold. Sexuality education is about how we live, who we are, and our collective potential—individually and societally.

Understanding that the facts of sexuality education cannot be separated from the meanings they represent for people provides impetus for and emphasizes the importance of providing affective educational experiences in both teacher education programs and instructional programs for youth. Sexuality education is utterly relevant to our lives and must therefore incorporate much affective content, qualitative as well as quantitative. To be blind to affect and its influence on the actions and attitudes of teacher trainees and students is to abandon our mission as sexuality educators.

What Is the Affective Dimension?

The affective dimension involves the feelings, emotions, attitudes and values which individuals have in regard to any topic or issue. These affective realities become a significant part of the learning equation when combined with cognitive input and ultimately influence the behavioral responses of the learners. Consider a teaching/learning scenario such as avoidance of unwanted pregnancy. A wealth of facts and data about pregnancy may be acquired through sensory inputs. These "facts" become superficial, however, if the feelings, emotions and attitudes of the learner are not engaged in a manner that has personal relevance to the decision-making process in future behavioral choices.

Krathwohl (1964) presented the affective domain in the early sixties in the second handbook of the *Taxonomy of Educational Objectives*. This classification placed attitudes, values, appreciations, etc., in hierarchical order in categories of receiving, responding, valuing, organization and the characterization by a value, or value complex. Vincent (1991) defined affective health education as the organization of learning experiences that emphasize beliefs, attitudes and values as integral contributors to the health decision-making process.

Kirschenbaum (1992) breaks down values clarification, a major application of affective education, into four components:

1. A value-laden topic or moral issue is selected—perhaps an issue related to politics, work, family, friends, love and sex, drugs, leisure time or personal tastes.
2. The teacher or leader introduces a question or activity to help learners think, read, write and talk about the topic.
3. During the learning experience, the leader ensures that all viewpoints are treated with respect and that an atmosphere of psychological safety exists in the classroom.
4. The activity encourages students to employ an array of "valuing processes" or "valuing skills" while considering the topic. These skills involve understanding one's feelings, examining alternative viewpoints, considering the consequences of various choices in a thoughtful manner, making a choice free from undue pressure, speaking one's views and acting on one's beliefs.

Youth who use these processes in making decisions will lead more personally satisfying and socially constructive lives (Kirschenbaum, 1992).

Affective education involves concern for the feelings, emotions and attitudes of students. This does not mean that we as sexuality educators must coddle our students or lower our expectations regarding their ability to achieve. It does not mean that we must forsake the cognitive elements of our curricula. On the contrary, in providing affective learning experiences, we actually raise our expectations of students and foster high levels of understanding and critical thinking.

In opening students' minds to possibilities heretofore unthought of or discussed, we speak to the whole student and to the realities students live each day. Thus, our message becomes meaningful, powerful and potentially freeing. Affective education creates an environment conducive to questioning and thinking critically about people, ideas, various cultures and our society. It produces students who can empathize with the perspectives and perceptions of others, who have good interpersonal skills, who have positive attitudes about sexuality and life, who respect others, and who are unafraid of challenging the system after critically examining it.

Affective education positively affects students' self-concept, which, in turn, can help them to move toward self-actualization and personal fulfillment. These are all things our educational system should strive for. A happy, self-actualized person is likely to be a good citizen who actively participates in our democracy, and through her or his participation makes life better for all.

Affective Dimensions in Teacher Preparation

Preparing teachers to become effective sexuality educators involves multiple components. It is an absolute given that the teacher should acquire a solid understanding of traditional content: a working understanding of reproductive anatomy and physiology, physical growth changes, psychosocial growth changes, reproduction, reproductive health/disease, sexually transmitted disease, including HIV/AIDS, and other basic content components. The sexuality education teacher should be armed with epidemiological and statistical data related to every aspect of sexual development and sexual behavior.

There is also a body of knowledge, with a greater emphasis on affect, that must be used when considering gender identity, sex-role socialization, intimacy, love, marriage, sexual response, sexual dysfunctions, laws, religion, families, parenting, and so on. Understanding structure, function, statistical relationships, theories and other traditional learning experiences will not suffice if we expect teachers to conduct sexuality education with an emphasis on affect. Knowledge of the content areas does not always translate to having the "heart" to teach the psychosocial decision-making components of good sexuality education.

For example, a teacher may cite various statistics on teen pregnancy, rates of intercourse, contraception usage, etc., when teaching a unit on pregnancy prevention. These statistics, however, may have no effect on a 14-year-old virgin female who will not admit the possibility that she may become sexually active, for whatever reasons (her parents' beliefs, her religious beliefs, etc.). Yet this same girl may well accept the romantic notion of being "swept off her feet" by the love of her life. Should this occur, the girl will most likely not contracept and could end up pregnant and/or infected with an STD.

The teacher must consider the psychosocial decision-making components, the "whys" and "hows" of decision making for teens, and provide a way for students to identify their own values. If the girl in the example were able to recognize that a pregnancy would be unacceptable to her or to her family, she would be more likely to consider the possible outcome of a romantic encounter if she failed to use contraception. The teacher must consider the ways students make decisions and provide them with tools for better understanding themselves as they make health choices. For teens especially, the social dynamics within their peer group and the psychological dynamics play an enormous role in the decision-making process. By exploring these dynamics within the content of sexuality education we can foster better decision making by our youth.

It has been written many times that most teachers in sexuality education are not adequately prepared. Thus, they often rely on lecture to present facts about biological reproduction, without delving into the affective concerns of students. These teachers often unwittingly send students the nonverbal message that sexuality is a subject of embarrassment that is uncomfortable to discuss

(George and Behrendt, 1985). In this way, teachers actually "become the curriculum" and teach, covertly, their own awkward feelings and attitudes about sexuality.

Sexuality Comfort

Marshall Kreuter (1992) has eloquently described how health educators are involved with "wicked stuff." How very true this is in the sexuality arena! We deal with premarital sexual intercourse, unintended pregnancy, contraception, abortion, sexual assault, love, homosexuality, masturbation and other controversial content. Our past socialization, familial influences, religious beliefs and other contributors to our values provide a framework for our responses. Cognitive dissonance will surface when we are confronted with behaviors, attitudes and beliefs which differ from our own. Embarrassment may be a natural response to such situations.

When teacher preparation programs do not provide affective experiences, teachers lose the opportunity to become truly comfortable with sexuality education. This is a huge shortcoming; it has long been recognized that sexuality educators with low comfort levels are less effective (Schultz and Boyd, 1984). Teachers' comfort level has also been shown to be associated with the actual topics covered (or not covered) in sexuality education classes.

Graham and Smith (1984) note that there are three specific components of sexuality comfort:
- sexual feelings and attitudes
- respect for and acceptance of others
- communication skills

These three components should be dealt with in teacher education methods courses. In fact, these authors believe that a core objective of a sexuality education methods course should be the development of sexuality comfort.

In courses for future sexuality education teachers, groundrules should be established that (1) invite participants to reflect upon their own experiences in the sexuality life cycle; (2) encourage disclosure of one's own experiences, joys, frustrations, feelings, etc., as well as tactful inquiry about others' experiences in this cycle; and (3) reassure participants that they have the right to disclose as much or as little as they desire and have the right to remind others of this if they are getting too personal in their questions.

Personal Reflection

The use of interactive discussions, roleplays, decision-making situations, collages and other facilitative methods, focuses the adult learner on his or her own personal sexuality issues and history: "how I learned," "what created good feelings, ambivalence or fears," and "what I wish had been different in my early sexual growth and development." The point is to *personalize* the learning experiences to foster introspective assessment of one's own sexual maturation. Learners think about whether they matured in a sexually healthy manner. Such exercises often illustrate how some unfortunately mature with the negative view that "sex" and "sin" are one and the same, with the consequence of feeling badly about one's body, feelings, fantasies, relationships and future marital perspectives.

The skilled facilitator can create powerful learning opportunities when he or she poses questions such as the following:
- How was the language of sex handled by your parents? Were the reproductive parts given euphemistic names? Was it allowable to ask questions about Aunt Mary's pregnancy?
- How much or how often did Mom and Dad touch each other? Was affection visible and positive?
- How was nudity dealt with in the home?

- Do you recall toilet training? How do you handle toilet training with your children?
- Were you allowed to play with toys of your choice, or was there gender specificity about appropriate toys and recreation?
- How much freedom did you have to make decisions? Were your parents hovering, suspicious, lax, etc., in their supervisory behaviors?
- What do you recall about your same-sex friends? What activities did you enjoy or participate in?
- Was there anything said about autoerotic behaviors, fantasies or dreams?
- How comfortable were your mother, father, siblings, friends, etc., with your body changes—genital growth, breast development, increased need for privacy? Did your relationships change as you matured?
- Were you encouraged or discouraged to pursue friends of the other sex? Were you given positive assurances and skills regarding these relationships?
- How did your parents, friends and siblings adjust to your dating and intimate relationships with others? Would you consider their suggestions as positive or fear-provoking?
- How prepared were you to select a lifetime marital partner?

Skilled teachers and facilitators can address the above topics in many ways. Preliminary thought can be initiated through assigned readings, audiovisual illustrations, case studies, personal inventories, value/decision sheets and other teacher-designed learning strategies. Interaction, expression of viewpoints and the creation of dialogue among learners, whether this occurs in one-on-one, small group or large group discussions, is essential.

Some adult learners are very ready for such personal reflection—others are not. The reticence by some adults to interact and disclose is perfectly acceptable; most will usually respond in future class sessions. Such methods are not only excellent for enhancing learners' personal growth and comfort level but give participants a firsthand experience of how a teacher can facilitate interactive learning designed to link attitudinal stances with cognitive information. One could cite many excellent affective methods used by sexuality education professionals in training programs. Basic to most is an emphasis on examining one's own sexuality.

The following list of questions can act as a springboard to help future teachers empathize with students, give thought to the potential exchanges that may take place in the classroom, and understand their own attitudes and feelings about sexuality and sexuality education. Until we can do these things we will be hindered in our efforts to provide effective sexuality education.

- What personal biases might I have?
- How comfortable am I with the various topics within a sexuality curriculum?
- How might my feelings and attitudes differ from my students'?
- How might this affect student learning?
- How prepared am I to understand and respond to questions posed by my students?
- Will I listen and hear what others really mean when they express themselves?
- Will I be able to communicate well with my students?
- How might I respond to personal questions that may come up in the course?
- Can I teach without personal biases being communicated? Should this even be attempted? Is value-free sexuality education a realistic notion?

These affective aspects should be incorporated into training prior to becoming a sexuality educator. Ironically, they are also the aspects often ignored by teacher training institutions. Educators may not have had the opportunity to experience the affective dimension as a student, a critical step in being able to create an affective dimension in future teaching situations.

Due to the personal nature of sexuality and its intimate connection with past life experiences prospective teachers cannot expect to attain affective skills in a week-end or a series of short inservice sessions. More extensive preparatory experiences are necessary. It isn't easy to acquire sexuality comfort, but it is certainly worth the effort. Introspection can be painful and frustrating at times, but the rewards are far greater than the costs. We will live better because of it; we will be more satisfied in our relationships with others; we will have a better understanding of ourselves and knowledge of self helps us become better teachers. Sexuality educators are a special breed. They strive for growth and recognize limitless potential to change themselves and society for the better.

Scales (1986) delineates two goals of professional sexuality educators that have emerged over the years: "How to help people avoid negatively valued consequences of sexual decisions such as unplanned pregnancy and sexually transmitted diseases, and how to help people accept and enjoy their sexuality as a positive aspect of their lives and a contributor to their overall mental health." Though at different times in history one or the other of these themes has been predominant, both are very important and worthwhile goals. The work of sexuality educators is extremely valuable to both individuals and society. This is why we go through such rigorous self-study. Sexuality educators know that anatomy and physiology are but small parts of sexuality. It is the context in which cognitive understanding occurs that is most important, a context fraught with affective concerns.

Affective Dimensions in the Classroom

Just as teachers cannot devote themselves solely to objective cognitive aspects in their own learning, so must they help their students delve into the subjective experiences that allow people to apply meaning to information. Rather than have students memorize facts about various STDs, we desire them to understand how to protect themselves and what to do if they do contract an STD. We want them to value their bodies and want to protect themselves from harm. We want students to respect and value others and avoid spreading STDs. We want them to understand the consequences of contracting an STD, the situational conflicts, the feelings which surface and the options available in making better, more-informed choices.

Three important goals of sexuality education have been identified (George and Behrendt, 1985):
1. An increase in the general knowledge and comfort of the learner about his or her sexuality and the sexuality of others.
2. The identification and clarification of values and attitudes, followed by their affirmation, reaffirmation and/or modification.
3. The acquisition of decision-making skills.

These are respectable and desirable goals that by their very nature call for an affective component. Increasing comfort, for example, is not something that can be achieved by student memorization, neither is values clarification, nor decision making. The affect in sexuality education is not a luxury, but a requisite. It is not something to be added on to a curriculum plan; it should be the basis for that plan.

Classroom experiences must foster critical examination of "facts." We must help students become comfortable with their own and accepting of others' sexuality. We must help them develop good decision-making skills—how to arrive at alternatives and then rank and choose among them, a characteristic of good problem solvers. In pursuing these objectives we can foster a sense of interdependence, and teach students the interpersonal skills required to work together.

All the affective-oriented activities we select to help teach students will also help them as they grow and mature. We are fortunate that many of the topics in sexuality education are rife with moral dilemmas and beg for discussion and expression of thoughts, feelings and attitudes. It is doubtful that any other subject matter has more opportunities to apply affective content, to foster important discussion and thought, or to allow valuable opportunities for learning about the self and others.

Personalizing the Facts

"Learning always involves two things: exposure to new information or experience and the personal discovery of what it means" (Combs, 1982). Thus, sexuality educators seek to help their students find personal meaning in the facts. Learning in the absence of affect is unlikely to influence behavior, so educators must present students with an opportunity to explore their feelings and emotions regarding the subject matter. The closer an event is perceived to the self, the greater the affect and the potential ability to change behavior (Combs, 1982). Humans naturally strive for meaning. To ignore this in our classrooms is to defeat the purpose of being there.

Self-Concept

Another factor cited by Combs that is involved in learning is the learner's self-concept. What students believe about themselves affects their learning. There is also a reciprocal relationship between the self-concepts of the learners and quality of learning in the classroom. Students who feel they are failures in the classroom reduce the quality of learning that could potentially take place. If these same students begin to experience success in the classroom, however, the quality of learning rises and their self-concepts become more positive.

Self-concepts tend to corroborate themselves. That is, students who expect to be successful in the classroom are more likely to succeed. This demonstrates the circular effect of the self-concept (Combs and Avila, 1985). As teachers, we must be ever-aware of this effect and strive to make it work in the right direction for our learners.

Teachers can help students experience the circular effect of the self-concept by making sure each student can succeed in some way every day. The teacher may do this by asking students questions that should be easy to answer, by drawing them into the discussions that take place by using references that personalize the topic for the students, by assigning them roles in group work and by praising their participation. Teachers can talk to their students individually before and after class, get to know them and learn which buttons to push to gain their interest. The beauty of sexuality education is that most students will be keenly interested in the subject, so educators can focus on creating an environment that is supportive and nonjudgmental.

One note of caution: a teacher must be careful in attempts to build healthy self-concepts to avoid complimenting students on their looks or clothes. Sending the message that students are valuable because of their looks or their wardrobe does little to foster healthy self-concepts. However, sending the message that the student is an asset to the class, that his or her input is important, that these ideas and thoughts are helpful to others, and that he or she is a capable student can have a profound effect on the self-concept of individual students as well as the classroom environment. A class full of students with healthy self-concepts is a classroom conducive to open discussion and learning.

Classroom Environment

Teachers must be aware of student perceptions of the classroom environment. An environment set up to challenge students can be a powerful motivator. One perceived as threatening, however, will inhibit learning. By ignoring the possibilities of threat and challenge in the classroom, teachers may inadvertently reduce the level of communication and learning that can take place. We must continually consider the feelings, attitudes and beliefs of our students as we set up learning situations.

For example, if educators set up classrooms where it is OK for students to ridicule one another, obviously learning and discussion will be inhibited; students will refuse to participate from fear of ridicule. A threatening environment dramatically decreases the potential for learning. The classroom in effect shuts down when the threat of ridicule inhibits dialogue and the free exchange of information. The students may as well be reading to themselves as sitting in a class with others.

A challenging environment, on the other hand, is one that invites learning. Students make an effort because they feel they can be successful. They are eager to do better work. A challenging classroom environment is the ideal we strive for as sexuality educators. However, it is not a simple thing to achieve. A challenge to one student may be a threat to another. Asking students to share their feelings about teen pregnancy may be a challenge to one student to concisely detail his or her views, while the same questions are perceived by another student as too personal and therefore threatening, putting him or her on the defensive. Thus, while we try to challenge our students, we must be ever-wary of the potential for threat. Everyone is on his or her own individual path to "becoming," and we must allow our students to grow at their own personal rates. Through it is impossible to individualize every lesson for all students at one time, we must be alert and observant and make adjustments if we note that some are threatened.

Bell and Schniedewind (1989) suggest we strive to promote and develop a climate of caring, respect and trust by working cooperatively with students to establish guidelines and by using structured activities to help students build positive self-concepts, develop communication skills, practice listening skills, express their feelings and resolve conflicts. Students can learn to examine group process and understand how to effect change in these processes.

While such a climate can be very helpful for students in all areas, it is absolutely imperative for the sexuality education classroom because of the very sensitive nature of the various topics in the curriculum. Without a climate of caring, trust and respect, students will not feel free to express their feelings, attitudes and beliefs.

Values

Another concept to address is values in the classroom. Combs notes that universal values such as valuing learning, critical thinking, and good citizenship, are involved in the business of schooling. He suggests that the role of the school is to facilitate the exploration of many values and their bases, while respecting the individual student's right to derive and express his or her own set of values without ridicule or condemnation. We as educators simply cannot separate values from our students or the classroom. Values are often determiners of human behavior and goals (Combs, 1982).

We all make decisions and usually utilize our own value systems in the process. As teachers of sexuality education, we hope for our students to make good decisions with regard to their sexuality. Many students, however, may not consider their values when making decisions. For the most part in their school experience, they are not forced to look at their personal values. Thus, they make decisions without serious thought to what they believe and value. Sexuality educators try to counteract these tendencies by giving students the tools to evaluate, express and derive a values framework consistent with their familial, religious and cultural views. Values clarification exercises are crucial to our mission.

There are numerous ways to help students identify their values. We can have students participate in roleplays, give them questionnaires to answer about their values, and have them write in journals in response to carefully chosen values clarification types of questions. We can ask them questions as a large group, encourage volunteers to share their answers and continue the discussion from there. We can present case studies for them to analyze the behavior of others and apply their own values. Teens could be presented with scenarios of different couples experiencing different levels of commitment, intimacy and passion. The students could then decide whether the couples should or shouldn't have sexual intercourse and explain why or why not. An exercise such as this forces students to look at their own values and listen to those of others. It fosters acceptance of others and helps students understand their own values and the impact these have on their behavior. These types of activities help students become aware of their own values and can thus help them to make better decisions and be true to themselves.

Summary

Affective learning is critical in sexuality education. Affective sexuality educators possess the following characteristics or traits:

- comfort with the language of sexuality
- ability to help the learner recognize the issues and different viewpoints expressed in a free society
- ability to facilitate/orchestrate meaningful and fair discussions
- ability to objectively help learners analyze moral and ethical dilemmas
- knowledge of how to structure a warm and inviting climate for learning and the expression of feelings, attitudes and beliefs
- recognition and rethinking of personal biases and the preparation to deal with them as they may occur in a teaching/learning situation
- openness to learning new ideas, beliefs and values held by others and acceptance of the right to think differently in a democratic society
- caring enough to sympathize with student problems and to look beyond the surface of questions to understand the hidden questions
- belief in the goodness of people and in himself or herself as a professional
- caring and thoughtfulness in dealings with students and a desire to enhance the self-actualization process of students while avoiding potential negative effects on student self-esteem

The affective sexuality educator will need certain skills and training to be effective. She or he must understand group dynamics and know how to lead discussions. She or he must be trained in listening and responding skills and in sensitivity toward others.

She or he must be skilled in conflict management and in handling censorship, as these issues may arise with parents, opponents of sexuality education and reluctant school administrators. She or he must understand how to structure classroom activities to maximize affective content.

The affective sexuality educator must incorporate all of these skills in addition to the normally expected basic teaching skills, including maintaining student involvement and good behavior within the classroom. She or he must also be able to incorporate these affective efforts while concomitantly teaching the required content of the curriculum.

The excellent affective sexuality educator is thus an excellent cognitive educator as well. She or he has the appropriate background and knowledge, understands generic teaching methodologies and understands the importance of the affective dimension. She or he teaches sexuality education concepts using affective education principles.

What happens to students after they complete the sexuality education class? If we have based our teaching/learning situations on affective education, one very real possibility is that the valuing, decision-making, problem-solving, communication and relationship skills learned will be retained and used long after the student has forgotten detailed specifics of the subject matter content. And this, of course, is why we sexuality educators are here.

References

Bell, L., and N. Schniedewind. 1989. Realizing the promise of humanistic education: A reconstructed pedagogy for personal and social change. *Journal of Humanistic Psychology* 29 (2): 200-223.

Combs, A. W. 1982. Affective education or none at all. *Educational Leadership* 39 (7): 495-97.

Combs, A. W., and D. L. Avila. 1985. *Helping relationships: Basic concepts for the helping professions.* 3d ed. Newton, MA: Allyn and Bacon, Inc.

George, K. D., and A. E. Behrendt. 1985. Sex education: Future research priorities in sex education. *Journal of Sex Education and Therapy* 11 (1): 56-60.

Gordon, S. 1990. Sexuality education in the 1990s. *Health Education* 21 (1): 4-5.

Graham, C. A., and M. M. Smith. 1984. Operationalizing the concept of sexuality comfort: Applications for sexuality educators. *Journal of School Health* 54 (11): 439-42.

Kirschenbaum, H. 1992. A comprehensive model for values education and moral education. *Phi Delta Kappan* 73 (10): 771-776.

Krathwohl, D. R. 1964. *Taxonomy of educational objectives: Handbook II: Affective domain.* New York: David McKay Co.

Kreuter, M. 1992. Speech delivered at the Adolescents At-Risk Conference, Wichita, Kansas, December 2.

Scales, P. 1986. The changing context of sexuality education: Paradigms and challenges for alternative futures. *Family Relations* 35 (2): 265-74.

Schultz, J. B., and J. R. Boyd. 1984. Sexuality attitudes of secondary teachers. *Family Relations* 33 (4): 537-541.

Vincent, M. L. 1991. With high tech are we losing touch: The time to re-emphasize affective health education. *Journal of Health Education* 22 (5): 272-81.

Chapter 15

The Power of Words: Talking About Sexuality

Robert J. McDermott, PhD

C ommunication is not always easy. When the subject under consideration is sexuality, significant roadblocks to communication can, and often do occur. Robert Crooks and Karla Baur (1990) point out that some of the difficulty inherent in sexual communication lies in our socialization and the language available for talking about sexuality.

Perhaps the most significant impediment to healthy sexuality education among youth is the so-called conspiracy of silence that pervades many households. More than forty years ago, Howard S. Hoyman observed that the "sentimental myth" approach to dealing with sex failed to meet both the immediate developmental needs of youth and the needs of modern living. Hoyman (1953) pointed out that sex education was viewed as a family task, with the school, church and community playing some role as well, mostly in developing character and stressing the importance of ideals and innocence. Many of the issues pertinent to sexuality education were overlooked or ignored.

The problem of home-based sexuality education is one of both lack of literacy and lack of technical knowledge. It has been noted that the tendency of lower socioeconomic status parents to impart sexual knowledge to their children is slight at best. The children of these parents also tend to be less literate, less likely to read books, and less exposed to sources of accurate, printed information (McDermott, 1977).

While more affluent and well-read parents are more likely to impart information than less knowledgeable parents, even educated parents often view their technical preparation as less than adequate, and, hence, do nothing at all. Whatever the reasons, not talking about sex, in fact, sends a loud message about the subject being too taboo or too impolite to mention.

The Right Words

Beatrice M. Gudridge (1969) once observed that parents are hindered by their own ambivalence about sex. Parents teach a child attitudes about sex long before the child enters school. Strong negative messages are conveyed by means of lifted eyebrows, strained looks or slaps when the genitals are touched. These are further reinforced by parents' reaction when a child uses certain four-letter words experimentally, and when coy babytalk is substituted for the formal names of sex organs and bodily functions. Gudridge (1969) writes:

> It is no wonder that many a child, from the primary grades on, does not ask [the] parents about the things that are bothering him [or her] regarding...sexuality, but turns to...friends (who are just as uncertain)....
> And when the time comes for that once-in-a-lifetime heart-to-heart talk with father or mother about the

"facts of life" at age 10 or 12, it is already too late. Communication on this subject broke down a long time ago.

Crooks and Baur (1990) suggest that this lack of communication and the absence of a "suitable language of sex" early in life have lasting influences. By the time many people are old enough to want to communicate sexual feelings and needs, they are stymied by a lack of knowledge as to how to proceed. Many of the relevant words have become associated with negative emotions instead of positive ones.

Thus, much of the mislabeled and otherwise incorrect knowledge about sex is the result of pooled ignorance, further compounded by adult noncommunication. Three decades ago, in the monumental School Health Education Study, it was found that three-fourths of the boys and one-half of the girls would never or only rarely turn to a parent for help when bothered by a sexuality-related question (Sliepcevich, 1964). This problem is exacerbated when no formal dialogue is offered at school and young people must rely on information provided by peers.

Wardell B. Pomeroy (1974) encourages parents of even very young children to teach the proper words for things, including bodily functions and parts of the sexual anatomy. He refers to the "sentimental pandering" that occurs when adults teach children phrases such as "wee-wee" instead of "penis," and so on. The babytalk is not the child's idea, but springs from the parents' lack of comfort with the subject.

Crooks and Baur (1990) suggest that our language lacks a comfortable sexual vocabulary. Sexual words often register as too clinical, too juvenile or too harsh. Consequently, our sexual vocabulary becomes paralyzed. Some words (e.g., *penis, vagina, coitus*) seem too medical or technical, while other terms (e.g., *prick, cunt, screw*) are more likely to be perceived as insulting or used to describe acts of aggression.

Sexologist Gary F. Kelly (1990) seems to concur with this analysis when he writes:

> In our culture, people are not encouraged to talk openly about sexual issues. Such discussions are often avoided altogether or at the very least approached with some discomfort and embarrassment. For some people, and in some contexts, the "proper" scientific terminology may seem more embarrassing than slang terms. This is probably one of the reasons why so many slang terms exist for the description of sex-related body parts and sexual activities.

Categories of Sexual Speech

Many people exert great effort to avoid direct references to sexual matters in their speech. Sexual speech can, in fact, be organized around a series of categories that reflect the discomfort people have in making references to sex:
- childhood vocabulary
- colloquial language
- formal words and expressions
- euphemisms

Childhood Vocabulary

One's first encounter with sexual speech is in childhood when a parent or other adult labels body parts and functions. Often these are named in ways that Gudridge (1969) calls "coy," and Pomeroy (1974) describes as "sentimental pandering." Childhood vocabulary or babytalk stays with some people into adulthood when they pass it along to their own children, never having become comfortable with or perhaps learned more appropriate sexual vocabulary.

Colloquial Language

So-called street language, labeled as colloquial vocabulary by Simkins and Rinck (1982), is usually considered offensive in polite circles. Crooks and Baur (1990) provide illustrations of street vernacular for the vulva or vagina (*snatch, pussy, cunt, muff, bearded clam, hair pie* and *beaver*) and the penis (*cock, dick, wang, prick* and *reamer*). Kaplan, Meeks and Segal (1978) explain that depending on the circumstances and the context, colloquial language may provide sexist commentary, may be used to shock vulnerable ears, may be used as substitutes for formal, medically oriented terms which actually seem more offensive to either the sender or the receiver, or may be used simply when available vocabulary offers no alternative. Whatever the motive for its use, this type of language definitely communicates, even if the message is emotionally laden and likely to be interpreted negatively.

Formal Words and Expressions

Somewhere in our education we learn what Crooks and Baur (1990) and Goldman (1990) refer to as clinical vocabulary, what Simkins and Rinck (1982) call formal vocabulary, or what other sexologists label as "medical" or "scientific" language. Although accurate, scientific and "proper," words such as *penis, vagina, vulva, testicles, coitus,* and *external genitalia* can be more upsetting and embarrassing for many people to articulate than some of their colloquial counterparts.

Some researchers have attempted to assess the impact of specific interventions to increase the use of scientific language between partners in describing sexual anatomy and sexual practices. Results have been inconclusive. Following a course in human sexuality designed to promote the use of scientific terms, the use of *penis* to refer to male genitalia increased, and the use of no word (i.e, the avoidance of the use of any term) decreased. However, an increase in the use of scientific terms to refer to female genitalia was less marked, and the use of the term *intercourse* in place of euphemistic or colloquial expressions was rare. Gloria J. Fischer, who performed the study, concluded that the term "intercourse" was one "simply not used by students" (Fischer, 1989).

Euphemisms

With many people ambivalent about both formal and colloquial terms, but not wanting to resort to their childhood words, euphemistic terminology, also known as "common discourse," surfaces as an alternative. Thus, sexual intercourse or coitus becomes "making love" or "getting it on." Simkins and Rinck (1982) describe a group of people for whom even euphemisms are too embarrassing. These people avoid any direct reference to sexual matters. Genitalia are "down there," and coitus is simply "you know."

Gender Differences in Sexual Language

Adelaide Haas has observed gender differences in the use of sexual language. She contends that men use more informal (i.e., slang) expressions than women, especially phrases involving profanity and obscenity (Haas, 1979). Women's speech seems to be more laden with euphemisms, polite expressions and unfinished sentences.

Walsh and Leonard (1974) asked 248 subjects to list as many words as possible that they believed were synonymous with the phrase "sexual intercourse." Males listed more unique terms than did females. The researchers explained their observation in the following way:

Why do females have a smaller vocabulary in the area of sexual synonyms? The answer may be due to differential cultural conditioning, in which case it may be argued that females actually do have an "impoverished" vocabulary in this area. Another explanation might be that females know as many synonyms as do males, but either consciously or unconsciously are blocked from using them.

Evidence provided by a team of investigators headed by M. Cecile Fraley supports the hypothesis that girls are provided less opportunity to learn sexual vocabulary even as toddlers (Fraley et al., 1991). Mothers of 63 girls (mean age = 26 months) and 54 boys (mean age = 29 months) were asked which words for genitals, if any, they used. Neither boys nor girls were likely to be given a standard anatomical term, although some received colorful colloquial expressions. Girls were less likely than boys to receive a term to refer to their genitals.

Sanders (1978) found that men and women used different vocabulary when communicating with a partner about sexual anatomy and sexual intercourse. Males made more use of the vernacular in their intimate interactions with sexual partners. For example, women tended to use "cute" names to refer to their partner's penis (e.g., *penie, oscar, baby-maker*), while men used what Sanders calls "power slang" (e.g., *rod, womp, pistol*) to refer to their own sexual organ.

Kelly (1990) found additional gender difference in the discussion of masturbation. "When it comes to some things such as masturbation, there are far more slang terms used to describe male masturbation than female masturbation." Jay (1980) indicates that sexual words and expressions go hand-in-hand with sex roles. The subject of menstruation is one about which many expressions, euphemistic, demeaning or sexist in nature, have emerged. In

1948, N.F. Jaffe found that in referring to a woman's menstrual period men might declare "she's waving the red flag," while women might refer to "having my friend." Over four decades later, such expressions persist. Men might refer to a woman as "riding the cotton pony," while women speak of a "visit from my red-haired friend." Cross-cultural studies on the use of sexual language (Jay, 1980) and on distortions in the way sexual vocabulary is presented to children and youth (Goldman, 1990) suggest that these phenomena are not unique to the United States.

Sexual Language in Context

Simkins and Rinck (1982) asked 202 subjects to identify the words they would use to refer to female genitalia, male genitalia, and sexual intercourse when they were (1) in mixed company; (2) engaged in conversation with people of the same sex; (3) engaged in conversation with their parents; and (4) discussing the concepts with their spouse or lover.

For circumstances of mixed company there were no gender differences. Respondents indicated they would use formal terminology. In conversations with members of the same sex, there were significant gender differences for all three terms. In all instances, males showed a preference for colloquial expressions, whereas females indicated a preference for the use of formal language.

For conversations with parents, respondents showed no gender differences for references to female genitalia or to sexual intercourse. In these instances, formal language would be used. There was a significant difference with regard to male genitalia, however. The majority of males and females used formal terms, but males were more likely to use colloquial or euphemistic expressions while females were more likely to avoid any direct reference.

Overall, the researchers concluded that language used with parents was the most restrictive. For conversation about these things with a spouse or lover, there was no gender difference concerning female genitalia—both males and females used formal expressions. However, males were more likely to use colloquial terms to refer to male genitalia, while females were more formal. Regarding references to sexual intercourse, females tended to use euphemistic language while males used more colloquial terms.

When it comes to discussing matters of sex, the vocabularies of males and females differ. The nature and extent of this difference is dependent, in part, on the circumstances and context in which the conversation occurs. Sexual language is more inhibited in some settings and with certain individuals than others. Walsh and Leonard (1974) ask:

> Why is it, then that we tend to inhibit our expression of sexual language? To answer this question, it seems necessary to explore what linguists call the "meaning of meaning." In particular, it seems important to distinguish between the denotative and connotative meanings of sexual language.

The Power of Words

The denotative or "dictionary" meaning of a word is easily determined by anyone with a standard reference dictionary. Connotative meanings, on the other hand, vary since they are influenced by culture and experience, and thus, have particular representational characteristics. In one study, researchers examined the attributes assigned by 1,111 university undergraduate students to fifty sexuality-related words (McDermott, Drolet and Fetro, 1989). They

identified a series of "high impact" words having negative connotations and words whose semantic representations differed along
gender lines (e.g., *erection, extramarital sex, orgasm, homosexual,
lesbian, vagina, pornography, virginity,* and other terms). Their
data imply that an emphasis on the psychological and emotional
impact of sexuality-related terms is warranted in classroom discussions, and that an educator's use of language may bring about
connotatively different responses from individual to individual.

What practical implications does this observation have for the
classroom teacher? First, teachers need to realize that a particular
word is likely to cause a myriad of reactions in students based upon
its connotative meaning for each person. The range of connotative
meanings for a term such as *homosexual* is likely to include everything from "a loving, caring individual" to "a filthy degenerate."
Similarly, *pornography* may either be "erotica" or "exploitation."
Second, the multiple connotative meanings that sexual language
may have suggests that in a human sexuality class there should be
a day designated on which the teacher permits the liberal use of
colloquial terms and other slang. This activity may diffuse the
"power" that language can over people.

In another study, Preston and Stanley (1987) asked 164 college
students four questions: (1) What is the worst thing a woman can
call a man? (2) What is the worst thing a man can call a woman?
(3) What is the worst thing a man can call another man? and (4)
What is the worst thing a woman can call another woman? Seven
different categories of responses were derived, with a number of
the categories having sexual connotations (e.g., unattractive, sexually inadequate, sexually promiscuous, homosexual, and so on). It
is unfortunate, indeed, that the power afforded to words is so
frequently exercised to insult rather than to praise.

Sexual Language in the Classroom

Which terminology should a classroom teacher use? Is it wise, as a rule of thumb, to apply the scientific or formal terms? As indicated earlier, it may be useful to permit the use of colloquial expressions under some circumstances, such as when the intent of the lesson is to diffuse the potency of certain words. Moreover, some young people may be familiar with nothing other than the street vernacular. Teachers must not shrink from the frankness that is called for in this era when sexual communication is more critical than ever before. Teachers and other school personnel who deliver sexuality education, or who are involved in its planning and administration, must be comfortable with the entire range of sexual language. More to the point, a teacher who shows embarrassment and is uncomfortable saying the word *condom*, is not likely to be perceived as a credible source of information about the subject, nor is he or she likely to impress young people with the importance of using condoms correctly if they are having sex.

McDermott and Marty (1983) describe a desensitizing activity for teachers that can be conducted during an inservice training. Given the formal, scientific term (e.g., *vagina* or *penis*) members of the group are asked to provide as many terms as possible from other categories (i.e., childhood, colloquial, euphemistic) that are synonymous with the formal term. The exercise can be set up as a game or contest with one half of the group pitted against the other half. In addition to releasing tension about sexual language, this activity virtually eliminates taboos on slang or other terminology for the remainder of the sessions.

Some teachers are able to adapt this exercise successfully for the high school classroom with similar results. An exercise of this nature is relevant in the classroom in a number of ways. First, the generation of sexual words offers a valuable clue to the teacher as to the comfort level of students in matters of sexuality. Second, the activity gives an indication of students' familiarity with sexual language and the variation within the group. Third, it may bring to light some of the sexual myths that are propagated among youth. Fourth, since a number of colloquial street slang terms are highly sexist, it provides an opportunity to talk about sexism and its potentially damaging effects. Finally, altering the context of words that are often used to display anger, show aggression, insult, or in any general way manifest power and control, not only diffuses their impact, but also decreases the likelihood of their being used for these purposes in the future.

Not only must the conspiracy of silence be eliminated, but education about sexuality must be made relevant to those persons who can most benefit from it. Educators need to start at the point where their students are. This starting point will not be the same for all groups; age, culture, ethnicity, gender, socioeconomic status and other other variables will influence where to start. Student groups will include children from low-income families, minority youth, gay and lesbian youth, and children with other characteristics and needs. In some instances, liberal use of the vernacular may be appropriate and will increase the probability that messages about safer sex practices and nonexploitation will be received and understood.

Dunkle (1990) suggests that effective school health education programs consider the salient preferences and nomenclature of the target population and be sensitive to its norms. Her point is particularly relevant to sexuality education because youth at risk must be met on their terms, and, if necessary, with their vocabulary. It may not be feasible or practical to ask an adolescent who is already skeptical about adult intervention to respond to *our* terms. In some schools and communities, being sensitive to youth norms may bring the sexuality educator into conflict with parents' perceptions of what the norms should be, a conflict whose resolution Dunkle says may be about as easy as "dancing with an octopus" where "you quickly learn that the old ways of moving do not work, and the chances are good that your feet will be stepped on more than once."

Educators need to be prepared for certain events that can occur when sexual language is used in the classroom. Sexual language can elicit emotional reactions such as embarrassment, guilt, shame and anger. Educators need to realize in advance that for some students the choice of words may interfere with thoughtful discourse. As discussed earlier, girls may be more reluctant than boys to make use of sexual vocabulary. Boys may, in fact, exhibit a great deal of latitude in their sexual language and speech. Some students may try to shock the teacher with use of colloquial street words. A teacher who is properly desensitized to sexual language will survive such tests.

Language is a tool for thinking, problem solving, learning and gaining perceptions of the world. Words also may act as barriers to learning, self-acceptance, communication and gaining new insights. The challenge, whether the communicator is a parent talking to a child, a teacher talking to a student, a health practitioner talking to a patient, or a lover talking to a sexual partner, is to possess as broad and diverse a sexual language as possible, and to use words that foster goodwill, trust and communication among people.

References

Crooks, R., and K. Baur. 1990. *Our sexuality*. 4th ed. Redwood City, CA: Benjamin Cummings.

Dunkle, M. 1990. Asking the right questions about school health programs: A commentary. *Journal of School Health* 60 (4): 147-148.

Fischer, G. J. 1989. Sex words used by partners in a relationship. *Journal of Sex Education and Therapy* 15 (1): 50-58.

Fraley, M. C., W. C. Nelson, A. W. Wolf and B. Lozoff. 1991. Early genital naming. *Journal of Developmental and Behavioral Pediatrics* 12 (5): 301-304.

Goldman, J. 1990. The importance of an adequate sexual vocabulary for children. *Australian Journal of Marriage and Family* 11 (3): 136-148.

Gudridge, B. M. 1969. Sex education in the schools. *Education U.S.A. Special Report.* Washington, DC: National School Public Relations Association.

Haas, A. 1979. Male and female spoken language differences: Stereotypes and evidence. *Psychological Bulletin* 86 (3): 616-626.

Hoyman, H. S. 1953. Basic issues in school health education. *Journal of School Health* 23 (1): 14-22.

Jaffe, N. F. 1948. The vernacular of menstruation. *Word* 4 (2): 181-186.

Jay, T. B. 1980. Sex roles and dirty word usage: A review of the literature and a reply to Haas. *Psychological Bulletin* 88 (3): 614-621.

Kaplan, R., L. B. Meeks and J. S. Segal. 1978. *Group strategies in understanding human sexuality: Getting in touch.* Dubuque, IA: W.C. Brown.

Kelly, G. F. 1990. *Sexuality today: The human perspective.* 2d ed. Guilford, CT: Dushkin Publishing Group.

McDermott, R. J. 1977. A curriculum in family life and sex education for pre-adolescents: Rationale, content, and method. Masters thesis, University of Wisconsin, Madison.

McDermott, R. J., J. C. Drolet and J. V. Fetro. 1989. Connotative meanings of sexuality-related terms: Implications for educators and other practitioners. *Journal of Sex Education and Therapy* 15 (2): 103-113.

McDermott, R. J., and P. J. Marty. 1983. Teacher education in human sexuality: Design for improvement. *The Teacher Educator* 18 (4): 2-10.

Pomeroy, W. B. 1974. *Your child and sex.* New York: Delacorte Press.

Preston, K., and K. Stanley. 1987. "What's the worst thing...?" Gender-directed insults. *Sex Roles* 17 (3/4): 209-219.

Sanders, J. S. 1978. Male and female vocabularies for communicating with a sexual partner. *Journal of Sex Education and Therapy* 4 (1): 15-19.

Simkins, L., and C. Rinck. 1982. Male and female sexual vocabulary in different interpersonal contexts. *The Journal of Sex Research* 18 (2): 160-172.

Sliepcevich, E. M. ed. 1964. *School health education study: A summary report.* Washington, DC: School Health Education Study.

Walsh, R. H., and W. M. Leonard. 1974. Usage of terms for sexual intercourse by men and women. *Archives of Sexual Behavior* 3 (3): 373-376.

Chapter 16

HIV and STD: What Educators Need to Know

Chwee Lye Chng, PhD

About 20 percent of people with AIDS are in their twenties (Stackhouse, 1990). Given a latency period of 8 to 10 years, these young adults could have been exposed to HIV during adolescence. Surveys among teenagers report poor understanding of both HIV transmission and prevention (Strunin and Hingson, 1987; DiClemente, Boyer and Morales, 1988). In addition, teenagers are prone to risk-taking behavior, motivated, in part, by the misperception that they are invulnerable. They continue to engage in behaviors that place them at risk for HIV infection.

The combination of ignorance, impulsive participation in high-risk behavior, and a sense of invulnerability places the adolescent at high risk for HIV infection. By age 17, 50 percent of all boys and 34 percent of all girls have had sexual intercourse; by age 19, 83 percent of boys and 74 percent of girls have done so (Turner and Miller, 1989; Zabin et al., 1986). Since full-blown AIDS cases represent only about 14 percent of the HIV-infected, there may be about 21,000 children and teenagers who are HIV-infected (Hein, 1987). More than 47 million students attend 90,000 elementary and secondary schools in the United States daily (Yarber, 1987). Because schools have the potential to reach millions of students annually and because most adolescents under the age of 18 are enrolled in school, school-based programs are an efficient way to reach a substantial portion of the adolescent population.

While diagnosed HIV infection is currently rare among teenagers, a significant number of them engage in activities that place them at risk for HIV infection (Hein, 1987). During adolescence, a time of sexual awakening, few know of ways to express intimacy and acceptance other than sexual behaviors. Nationally, about 75 percent of all cases of sexually transmitted disease (STD) occur in people between the ages of 15 and 24 (Bell and Holmes, 1984), and, except for gay men and prostitutes, teenage girls have the highest rates of gonorrhea and chlamydia of any age or sex group (Turner and Miller, 1989). It is estimated that 25 percent of all teenagers will contract an STD before graduation (Kroger and Wiesner, 1981). Some evidence also suggests that STD is a greater problem in teenagers than among adults. When the denominator for national STD rates is corrected to include only the sexually active portion of the adolescent and young adult populations, 10 to 19 year olds have the highest rates of gonorrhea and syphilis.

Based on these high STD prevalence rates, HIV as an STD has the potential of becoming a major health threat to teenagers. Teenagers also report an increase of multiple sexual partners. About 16 percent of high school females report four or more sexual partners. Most are not using condoms, even though they may know about HIV transmission. Not surprisingly, more than 1 million teenage pregnancies occur annually in the United States (Zabin et al., 1986).

HIV/STD Prevention and Sexuality Education

The HIV/AIDS crisis has forced many people to recognize the need for sexuality education for teenagers. A majority of American adults are in favor of teenagers learning about HIV in school, and some states have mandated such curricula (Centers for Disease Control, 1988). By 1991, 21 states required all school districts to provide sexuality education, and 33 required HIV/AIDS education. An additional 24 states recommended sexuality education in their schools (Britton, de Mauro and Gambrell, 1992). Many school administrators who previously opposed sexuality education programs are today providing HIV/AIDS education for their students.

However, many teachers do not and cannot present HIV information within a positive context of human sexuality. For example, the HIV/AIDS education curriculum in Utah has strict prohibitions on any information about sex and homosexuality. It prohibits discussion of the intricacies of intercourse, sexual stimulation and erotic behavior; homosexuality as an acceptable lifestyle choice; and contraceptive methods. If teachers violate these guidelines, they can be charged with Class B misdemeanors (Britton, de Mauro and Gambrell, 1992).

Although many people agree that HIV education must be a high priority for teenagers, there is controversy over the age at which such education should begin and what its content should be. In many ways, these controversies are extensions of continuing debates in the field of sexuality education. Advocates and opponents of HIV/AIDS education have debated for years over the need to offer "realistic" guidance to teenagers about condoms or the need to promote abstinence from premarital sex and sexual fidelity in marriage. Whatever the outcome, evidence suggests that HIV/AIDS education is being implemented into school systems half-heartedly at best (Calamidas, 1990).

Where Does HIV Prevention Fit?

HIV/AIDS education, although often presented as part of the human sexuality curriculum in the school, is quite different in both goals and scope from sexuality education. Sexuality education examines the biological, psychological and cultural aspects of human sexuality; it explores the influence of culture on a person's sexual attitudes, feelings and behaviors, as well as sexual interactions with others. The purpose of sexuality education for teenagers is much more than just learning about reproduction and STD. Teenagers want to feel comfortable with their own sexuality and to feel good about themselves. Minimally, they need information on sexual pleasure, love and intimacy, dating, communication, relationship and personal fulfillment. HIV/AIDS education in the school, however, focuses exclusively on transmission and prevention of HIV.

HIV/AIDS education could be positioned in several different areas of the sexuality education curriculum. There are advantages and disadvantages to each of the following presentations.

As Part of an STD Unit

In many school systems, HIV/AIDS education is presented through the health education curriculum, usually as a part of the unit on STD. STD provides a useful framework for considering HIV/AIDS since the behaviors associated with HIV/AIDS are also those that are linked with increased risk for other STD. These behavioral risk factors include having multiple sexual partners, participating in high-risk sexual behaviors and not using protective measures. The preventive measures against HIV transmission will also protect students from contracting other STDs.

Because of the similarity between risk factors for HIV and those for other STD, increases in HIV infection are expected to occur primarily among teenagers at risk for other STD. This expectation is supported by research showing higher rates of HIV infection among patients from STD clinics (Quinn, Glasser and Cannon, 1988). There is, however, a potential negative effect of presenting HIV information within STD education—teachers are forced to introduce sexual behavior within the context of disease, disfigurement and death.

The message about the potential danger of sexual relationships in an age of HIV/AIDS is an important one, but not at the price of distorting the value that human sexuality is wholesome, beautiful and positive. Unfortunately, for many teenagers today the word "HIV/AIDS" brings associations of sex and death and unleashes irrational feelings and thoughts. A lesson on HIV/AIDS and STD may be some young teenagers' first tentative introduction to sexuality education. Unfortunately, the fusion of HIV/AIDS, STD, and human sexuality reinforces the notion that human sexuality itself entails dysfunction, disfigurement and death. In addition, there is a danger that using fear messages with teens will not be an effective prevention strategy.

As Part of a Unit on Disease

HIV education could be placed within a unit on disease. The history of diseases and ways in which certain groups were targeted and blamed for plagues and other health problems could be highlighted. This strategy may serve to remove the stigma from HIV-infected individuals, and also points out that it is risky behaviors and not group membership that places a person at risk.

Some people believe that STD should only be discussed in connection with infectious diseases (such as in the biological sciences curriculum) and not as part of the sexuality education curriculum. They feel that a discussion of STD detracts from the "beauty" of human sexuality. Inadvertently, however, this attitude promotes the idea that "nice" people do not contract and should not discuss STD, although an examination of health statistics indicates that scores of "nice" people acquire STDs nonetheless. In fact, a possible reason that STDs continue to exist and spread is that they are not discussed candidly.

STD should not be separated from other aspects of sexuality education. STD should be discussed in the context of intimacy and relationships, with a focus on personal responsibility that includes not transmitting STD to others. It is a mistake to discuss HIV transmission outside the context of human sexual relationships and focus exclusively on the biomedical aspects of the disease. Although this strategy may be less threatening to some communities and parent groups, it is not an effective means of educating adolescents about HIV, since teenagers contract HIV primarily through unprotected sexual intercourse.

As Part of a Comprehensive Sexuality Education Unit

To counteract potential negative effects, education about HIV/ AIDS should be provided as part of a comprehensive sexuality education curriculum in a general context of health education. HIV/AIDS education fits into lessons on human sexuality and drug prevention. A comprehensive health education curriculum lays a foundation of health knowledge and principles so that HIV-related concepts are easier for students to understand and accept. If teenagers have already heard and understood that sexuality is a normal, natural, affirming component of life, HIV/AIDS education will not lead them to permanently associate sex with death.

In the United States, it is estimated that fewer than 10 percent of all students take comprehensive sexuality education courses. The majority of school-based sexuality education programs are ten hours or less and tend to focus on the basics of anatomy, human reproduction, and physical and psychosocial changes during puberty (Hayes, 1987). Unfortunately, the scope of many programs is too limited. The focus is often restricted to biological functions, and the importance of interpersonal relationships and responsibility is omitted. The information conveyed in such programs is aimed at preventing pregnancy and avoiding STD and seldom focuses on how sex might be a means of personal enjoyment and a way of enriching intimate relationships. To highlight HIV/AIDS while ignoring pregnancy, acquaintance rape, personal hygiene, communication and other STD not only ignores important health issues related to sexual behaviors, but overemphasizes the importance of HIV/AIDS in human sexuality.

Educational programs designed to increase teenagers' awareness of HIV and sexuality will be more effective if they treat adolescent sexuality as a positive aspect of humanity rather than something that is shameful or wrong. A teenager who has a positive and accepting attitude toward his or her sexuality is more likely to use protection effectively (Baker, Thalberg and Morrison, 1988).

Fear-Based Prevention Messages

Many STD prevention programs rely to varying degrees on threatening messages that evoke anxiety and fear in the audience. Research suggests that the value of fear messages is limited. School-based programs that rely heavily on fear have not been successful, apparently because the fear is associated with an event that students often perceive to have low probability, and because a substantial time lag exists between risk-associated behavior and negative outcomes (Des Jarlais and Friedman, 1987). Ideally, the level of fear evoked by threatening messages should be sufficient to create awareness of a potential problem, but not so great as to evoke denial. The fear level should also be low enough to be effectively dispelled by the adoption of the desired behavior (Job, 1988).

Teachers need to guard against over emphasizing horror and fear in their lessons. For example, messages such as "Bang, bang, you're dead!" have been used to call attention to the fatal consequences of HIV infection. The assumption of these fear-based programs—that teenagers will abstain from sex if informed about the inherent dangers of unprotected sex—does not take into consideration the social factors involved in initiating and maintaining risky sexual behaviors.

Fear can sometimes cause anger in people and lead them to disregard health messages if they believe the messages are manipulative. Shilts (1987) describes such a reaction to early AIDS warnings, when gay men often saw political motives behind messages on risk reduction. To base the discussion of sexuality and HIV prevention entirely on fear may be counterproductive; and yet, human sexuality can be frightening and has vast potential for abuse. An element of fear, although detrimental in some respects for some individuals, may more truly reflect the human condition. Keeping delicate balance between realistic fear and an overall positive view of sexuality in HIV prevention, STD education and sexuality education can present difficulties for the untrained or inexperienced educator.

Discussing Sensitive Issues

Although a majority of American adults favor sexuality education in the schools, conflicts still arise over the inclusion of specific controversial topics such as contraception, abortion or homosexuality (Hayes, 1987). Because HIV is sexually transmitted, it is not surprising that value conflicts surrounding HIV/AIDS education are similar to those that have historically accompanied the more general topic of sexuality education in the schools.

Homosexuality is an essential but often controversial topic in HIV education for teenagers. The topic is important for two reasons: at least 10 percent of teenagers are gay or lesbian with unique health and sexual needs; and HIV education often provokes homophobic reactions from adolescents who are insecure with their own emerging sexual identities. The creation of a classroom environment in which homosexuality is not automatically a subject of condemnation or hostility is of paramount importance. Although questions about sexual identity are intense between the ages of ten and eighteen, in many school health education programs, the topic of sexual orientation is omitted or deemphasized, either because of the teacher's own discomfort or the mandate of the school district.

To avoid or minimize the controversy that can arise around HIV education it is important to involve parents in curriculum development. Homework assignments involving parents can help to establish a sense of partnership and collaboration between family and school, as well as provide an opportunity for parents to explain their values to their children. It is important to establish specific groundrules for classroom discussion. These could include students' and teacher's right to pass or to decline to answer personal questions; not asking intimate questions about personal sexual practices; confidentiality; and what language will be used in the classroom.

Personalizing Adolescent Risk

Given the lengthy incubation period for HIV, teenagers almost never know any peers with AIDS, even in communities where

AIDS is commonplace. When the risk of HIV infection is perceived to be remote and irrelevant to teenagers' daily lives, their mistaken belief that "it can't happen to me" is understandable. Cognitive immaturity may influence teenagers' risk perception. Teenagers tend to be too optimistic about their likelihood of risk and rarely use appropriate estimates of risk in personal decision making (Hein, 1987).

Most teenagers are not personally familiar with HIV infection, so consequences of behavior are difficult to evaluate. This may be particularly true for younger teenagers, for whom immediate pleasure often obscures long-term consequences. In sexual behavior the pleasure is immediate and the negative consequences are a statistical probability in the future.

The long latency of symptoms of HIV precludes effective trial-and-error learning among teenagers. Their preoccupation with the present makes it unlikely that delayed consequences, no matter how dire, will be a deterrent to action. To pierce teenagers' sense of invulnerability, the risks must be presented as concrete and relevant to them. The example of other STDs can be used. Compared to HIV, the incubation periods for some STDs such as gonorrhea (two to ten days) and genital herpes (two weeks) are almost immediate. It may be easier to demonstrate and personalize the negative consequences of risky behavior for teenagers using these examples. Since the behaviors associated with such STDs include those linked with increased risk for HIV, reducing risk for these STDs in effect minimizes the possibility of HIV infection.

Peer educators are also effective in piercing through teenagers' perceived invulnerability. Adolescents often have more trust in their peers and feel greater rapport with other teens than they do with adults. Encouraging teen participation as peer educators includes adolescents in the development and implementation of prevention programs and makes them part of the solution to a problem rather than targets of interventions. Peer educators have been used in HIV education programs based on the assumption that teenagers are less embarrassed about discussing sensitive issues among themselves and are more likely to follow the advice of other teens. Peer leaders can also help to monitor homophobic or racist responses arising from HIV instruction. Peer educators should be students who are accepted by other students, are opinion leaders in the target group, and exhibit a concern for peers and a willingness to be trained to work with HIV education.

Information and Prevention Skills

Sexuality education programs that are "mechanical" in nature are better than none at all, but may not meet the practical needs of students. Because teenagers need more than information about sexual intercourse, HIV transmission and negative consequences of sexual activity, in some schools attention is being focused on a cognitive-behavioral approach. This approach recognizes that teenagers need intellectual skills to understand the consequences of their actions and behavioral skills for communicating with others about sexual issues (Mitchell.and Brindis, 1987). A single pamphlet, film or lecture about HIV/AIDS will be insufficient to influence the behaviors associated with transmission. Similarly, education about the biology of HIV, the symptoms of the disease or the social consequences of the epidemic will do little to affect its spread among teenagers, unless they have access to condoms and are skilled in risk-reduction behaviors.

HIV/AIDS education should use multiple venues and formats of communication to deliver clear, consistent messages about HIV-related behaviors and ways to reduce risk. Teenagers in the same classroom may have different HIV-related educational needs. The sexually active teen may require specific information about condoms and support in their consistent use, while another student may need to develop skills to help resist pressure to initiate sexual activity until he or she can engage in it responsibly. Students in denial may need help in personalizing their risk of HIV infection. Those who deny their risk for HIV may also avoid confronting the risk of their sexual and drug experimentation.

Changing behavior involves not just knowing what to do, but knowing how to do it. In addition to information, teenagers need skills to apply their knowledge to real-life situations. Broaching controversial topics in conversation, resisting peer pressure to have unprotected sex or to use drugs, and negotiating less risky activities may be more difficult than learning biomedical facts about HIV transmission. A comprehensive sexuality education program addressing HIV/AIDS should assist teenagers to delay the initiation of sexual activity, facilitate sexually active teenagers' access to contraceptive services and condoms, and increase all teenagers' ability to make responsible sexual decisions. It should ensure that teachers are well trained to instruct about HIV/AIDS and sexuality, and that programs are developed and implemented with appropriate parent and community involvement.

Guidelines for HIV/AIDS Educators

In order to teach about HIV/AIDS effectively, teachers must be aware of their own feelings, biases, prejudices and values related to HIV, and must be comfortable with their own sexuality. For some teachers, discussion of aspects of human anatomy may cause acute discomfort, and they may convey this attitude to their students, reinforcing the view that sex is "dirty" and should not be discussed candidly. Other teachers may be unable to freely discuss topics related to HIV such as anal sex, bisexuality, oral sex and sexual variation.

It has been recommended that professional preparation programs include preservice and inservice HIV training for health educators. If nonspecialist teachers are used to teach HIV education, they should receive ongoing practical support from health specialists and coordinators. It would be prudent for the teacher to enlist the support of HIV experts in the community to provide current and relevant information for the students.

Beside knowledge and skills to plan, implement and evaluate teaching activities, sexuality educators who work with teenagers must
* gain an increased awareness and comfort level with personal sexual feelings, attitudes and behaviors
* clarify personal values related to sexuality
* become more aware of the sexual ideas, opinions, concerns, attitudes and values of teenagers
* increase acceptance of the variety of sexual opinions, attitudes, values and behaviors of others

Well-prepared HIV/sexuality educators need to have a working knowledge of the biological, psychological, sociocultural and ethical aspects of human sexual behavior, including the integration of love and sexual behavior, as well as the relationship between sexuality and value systems, lifestyles and dysfunctional behavior.

The advent of HIV/AIDS has led to calls for more comprehensive and effective sexuality education programs in the school.
* To be effective in modifying sexual behaviors of students, HIV/AIDS education programs must be consistent, intensive, systematic and combined with other strategies.
* Educational materials and behavioral change interventions must be culturally and linguistically relevant, sensitive and specific to the adolescent populations.

- The saying "multiple channels, repeated multiple times," applies to HIV/AIDS education for teens. Do not expect one approach to work for all teenagers. Adolescents within any given subculture are highly different from one another. Early, middle and late adolescence are different physical, social and psychological phenomena.

- Increased attention should be focused on cognitive-behavioral approaches, which recognize that adolescents need cognitive skills to understand the consequences of their actions and behavioral skills for communicating with other adolescents about issues pertaining to sexuality (Mitchell and Brindis, 1987).

- The likelihood that an HIV/AIDS education program will be effective increases when adolescents feel they have a significant role in identifying the problem and in designing, implementing and evaluating that intervention. Teachers, parents and student must be partners in this important process.

References

Baker, S., S. Thalberg and D. Morrison. 1988. Parents' behavioral norms as predictors of adolescent sexuality activity and contraceptive use. *Adolescence* 23 (90): 265-282.

Bell, T. and K. I. Holmes. 1984. Age specific risks of syphilis, gonorrhea and hospitalized pelvic inflammatory disease in sexually experienced U.S. women. *Sexually Transmitted Disease* 11 (4): 291-295.

Britton, P. O., D. de Mauro and A. E. Gambrell. 1992. HIV/AIDS education: SIECUS study on HIV/AIDS education for schools finds states make progress but work remains. *SIECUS Report* 21 (1): 1-8.

Calamidas, E. 1990. Effects of sex education on the sexual anxiety of medical students. *Journal of Sex Education and Therapy* 13 (1): 1-3.

Centers for Disease Control. 1988. Guidelines for effective school health education to prevent the spread of AIDS. *Mortality and Morbidity Weekly Review* 37 (S-2): 1-14.

Des Jarlais, D., and S. Friedman. 1987. HIV infection among intravenous drug users: Epidemiology and risk reduction (editorial review). *AIDS* 1 (1): 67-76.

DiClemente, F., C. Boyer and E. Morales. 1988. Minorities and AIDS: Knowledge, attitudes and misconceptions among Black and Latino adolescents. *American Journal of Public Health* 78 (1): 55-57.

Hayes, C. 1987. *Risking the future: Adolescent sexuality pregnancy and childbearing.* Washington, DC: National Academy Press.

Hein, K. 1987. AIDS in adolescents: A rationale for concern. *New York State Journal of Medicine* 87 (3): 290-295.

Job, R. 1988. Effective and ineffective use of fear in health promotion campaigns. *American Journal of Public Health* 78 (2): 163-167.

Kroger, G. and O. Wiesner. 1981. STD education: Challenge for the 1980s. *Journal of School Health* 51 (4): 242-246.

Mitchell, F., and C. Brindis. 1987. Adolescent pregnancy: The responsibilities of policymakers. *Health Services Research* 22 (3): 399-437.

Quinn, T., D. Glasser and R. Cannon. 1988. Human immunodeficiency virus infection among patients attending clinics for sexually transmitted diseases. *New England Journal of Medicine* 318 (4): 197-203.

Scales, P. 1984. *The front lines of sexuality education.* Santa Cruz, CA: ETR Associates.

Shilts, R. 1987. *And the band played on: Politics, people and the AIDS epidemic.* New York: St. Martin's Press.

Stackhouse, W. 1990. The impact of religion on sexuality education. *Siecus Report* 18 (2): 21-27.

Strunin, L., and R. Hingson. 1987. Acquired Immunodeficiency Syndrome and adolescents: Knowledge, beliefs, attitudes and behaviors. *Pediatrics* 79 (5): 825-828.

Turner, C., and H. Miller. 1989. *The National Association of State Boards of Education HIV/HIV Education Survey. Profiles of state policy action.* Alexandria, VA: National Association of State Boards of Education.

Yarber, W. 1987. School AIDS education: Politics, issues and responses. *SIECUS Report* 15 (6): 1-5.

Zabin, L., M. Hirsh, E. Smith, R. Street and J. Hardy. 1986. Evaluation of a pregnancy prevention program for urban teenagers. *Family Planning Perspectives* 18 (3): 119-126.

Chapter 17

Adolescent Pregnancy Prevention and Sexuality Education

Claire Brindis, DrPH

A dolescent sexual activity, pregnancy and out-of-wedlock child-birth, especially among younger adolescents, have escalated over the past two decades. The time gap between biological ability to bear children and readiness to raise them has widened: the number of years during adolescence when pregnancy can occur, and the length of time it takes to prepare adolescents for full participation in our complex society have both increased.

The negative effects of early parenthood have been amply documented: health, education, and future employment are adversely affected; poverty is a frequent outcome. Both individuals and society pay a high price. The expanding number of teenagers bearing babies at ever-younger ages, with a growing proportion of these births to unmarried mothers who often lack both financial support and the educational skills to become economically self-sufficient, has shifted the economic burden from the family to the public.

As a result, adolescent childbearing increasingly has become an issue of national concern. Policy-makers generally have felt much more comfortable supporting programs that help pregnant teenagers and their infants than supporting programs aimed at postponing a first pregnancy. They have focused on whether the mother and infant are healthy, rather than dealing with the controversy surrounding publicly acknowledging that large proportions of adolescents are sexually active, and funding programs that help adolescents avoid pregnancy.

In response to the acknowledged problem of too early childbearing, a diverse array of health and social service professionals, religious and community leaders, parents, teachers, policy-makers and others are striving to develop effective strategies that will prevent unintended adolescent childbearing. These strategies have ranged from educational programs in classroom settings to increasing access to family planning services to model community-based programs that respond to the variety of problems that adolescents face, including efforts to increase adolescents' motivation to delay childbearing.

There is a growing recognition of the diversity that exists among adolescents, and, thus, of the need for strategies at the local community, city, county, state and national levels that are simultaneously comprehensive and diversified. There is also a recognition that appropriate interventions targeted to specific groups of adolescents—adolescents who have not initiated a sexual relationship, adolescents who are sexually active and adolescents who are already pregnant and parenting—are needed within the same community.

Those engaged in adolescent pregnancy prevention must understand adolescent pregnancy and parenting in terms of the life options available to adolescents and then work toward empowering adolescents to make conscious choices—choices about their sexuality and reproduction in particular, but also about their personal relationships, health, education and economic future (Brindis and Jeremy, 1988). Thus, the adolescent pregnancy prevention agenda often resonates with the goals and objectives of professionals engaged in sexuality education. Sexuality education has been and continues to be an important component in any pregnancy prevention program. This chapter examines the role of sexuality education within the field of adolescent pregnancy prevention.

Goals of Programs

From the mid-1970s, pregnancy prevention programs and services for adolescents appeared in increasing number, but there was little discussion about which programs worked and why. In 1985, the prestigious National Research Council (NCR), which draws its members from the National Academy of Engineering and the Institute of Medicine, appointed a 15-member expert interdisciplinary panel (the Panel on Adolescent Pregnancy and Childbearing) to study the issues and document how various interventions affected teen pregnancy rates. In 1987 the NRC released the study results in three volumes: *Risking the Future: Adolescent Sexuality, Pregnancy and Childbearing*. The report provided a comprehensive review of programs, formulated a series of goals, and recommended program areas and strategies to accomplish those goals.

The NRC panel suggested three broad goals related to adolescent pregnancy: reduce the rate and incidence of unintended pregnancy, especially among school-age teenagers; provide alternatives to adolescent childbearing and parenting; and promote positive social, economic, health and developmental outcomes for adolescent parents and their children.

The panel recommended three goals to reduce unintended pregnancy among school-age teenagers: delay the onset of sexual activity; encourage sexually active teens to use contraceptives; and find ways to enhance the life options of those adolescents for whom pregnancy might appear to be a positive alternative.

The Sexuality Education Component

Early pregnancy prevention efforts had a strong sexuality education component. At the core of many of the "information-based" curriculum models was a strong emphasis on increasing the overall level of knowledge regarding contraceptive choices and how each method worked, and material designed to create positive attitudes towards using contraceptives. Many of these early prevention efforts, begun in the 1970s, dovetailed with the increased availability of the birth control pill and the development of a network of publicly subsidized family planning clinics throughout the country that provided adolescents with access to care without the need for parental consent (Hayes, 1987).

Initially, there appears to have been a relatively naive belief that providing information about sexuality and contraceptive methods would resolve the issue of adolescent pregnancy. Programs appeared to function on the premise that information would be readily absorbed by students, and that students consequently would develop the necessary skills to both seek contraceptive services and become effective contraceptive users.

Studies that measured the effect of these early curricula on teen pregnancy rates were not encouraging (Kirby, 1984; Marsiglio et al., 1986; Kirby, 1989). Ironically, the lack of effect on the incidence of adolescent sexual activity has been important in its own regard. A number of accusations have been made by opponents of sexuality education that sexuality education is in itself a major contributing factor to increasing numbers of adolescents engaging in early sexual behavior. In fact, the majority of the studies demonstrated that sexuality education neither contributed to nor diminished the likelihood that a teenager would become sexually active and that sexuality education did not significantly affect the amount of sexual activity among students (Dawson, 1986; Marsiglio and Mott, 1986).

Recent studies show that some programs can have positive effects in the areas of (1) knowledge (particularly for younger adolescents) about abstinence, birth control, sexually transmitted disease and the probability of becoming pregnant; (2) skills, so that students show improvements in communication and decision-making skills; and (3) parent/child communication, resulting in a greater sense of comfort in discussing sexual issues within the family (Kirby et al., 1991). While each of these effects has intrinsic value, their impact on the incidence of adolescent pregnancy is indirect.

Impact on Pregnancy

A growing sophistication regarding the repertoire of skills that young people need in order to successfully avoid pregnancy contributed to the development of several generations of programmatic efforts, including curricula that focused on values clarification, development of problem-solving and decision-making skills, anticipatory guidance, communication and interpersonal skills and other cognitive behavioral skills (Kirby et al., 1991).

A significant evolution in the field occurred as the focus on adolescent pregnancy prevention was broadened to include a more comprehensive concept of sexuality education, one which encompassed a broader array of topics, skill areas and age groups. Thus, in addition to teaching about human reproduction, sexual decision making, abstinence and birth control, HIV and STD, comprehensive sexuality education programs include topics related to communication skills, gender issues, self-esteem and life planning (Stout and Rivara, 1989).

In addition to a more comprehensive curriculum, sexuality education advocates recommend a comprehensive curriculum that begins at or even before kindergarten and continues throughout high school. An assessment of whether such a comprehensive level of education can contribute significantly to adolescent pregnancy prevention has not been conducted.

Recent efforts aimed at decreasing the early onset of sexual activity have focused on targeting adolescents before they initiate sexual activity. Abstinence models such as *Postponing Sexual Involvement*, geared toward younger adolescents (ages 12 to 14), and *Reducing the Risk*, a model that combines aspects of social learning theory and social inoculation theory, appear to reduce the likelihood of unprotected sexual intercourse for youth without prior sexual experience. They have been shown to have a powerful impact on both delaying the onset of sexual activity and improving the incidence of contraceptive use among adolescents who delayed sexual activity (Kirby et al., 1991).

However, professionals concerned with those adolescents who are already sexually active note that even sexuality education curricula that are comprehensive in nature will continue to have limited impact on preventing pregnancy because they represent only a single strategy to adolescent pregnancy prevention. Increasingly there is a recognition that the right kind of information and skills are necessary, but not sufficient by themselves to prevent pregnancy (Forrest and Silverman, 1989).

Limits of Sexuality Education
Although "sexuality education" is taught widely, its content and timing tends to make its role in adolescent pregnancy prevention a relatively limited one.

- National surveys have documented that only about 60 percent of all adolescents receive at least some sexuality education. Within this group, only 35 percent received a comprehensive course that included birth control, reproduction and sexual development (Kenney, Guardado and Brown, 1989).
- Although four-fifths of the states either require or encourage the teaching of sexuality education in the public schools, only about two-thirds require or encourage the schools to teach about pregnancy prevention, specifically birth control methods (Kenney, Guardado and Brown, 1989).
- Although the majority of school districts across the country offer some type of sexuality education, it traditionally takes place in the ninth or tenth grade, long after a number of adolescents are already engaging in sexual activity (Forrest and Silverman, 1989).
- While most teachers believe that information should be made available to young people as to the sources of birth control methods in their community, only 48 percent of schools offer sexuality education that addresses this issue (Forrest and Silverman, 1989).

Other factors that weaken educational interventions to prevent pregnancy are the relatively limited length of programs and the lack of availability of teaching materials and strategies for teachers (Alan Guttmacher Institute, 1989).

In addition, sexuality education teachers find that though there is national support for teaching sexuality education in the school, local communities and parents often do not support this education. Policies that support teaching human reproduction may not support teaching about adolescent pregnancy prevention strategies, thus further diluting the potential success of this approach.

HIV/AIDS Prevention

To further complicate the picture, HIV and AIDS education appears to be receiving more attention and funding from federal, state and local school districts than sexuality education. Most new state personnel and expenditures are devoted to HIV/AIDS prevention education rather than sexuality education (Kenney, Guardado and Brown, 1989). Currently, school health teachers are more likely to teach about the prevention of HIV and STD than they are about the use of birth control to prevent pregnancy (Alan Guttmacher Institute, 1989).

Emphasis in many of these programs is on abstinence from sexual relations, although the majority of school districts also cover the topic of condoms as a means of preventing STD and HIV, with lesser emphasis on the use of condoms as a means to prevent pregnancy. The public recognition of the serious results of HIV/AIDS and adolescents' risk to the disease, as well as the lesser, but also serious implications of other sexually transmitted disease, has enabled health educators to make greater inroads in the provision of information surrounding HIV/AIDS in comparison to discussing the more value-laden topic of pregnancy prevention.

Ironically, efforts to prevent HIV/AIDS have been able to open classroom doors that had previously been closed to sexuality educators, but due to categorical funding and other policy restrictions they still are unable to bridge the schism that has occurred in a number of sites between the fields of pregnancy prevention and HIV/AIDS prevention. As the public increases its awareness of HIV and the disease affects greater numbers of adolescents and women, one can anticipate that more integrated efforts that emphasize condoms as a dual-purpose strategy will need to be developed. This merger is important; otherwise, pregnancy prevention will likely be less prominent than HIV/AIDS prevention.

What Works: Types of Approaches

The complexity of changing human behavior, particularly reducing the incidence of adolescent pregnancy through the adoption of consistent contraceptive behavior, and our greater understanding of the antecedents of adolescent pregnancy, have contributed to the development of increasingly sophisticated models of intervention. Community-based efforts that only increase young people's level of knowledge and skill about birth control or provide access to reproductive health services have limited success because these approaches do not address the root causes of adolescent pregnancy. Increasing young people's "capacity" to avoid an unintended pregnancy is not sufficient unless that young person also carries the hope of life opportunities which makes delaying parenthood a worthwhile option (Dryfoos, 1986).

Those who seek to reduce teen pregnancy have begun to recognize that adolescent pregnancy prevention requires a number of concurrent and reinforcing strategies provided within a comprehensive framework and made available on a continuous basis to adolescents, their families and the community at large. These strategies may begin, but cannot end, with sexuality education, even when such education is of high quality. It is also evident that few communities have been able to coordinate youth-serving programs and integrated services that include sexuality education and access to contraceptive care.

In considering adolescent pregnancy prevention efforts and emerging strategies, it is important to consider the necessity of joining sexuality education efforts, particularly comprehensive kindergarten through grade 12 efforts, with a number of additional school- and community-based strategies. If one visualizes a continuum of models, it could begin at one end with adolescent pregnancy prevention efforts that rely primarily on education-only approaches, and increase in complexity and use of multiple-strategies as one moves further along across the continuum.

Classroom Programs

As previously described, traditional adolescent pregnancy prevention models have relied on relatively short-term sexuality education curricula which may or may not include specific information pertaining to birth control or where to access contraceptive care. The more comprehensive sexuality education curricula are oriented to developing specific interpersonal skills among youth—for example, providing homework assignments that require students to speak with their parents regarding values pertaining to sexual and contraceptive behavior; to compare the prices of different contraceptives that are available over the counter; and to visit family planning programs to learn how they function, where they are located, and what the policies are regarding the provision of services to adolescents.

Parent sexuality education workshops are sometimes built into these programs to enhance parents' skills so that they can supplement and reinforce the instruction provided in the classroom. The primary participants in this approach are school teachers who are sometimes linked to outside community agencies. A Planned Parenthood affiliate or county health education department might provide classroom education on specific topics such as methods of contraception. This provides the opportunity to share information on available resources in the community. Parent/child workshops, which may be held at the school site, are also often offered by outside community resources.

Clinic Programs

Moving along the continuum, a number of adolescent pregnancy prevention efforts have combined sexuality education with clinical contraceptive services, either at the school site or in community-based clinics. Federal and state funds, as well as private fund-raising efforts involving foundations and other donors, support a network of family planning clinics across the United States. Family planning clinics have been shown to be an important resource for young people and have greatly contributed to reducing the incidence of adolescent pregnancy (Harlap, Kost and Forrest, 1991).

Today, however, lack of funding has contributed to a diminishing number of these services. A decrease of 1,000 family planning clinics since 1980 has resulted in fewer than 5,000 clinics funded throughout the country (Ku, 1993). Lack of resources has contributed to the fact that only about one-third of at-risk adolescents receive access to the contraceptive services they need (Levine and Tsoflias, 1993). An innovative approach for bringing services to adolescents was developed in the early 1970s when comprehensive primary health services, including family planning counseling and education, were brought directly from the community into schools. The majority of programs did not dispense contraceptives on campus, but the intent was to diminish the psychological barriers to accessing care by establishing a trusting relationship at the school site where information and counseling related to family planning could be provided in a confidential manner.

In over 360 school-based health centers across the country, students can receive contraceptive-related services, either through referral to an outside agency, a prescription to a local pharmacy or clinic, or services directly on campus. Health educators within the clinics have also played an important role in teaching or co-teaching sexuality education in the classroom. This approach often results in a number of students visiting the clinic. It is important to note that in spite of the availability of and easier access to family planning care, only about 15 percent of visits are related to contraceptive services (Waszak and Neidell, 1992). The majority of visits are either for primary care or for mental health services which appear to be far more pressing for adolescents and are part of the student's overall health status.

One of the most successful clinic models was established by the Johns Hopkins School of Medicine in two schools in Baltimore. This model was not a traditional school-based clinic (Zabin and Hirsch, 1988). Rather it helped to create a strong linkage between the school and clinical services provided off-campus. The program co-located a social worker and a nurse practitioner half-time in the two schools, and devoted the remaining time to providing clinical services at an off-site (but convenient) family planning store-front clinic. At the school sites, a classroom was designated where students could drop in for counseling and group discussions on a number of family life education topics.

In contrast to the school-based clinic model, the Baltimore program did not provide comprehensive primary care or mental health counseling. The program was more narrowly focused on family planning services, including the treatment of sexually trans-mitted disease and the provision of contraceptives. Students could make appointments with staff during the school hours and then see the same staff member after school when the clinic was open. Evaluation of this program demonstrated a dramatic decrease in the incidence of adolescent pregnancies and births, and a delay of seven months in the initiation of sexual relations among adolescents who were not sexually active (Zabin and Hirsch, 1988).

Community Programs

A number of efforts are underway in which sexuality education and access to contraceptive services are considered only two of a number of health, education and support services made available to adolescents. These approaches focus on maximizing the adolescent's capacity to make effective contraceptive decisions and on improving the adolescent's sense of future life options. One example of this approach is the New York City–based Children's Aid Society Holistic Model, a 15-week family life education and pregnancy prevention course that combines a range of interventions, including access to health and medical services (including contraceptive services), mental health services, academic assessment and homework help, and a job club and career awareness component where students can learn how to look for a job and get paid for participating in community work.

In this model, the adolescent receives self-esteem enhancement opportunities through participation in the arts, and opportunities to develop skills in lifetime individual sports, such as tennis, racquetball and swimming. College admission is guaranteed to Hunter College in New York for teens who complete high school, participate in the primary prevention program and are recommended by the program director. Financial aid is also available. The program is currently being evaluated, but initial findings indicate that very few of the participants experience an unintended pregnancy in contrast to other adolescents living in the same environment (Brindis, 1991).

Another recently developed model is oriented to reaching younger adolescents. Options for Pre-Teens (OPT) is sponsored by the American Association of School Administrators (AASA). OPT is a primary prevention program serving fourth, fifth, sixth and seventh grade boys and girls in urban school districts. Its purpose is to provide preadolescents with the motivation and the skills to abstain from early sexual activity and other risky behaviors and be successful in school (Card, Adams-Taylor and Miller, 1992).

Specific goals include developing students' life-planning and decision-making skills, improving school performance, developing closer ties between schools and communities, involving parents in the educational and social development of their children, and helping students and their families ameliorate the effects of poverty.

The OPT model is composed of several components:

- The Life Planning Curriculum teaches students about risky behaviors, gives them skills for resisting risky behaviors and provides information on family life, sexuality and careers.
- The Academic Skills Improvement Curriculum assists students to achieve grade level performance in reading, math and other subjects.
- The Service Learning component gives students the opportunity to assume responsibility, to explore adult roles and to learn about the world of work.
- The School Climate Enhancement component involves the adolescent in improving the school climate and in establishing action plans that set clear school goals.
- The Family Involvement component attempts to include parents through establishing a family volunteer program and a family room within the school, and supporting parents' direct involvement in their children's learning.
- The Student and Family Advocacy component provides counseling and continuous case management for students and their families.

In these two models, sexuality education becomes an integral approach within a broad-based program for adolescent pregnancy prevention. It is important, however, to note that few communities have been able to develop such comprehensive models and that the effectiveness of these approaches are still being studied. Yet it is anticipated that these integrated efforts may have much greater potential for success in preventing pregnancy among the most vulnerable segments of the adolescent population.

Environment Programs

Finally, there are those pregnancy prevention efforts that do not necessarily emphasize or highlight sexuality education, but strive to provide a nurturing environment for young people to achieve a reduction in both school dropout and adolescent pregnancy. An example of this model is the program established by New York businessman Eugene Lang. The "I Have a Dream" foundation provides college scholarships for students who graduate from high school. The program has been replicated in 14 cities across the country. Although it is not labeled an adolescent pregnancy prevention program, the strong emphasis on school continuation and the support provided by social workers in each program provides students with the necessary motivation and encouragement to continue with their education. In an initial analysis of the first group of students who have benefited from the program, only a handful had dropped out as a result of an unintended pregnancy (Brindis and Jeremy, 1988).

Another program with a relatively small emphasis on the provision of sexuality education, but which appears to be providing adolescents with the skills and self-esteem necessary to delay early childbearing, is the Teen Outreach Program (TOP). TOP is a school-based program that combines small group discussions based on a curriculum that emphasizes understanding oneself, dealing with life pressures, relationships, communication and community resources with volunteer service experience in the community (Philliber and Allen, 1992).

TOP programs are sponsored by local Junior Leagues and operated by schools. About two-thirds of TOP programs are offered after school hours, about one-third are offered during school. Students meet once a week throughout the school year to discuss both the curriculum and their experiences working in the community. Volunteer services include working in hospitals, nursing homes and the school, tutoring younger students, and many other types of activities. Evaluation results indicate that the program has been successful in reducing the incidence of pregnancy, school suspensions, course failure and school dropout (Philliber and Allen, 1992).

Some keys to the success of the TOP program have been mentoring from a caring and consistent adult; a work experience that offers opportunities for skill building; a peer support group atmosphere; and the opportunity to feel appreciated. Students also develop strong skills in assertiveness, decision making, communication and the use of community resources. These programs incorporate a number of life options and opportunities, which are at the heart of adolescent pregnancy prevention.

Communities striving to develop new approaches to preventing teen pregnancy may wish to review what youth serving resources already exist within their community and consider ways that "capacity" building efforts (e.g., sexuality education geared to supporting delayed initiation of sexual activity, as well as responsible sexual activity) can be formally connected to efforts geared to improving the life opportunities of young people. Joining forces and combining resources offers communities the opportunity to create coordinated and comprehensive efforts geared to both reducing the incidence of adolescent pregnancy and improving the life potential of youth.

Summary

With the increasing recognition that young people at-risk for an unintended pregnancy need more than the information and skills training provided in even a comprehensive sexuality education program, sexuality educators are joining other professionals to broaden the scope and focus of adolescent pregnancy prevention efforts. Combining the information and skills developed through comprehensive sexuality education programs with additional strategies that aim at expanding adolescents' level of confidence and the skills needed to build their futures will likely represent the next wave of activity in the field of adolescent pregnancy prevention.

These partnerships also have relevance for other efforts to decrease adolescent risk-taking behavior—for example, in the area of substance use and violence prevention. Along with these efforts, sexuality educators will need to continue to advocate for the implementation of curricula that range from abstinence education geared to younger adolescents to programs within a more comprehensive curriculum that support the development of specific personal and social skills that will enable young people to discuss responsible sexual activity and effectively use contraceptives. Too many young people have received very diluted efforts aimed at reducing their vulnerability to unintended pregnancy. Those who work to prevent adolescent pregnancy have a responsibility to continue to improve their interventions and to integrate these efforts within the larger context of a society committed to investing in young people.

References

Alan Guttmacher Institute. 1989. *Risk and responsibility: Teaching sex education in America's schools today.* New York.

American School Health Association. 1991. *Sexuality education within comprehensive school health education.* Kent, OH.

Brindis, C., and R. Jeremy. 1988. *Adolescent pregnancy and parenting in California: A strategic plan for action.* San Francisco: Center for Population and Reproductive Health Policy, Institute for Health Policy Studies, University of California, San Francisco, UCSF Publications Department.

Brindis, C. 1991. *Adolescent pregnancy prevention: A guidebook for communities, health promotion resource center.* Palo Alto, CA: Health Promotion Resource Center, Stanford Center for Research in Disease Prevention.

Card, J. J., S. Adams-Taylor and N. Miller. 1992. Options for pre-teens: Programs provide skills for the future. *Too Early Childbearing* 33 (June): 6-7. (Newsletter published by Charles Stewart Mott Foundation.)

Dawson, D. A. 1986. The effects of sex education on adolescent behavior. *Family Planning Perspectives* 18 (4): 162-170.

Dryfoos, J. 1986. Preventing teen pregnancy: What works. *Planned Parenthood Review* 6:6-8.

Forrest, J. D., and J. Silverman. 1989. What public school teachers teach about preventing pregnancy, AIDS and sexually transmitted diseases. *Family Planning Perspectives* 21 (2): 65-72.

Harlap, S., K. Kost and J. D. Forrest. 1991. *Preventing pregnancy, protecting health.* New York: Alan Guttmacher Institute.

Hayes, C., ed. 1987. *Risking the future: Adolescent sexuality, pregnancy and childbearing.* Washington, DC: National Academy Press.

Kenney, A. M., S. Guardado and L. Brown. 1989. Sex education and AIDS education in the schools: What states and large school districts are doing. *Family Planning Perspectives* 21 (2): 56-64.

Kirby, D. 1984. Sexuality education: An evaluation of programs and their effects. Santa Cruz, CA: ETR Associates.

Kirby, D. 1989. Sex education programs and their effects. *The World and I* (September): 591-603.

Kirby, D., R. P. Barth, N. Leland and J. V. Fetro. 1991. Reducing the risk: Impact of a new curriculum on sexual risk taking. *Family Planning Perspectives* 23 (6): 253-263.

Ku, L. 1993. Financing a family planning services. Research paper. Washington, DC: Urban Institute.

Levine, R., and L. Tsoflias. 1993. *Publicly supported family planning in the United States: Use in the 1980s.* Washington, DC: Urban Institute and Child Trends, Inc.

Louis Harris and Associates. 1988. *Public attitudes toward teenage pregnancy, sex education and birth control.* New York.

Marsiglio, W., and F. L. Mott. 1986. The impact of sex education on sexual activity, contraceptive use and premarital pregnancy among American teenagers. *Family Planning Perspectives* 18 (4): 151-162.

National Guidelines Task Force. 1991. *Guidelines for comprehensive sexuality education: Kindergarten-12th grade.* New York: Sex Information and Education Council of the United States.

Philliber, S., and J. Allen. 1992. Life options and community service: Teen outreach program. In *Preventing adolescent pregnancy,* ed. B. C. Miller, J. J. Card, R. L. Paikoff and J. L. Peterson, 139-155. Newbury Park, CA: Sage Publications.

Stout, J. W., and F. P. Rivara. 1989. Schools and sex education: Does it work? *Pediatrics* 83:375-379.

Waszak, C., and S. Neidell. 1992. *School-based and school-linked clinics: Update 1991.* Washington, DC: Center for Population Options.

Zabin, L. S., and M. B. Hirsch. 1988. *Evaluation of pregnancy prevention programs in the school context.* Lexington, MA/Toronto: Lexington Books, D. C. Heath and Company.

Diversity and Sexuality Education

Chapter 18

Cultural Competence and Sexuality Education

Lenora E. Johnson, MPH, CHES

*S*exuality is a term that carries a particular meaning to sexuality educators and health education specialists. It is also a term that is interpreted differently by every culture and every family represented in a classroom. To effectively deliver messages which will yield healthy, self-assured youth who are confident in making responsible decisions, sexuality educators must understand the various cultural values that surround sexuality and be sensitive to the cultural backgrounds and needs of their students.

Defining Culture

While there are many technical definitions and highly theorized explanations of culture, simply put, culture is how individuals color their picture of the world in which they live. John Ogbu (1987) defines culture as the design for living that people have worked out and continue to work out in the course of their history.

For purposes of this chapter, cultural diversity refers to those differences that result from ethnicity, heritage and historical background that have been carved into a person's inner belief system by the population in which he or she was reared. This is a somewhat narrow examination of cultural diversity; educators are encouraged to explore the further cultural differences that evolve as a result of religious affiliation, sexual orientation and physical abilities.

Sexual Attitudes, Values and Beliefs

It has been clearly documented that while the interest in abstinence-based programs for teens is on the rise, sexual activity rates continue to rise as well. What is not well documented are the explanations for the differences in the sexual practice among young people today. If socioeconomic status is not a variable, cultural differences in decision making may be based not on options but on differences in attitudes, values and beliefs that are rooted in, but to some extent transcend social and economic circumstances.

United States birthrates for White teenagers are higher than those for any other Western country. For African-American teenagers the rates are three times higher than that for Whites, and African-American teens are more likely to have had sex at an earlier age than White teens (Newcomer and Baldwin, 1992). More frightening statistics reveal that 75 percent of Hispanic and 66 percent of African-American female adolescents did not use any type of protection against sexually transmitted diseases or pregnancy the first time they had intercourse, compared to 45 percent of White females.

Findings of this nature are as dangerous to the efforts of educators as they are alarming to the general public. The danger comes from making generalizations about the findings—usually that adolescents from specific populations are more promiscuous or take greater risks. We tend to label these youth as "at-risk" or "high risk," terms that are highly offensive to the populations they are intended to describe. Special attention should be given to the terms and labels we attach to groups. Populations that might be "at-risk" as defined by statistical analyses may have other positive health attributes that enhance the quality of life and diminish the negative impact of the behavior being studied. Failure to recognize the strengths of a population prior to focusing on their needs results in failed programs and wasted energy.

Cultural Value Differences

Different cultures have different health-related cultural values. Sketchy examination merely reveals the problem areas. Deeper investigation will reveal that many cultural values can serve to develop or sustain positive health habits. For example, for youth in many American Indian cultures, self-esteem is often at "abysmally low levels." In a study by Rosenthal (1974), the Chippewa children exhibited the most negative and deprecating self-assessment of any minority group examined. While this information is vital to designing effective education opportunities for Native American youth, it does not begin to access the strengths of the Native American culture that can serve to enhance any educational intervention. Rarely is focus placed on the positive attributes of diverse cultures.

Hispanic youth have significantly higher marriage rates during their teenage years (Newcomer and Baldwin, 1992). African-American high school seniors are less likely to use drugs than their White counterparts (Hechinger, 1992). Eating disorders are not nearly as common in young adults of color as they are in the White youth population (Hechinger, 1992). Sexuality educators may not focus on such attributes because they are slightly removed from their primary focus. However, exploring the cultural attitudes and values that yield such positive behaviors will increase the understanding of cultural values directly related to sexuality.

The American culture imposes values that may or may not be the values held by distinct populations represented in the United States. American culture can be associated with the following values:

- personal control over environment
- time dominates
- individualism/privacy
- self-help
- competition
- practicality/efficiency

These values conflict with values held by many ethnic populations. For example, many cultures believe that fate overrides personal control, human interaction is more important than being on time, individuality should give way to group welfare and family cohesiveness, self-help is less important than birthright, competition should take a back seat to cooperation, and idealism and theory are more valuable than practicality and efficiency.

Examining some of the values that can be broadly associated with some of the populations we so often refer to as "minorities," and comparing these with the values of the dominant Euro-Anglo culture can be helpful in understanding issues that can arise in a classroom setting.

The Family Unit

The dominant culture assumes that the universal goal of childrearing and adolescence is to develop or become an individual able to function independently of the family unit (Isaacs, 1993).

However, for cultures representing people of color the reverse is often true. Young adults are reared to view the family unit as most important and to place the utmost confidence in it. For many cultures of color, the goal for every generation is to achieve a level whereby it can be of assistance and provide greater support to the family unit. Family roles are important and help develop self-concept. Self-esteem is centered around being a member of the family unit which emphasizes cultural pride.

Appropriate Sexual Behavior

In the traditional Hispanic culture "good girls" are sexually naive. Thus, it may not be perceived as appropriate for them to be prepared for sexual experiences by possessing a condom or being able to articulate desires in regard to sexual activity. Marriage and motherhood is highly valued in the Hispanic culture and is often associated with a higher level of respect. This value might affect decision making regarding contraceptive use (Brindis, 1992). In the Hispanic culture it is not always proper to discuss issues of health and well-being with persons outside the family unit.

Relationships

In Hispanic populations it is important to have a sense of values centered around relationships. *Sympathia* describes an individual who is well liked, fun, caring and kind. A person exhibiting *sympathia* is well respected and held in high regard in the community. While assertiveness is viewed positively by the Euro-Anglo culture, it is often perceived as aggressive and offensive in the Hispanic culture. While the term "macho" often has negative connotations in the dominant culture, it has positive dimensions for the Latin culture. *Respecto* refers to persons who are older, male and powerful. In most cultures, youth are raised to respect their elders. In Hispanic, African-American, Asian and Native-

American cultures, however, that respect carries over from childhood into adulthood and respect for all elders is a constant value.

Respect for Tradition

American Indian cultures value a cooperative spirit that accompanies shared property. Other strong values might include living in the moment without an inordinate emphasis upon future commitments or punctuality, and respect for tradition and the natural surroundings (Lamarine, 1989). Respect for the land and the environment is a strong value for American Indian cultures. In the Native American culture, land is sacred and cannot be exploited or seized. Native Americans avoid talk about death and illness and emphasize self-preservation.

Pride in Heritage

African Americans value self-image and pride in one's heritage. Far too often youth have been the subjects of negative comments and experiences that have been internalized and have served to erode their self-concept. African-American women are often socialized to be strong, assertive and economically independent. African-American men might evaluate their masculinity by their ability to take risks or to experience pain or discomfort without submitting to it. Mistrust of western medical practices can make means of birth control that are generally administered through clinical settings unlikely to be utilized. The African-American community welcomes and cares for children regardless of the age or marital status of parents, and tends to be more forgiving of sexual activity outside of marriage than some other cultures. Homosexuality is generally viewed as unnatural, immoral and something practiced by the White Anglo society (Pittman et al., 1992).

Challenges to Cultural Understanding

Three areas that affect education of any kind are especially important in the area of sexuality education. Language barriers, issues of trust, and economic factors need to be acknowledged, examined and addressed as part of the planning process in any successful sexuality education effort.

Language Barriers

By the year 2030, the Hispanic youth population will grow by almost 80 percent; the African-American youth population will increase by 14 percent; while the White youth population will decline by 10 percent (Duany and Pittman, 1990). In many states, particularly California, Texas and New York, Spanish-speaking populations are the emerging majority. Yet language barriers represent only the tip of the iceberg in working with individuals from diverse cultural backgrounds.

Language barriers are usually thought to exist with individuals whose native tongue is something other than English. However, such barriers exist among English-speaking populations as well. English does not always sound the same, nor is it always interpreted the same. Sociologist Rosalie Cohen discusses two basic language styles, analytical and relational. These styles affect not only language but thinking, learning and interacting as well. The analytical style, which is associated with many European Americans, is structured, ordered, controlled, logical, precise and cognitive. Other cultures, many African Americans, for example, tend more toward the relational style of language, which is free, creative, expressive, social, approximate and affective (Pittman et al., 1992).

Bias toward "proper English" has no place in health or sexuality education. Educators must recognize that many people prefer language that communicates what is felt. Simple and forthright words and messages are not only preferred but help to create an environment that is less threatening. Establishing trust and creating a safe environment for dialogue is key in sexuality education where topics for discussion are extremely private and personal.

Trust

In years gone by, the United States and the institutions of American society have not dealt well with diversity. As a result, mistrust exists and many ethnic groups view mainstream society with suspicion.

The nation's lack of attention to the needs of the emerging ethnic majority has established situations and circumstances that make it difficult to gain the trust of select populations. Without trust it will be impossible for people of color to gain access to the structures and systems that will enable them to acquire the security that was once referred to as "the American dream." Understanding the mistrust that people of color harbor is essential to successful sexuality education and health education programming.

For example, many Native Americans view the introduction of alcohol into their culture as a form of planned genocide introduced by the White male power structure. Similarly, African Americans may view the amount of drugs in their neighborhoods as an intentional plan to destroy the strongest segment of their community (Isaacs, 1993). Other conspiracy theories include the belief that HIV was deliberately created in a laboratory in order to infect African Americans, that AZT is designed to poison them, that condom distribution campaigns are a scheme to reduce the population of the Black community, and that needle distribution programs are a plot to encourage drug use (Thomas, 1992).

The evidence for planned destructive intervention focused toward specific communities is exceedingly convincing to those directly affected. Rebuilding trust will take time. Until then, educators may need to consider distributing their messages through deliverers who are seen as trustworthy, credible sources of information for their specific community, population or culture.

The Power of Poverty

The poverty rate for children is twice as high for Hispanics and almost three times as high for African Americans as it is for Whites. During the eighties the average unemployment rate for African Americans was 15 percent, a figure matched only by the average unemployment rate of Americans during the height of the Great Depression. The worst of times economically for Americans in general can be compared to the best of times for people of color today. African American and Hispanic adolescents are disproportionately represented among the poor and disadvantaged, and poorer youth are more likely to begin their sexual experiences earlier than their better-off peers (Newcomer and Baldwin, 1992).

In planning educational experiences for diverse cultures, it is critical that program planners examine indicators to determine whether they are based upon cultural beliefs and values or socioeconomic factors. Socioeconomic status (SES) clearly explains much of how young people of color paint their pictures of the world. Chronic poverty (and almost all poverty is chronic) "often leads to social isolation from mainstream America, diminished self-esteem, self-hatred, early school drop out and lowered hopes and life expectations" (Isaacs, 1993). Poverty is not a culture; it is a situation that many cultures experience. It can, however, be argued that poverty is a condition that serves to complicate our understanding of diverse cultures because it clouds our ability to distinguish between those beliefs and values that are imposed by culture and those attitudes that result from the erosion of the hopes of individuals who battle poverty on a daily basis.

Delivering Effective Messages

The basic tenet in working successfully with diverse populations is to understand the values of the families and communities to which individuals belong. Sexuality education must be framed within the context of these values. Partnerships between parents and guardians, community leaders and church officials are an integral part of every health promotion message for people of color.

"Multicultural education is education responsive to cultural differences with the aim of promoting individual students' achievement and promoting mutual respect and tolerance among students" (Fullinwider, 1993). Pittman and colleagues (1992) say that educators should not talk more than students. On that same chord, educators should not operate in and apart from those institutions that help students determine the picture of their world. The most important of these institutions are family and religion.

Since self-esteem, or lack thereof, is a thread that connects many of the issues facing people of color, strategies to develop positive self-esteem are key to successful sexuality education programs. A clear understanding of the concept of self-esteem along with an understanding of how people of color have been systematically excluded from opportunities to succeed can help educators determine how best to approach the development of culturally sensitive messages for sexuality education.

Teaching Strategies

Some strategies for increasing self-esteem might include using older students to teach or tutor younger students or siblings. This strategy, which is recommended for Native American populations by Lamarine (1989), concurrently helps enhance the self-esteem of older youth. Lamarine further recommends cooperative learning for Native American children. Cooperative learning activities allow students to work together to make discoveries about varying subjects. Specific group activities might include developing group presentations and group learning games that eliminate one-on-one competition.

Mixed teaching strategies work well with youth of diverse cultural backgrounds, particularly for young people who are still being acculturated into the dominant culture (Brindis, 1992). Such strategies include small group discussion, experiential teaching games, anonymous question and answer techniques and roleplaying. Brindis (1992) makes four recommendations for sexuality educators working with Hispanic populations. These recommendations can apply to all children of color as well as to children in general:

- For younger teens focus programs on delaying the onset of sexual activity. For older teens, focus programs on preventing pregnancy through contraceptive use.

- Special emphasis should be placed upon documenting and addressing common myths related to sexuality issues (menstrual cycles, contraceptives, etc.).

- Develop programs that will help young adults identify alternatives and realistic life goals that will override the notion that pregnancy heightens one's status or gains commitment from a partner. Steps for achieving the goals that are set should also be addressed.

- Work cooperatively with other responsible professionals who might have an impact upon youth to effectively deliver consistent, positive messages surrounding sexuality education. Such professionals might include clergy, community recreation leaders and leaders of youth clubs.

Mereasa Isaacs (1993) directs educators preparing programs for adolescents of color to pose five questions at the onset of planning.

1. How and by whom is the health problem being defined?
2. What factors should be assessed to determine whether there is a health problem and the nature of the problem?
3. How are health prevention and promotion programs to be offered and made accessible to the targeted community of adolescents of color?
4. Who should administer/provide the proposed intervention?
5. What are the expected or anticipated outcomes? How can effectiveness be measured?

By first becoming aware of the values and beliefs attached to the culture of the target population and then posing the above questions at the onset of planning the educational experience, messages can be designed to fit the world painted by that culture. The more the sexuality education message fits the student's cultural framework, the more likely that message will be received, internalized and acted upon.

References

Bean, R. 1992. *The four conditions of self-esteem.* 2d ed. Santa Cruz, CA: ETR Associates.

Brindis, C. 1992. Adolescent pregnancy prevention for Hispanic youth: The role of schools, families and communities. *Journal of School Health* 62 (7): 345-51.

Duany, L., and K. Pittman. 1990. *Latino youth at a crossroad: Report of the adolescent pregnancy prevention clearinghouse.* Washington, DC: Children's Defense Fund.

Fullinwider, R. 1993. Multiculturalism: Themes and variations. *Perspectives* 5 (2). (Newsletter published by the Council for Basic Education.)

Hechinger, F. M. 1992. *Fateful choices: Healthy youth for the 21st century.* New York: Carnegie Corporation.

Isaacs, M. 1993. Developing culturally competent strategies for adolescents of color. In *Adolescent health promotion: Proceedings of AMA state of the arts conference,* ed. A. Elster and K. Holt, 35-54. Arlington, VA: National Center for Education in Maternal and Child Health.

Lamarine, R. 1989. The dilemma of Native American health. *Health Education* 20 (5): 15-18.

Newcomer, S., and W. Baldwin. 1992. Demographics of adolescent sexual behavior, contraception, pregnancy and STDs. *Journal of School Health* 62 (7): 265-70.

Ogbu, J. 1987. Cultural influences on plasticity in human development. In *The malleability of children,* ed. J. L. Gallagher and C. T. Ramsey, 155-69. Baltimore: Paul H. Brooks.

Pittman, K., P. Wilson, S. Adams-Taylor and S. Randolph. 1992. Making sexuality education and prevention programs relevant for African-American youth. *Journal of School Health* 62 (7): 339-44.

Rosenthal, B. 1974. Development of self-identification in relation to attitude toward the self in Chippewa Indians. *Genetic Psychology Monographs* 90: 43-141.

Thomas, S. B. 1992. From where I sit. *Family Life Educator* 11 (1): 18-19.

Chapter 19

Gay, Lesbian, Bisexual and Questioning Youth

Warren J. Blumenfeld, MEd

This chapter focuses primarily on the issues of homosexuality as presented in the schools, and on the needs of lesbian, bisexual and gay (hereafter referred to as LesBiGay) students, as well as those who still are in the process of "questioning" their sexual identity. This chapter is based on two primary assumptions: (1) that all students have a right to the best education possible to achieve their *fullest* potential; and (2) that all students have the right to a safe environment in which to learn.

Background

LesBiGay people have gained a greater degree of visibility in many sectors of society. Literature on LesBiGay themes has exploded in recent years. Today there are more "open" elected officials than ever, and, except for some notable exceptions, more and more states and municipalities are passing "gay rights" laws. Greater numbers of people are "coming out" of a closet of denial and fear and into the light of day at younger ages than ever before. And the topic of homosexuality increasingly is being discussed in the schools.

Despite this increased visibility (or possibly because of it) LesBiGay people are among the most stigmatized groups in the United States today. According to the U.S. Department of Justice: "The most frequent victims of hate violence today are Blacks, Hispanics, Southeast Asians, Jews and gays and lesbians. *Homosexuals are probably the most frequent victims*" (Finn and McNeil, 1987). The National Gay and Lesbian Task Force surveyed over 2,000 people and found that 90 percent had experienced some form of victimization on account of their perceived or actual sexual orientation. More than one in ten had been threatened directly with violence.

This victimization was reported to have occurred at home, school and other community sites. Forty-five percent of the males and 25 percent of the females had been harassed or attacked in high school or junior high school because they were perceived as lesbian or gay. Approximately one-third of the 2,000 respondents were assaulted verbally, and more than one in fifteen were physically abused by members of their own family. These figures were substantially higher for young people who were open about their sexual orientation while still living at home.

In 1973, the American Psychiatric Association voted to eliminate homosexuality from its list of disordered mental conditions, referring to it rather as a variation in sexual orientation. Two years later, the American Psychological Association followed suit by resolving that, "Homosexuality *per se* implies no impairment in judgment, liability, or general societal or vocational capabilities," and urged psychologists "to take the lead in removing the stigma of mental illness long associated with homosexual orientations" (American Psychological Association, 1975).

However, some clinicians still hold views contrary to these written policies and many are ill-equipped to counsel LesBiGay clients. In one study, nearly two-thirds of school guidance counselors surveyed expressed negative attitudes and feelings about homosexuality and LesBiGay persons. Though most of these counselors reported knowing at least one LesBiGay student, few felt prepared to work with this population (Sears, 1988).

Prospective teachers likewise seem unprepared to respond supportively. Sears found that 80 percent of the prospective teachers surveyed harbored negative feelings toward LesBiGay students. Those pursuing certification in elementary education were more likely to express homophobic attitudes than those planning to teach in the secondary schools (Sears, 1989). A number of studies found that an overwhelming majority of school administrators would dismiss a teacher for disclosing her or his homosexuality to students and concluded that educators, in general, lack sufficient knowledge and training to address the needs and concerns of students with same-sex feelings (Sears, 1992; Dressler, 1985; Fisher, 1982; Griffin, 1992; Price, 1982; Smith, 1985).

Homophobia and Heterosexism

For purposes of this discussion, *homophobia* is defined as the fear and hatred of those who love and sexually desire those of the same sex. It has its roots in sexism and includes prejudice, discrimination, harassment and acts of violence brought on by this fear and hatred. Homophobia is therefore a form of oppression and not simply an irrational fear, such as a fear of spiders or of heights. Like other forms of oppression, homophobia is pervasive throughout our society.

Heterosexism is the system of advantages bestowed on heterosexuals based on the assumption that all people are or should be heterosexual. Heterosexism therefore discounts the needs, concerns and life experiences of LesBiGay people (Blumenfeld, 1992).

Within a school environment, homophobia and heterosexism compromise the learning environment and hurt everyone, irrespective of sexual orientation.

Adolescents and Sexual Orientation

Adolescence is usually an exciting and difficult stage of enormous change in a person's life. Adolescence is not a particularly easy period for most young people, but for heterosexual adolescents, social and educational structures are in place to support their emerging sexual identity formation. Through the process of socialization, their feelings are validated and mirrored by peers, supportive adult role models and positive portrayals in the media. School and home environments (primary places of socialization) permit them the opportunity to openly explore and rehearse behaviors necessary for the development of interpersonal skills.

The situation is often quite different for young people who experience strong same-sex attractions. The origins of sexual orientation are not completely understood, but it is generally believed to be established during early childhood, usually before the age of five (Bidwell, 1988). Though some young people do come to terms fairly early with their LesBiGay orientation and have little difficulty gaining the support they need, the enormous peer pressure to conform, coupled with the social stigma surrounding homosexuality and the lack of support systems in many quarters, cause many of these young people to turn inward. Seeing and hearing demeaning stereotypes and myths about homosexuals, derogatory epithets from peers and family members, negative and misleading media portrayals, little accurate information presented in the school, or, worse yet, absolutely nothing at all, their initial sense of being somehow different often turns into denial of their feelings or self-hatred. They may become isolated and withdrawn in order to keep their "hidden shame" a secret.

Young people who are perceived as gay, lesbian or bisexual or who are actually "out" are often the target of verbal or physical abuse from peers and even from family members. Poor self-esteem and fear often lead to poor school performance, chronic truancy, and, in many cases, dropping out of school all together. Other students compulsively bury themselves in their schoolwork or other activities. All these responses seriously impede their emotional and intellectual development, placing them at greater risk for general dysfunction (Remafedi, 1985).

Young people experiencing conflict over issues of sexual orientation often turn to substances to reduce the pain and anxiety they feel (Ziebold, 1979). One study found that 58 percent of young gay males interviewed could be classified as having a substance abuse disorder in the Diagnostic and Statistical Manual (Remafedi, 1985).

A homophobic environment affects heterosexual students as well as LesBiGay students. Young people of all sexual identities are often pressured to become heterosexually active to prove to themselves and others that they are "normal." Premature sexual involvement increases the chances of teen pregnancy and the spread of sexually transmitted disease (STD).

In addition, homophobia is responsible for the elimination of factual and open discussions of the lives and sexuality of LesBiGay people as part of school-based health education and sexuality education programs, keeping vital information from all students. Paroski (1987), in a study of LesBiGay adolescents, found that because of the lack of information in the schools, these youth learned primarily about same-sex sexuality through self-initiated exploration and personal contacts, which placed them at greater risk for STD, including HIV infection (Paroski, 1987).

Consequences of Alienation

Students from other minority backgrounds (e.g., African American, Asian, Latino, Jewish) often face instances of discrimination. However, since their families of origin are also members of these groups, these young people usually are supported by their families in their ethnic or religious identifications.

Since most LesBiGay youth are raised by heterosexuals, support for their sexual orientation is not automatic. Some youth are rejected by parents and guardians and become runaways. One study found that half the young gay males interviewed had experienced negative family reactions to their sexual orientation. Twenty-six percent were forced to leave home (Remafedi, 1985). Up to 40 percent of youthful runaways are LesBiGay (Gibson, 1989). Many of these youth turn to prostitution in order to live. Nearly half of all young male prostitutes are gay-identified (Yates, MacKenzie and Pennbridge, 1988). Like other youth living on the streets, LesBiGays have a high rate of substance use, depression and suicide attempts (Gibson, 1989).

These problems are not confined to LesBiGay youth who live on the streets. A report commissioned by the U.S. Department of Health and Human Services on the incidence of youth suicide found that most of the suicide attempts committed by LesBiGays occurred during their youth and that they were two to three times more likely to attempt suicide than their heterosexual counterparts. The report concluded that LesBiGay youth comprise up to 30 percent of the estimated 5,000 completed youth suicides each year (Gibson, 1989).

Other studies found that nearly all LesBiGay suicides occur between the ages of 16 and 21 (Pollak, 1985) and that the earlier young people are aware of same-sex attractions, the greater the problems they face and the more likely they are to develop suicidal feelings and behaviors.

Possible Strategies

Educational institutions can help lead the way to a future in which all students are free to learn to their fullest potential in a safe and supportive environment. Early in 1992, Governor William Weld of Massachusetts created, by executive order, the nation's first Commission on Gay and Lesbian Youth to examine the ways in which the state could respond to the needs of this often neglected population.[1] Educators, administrators, students and parents joined to form an educational committee to draw up a set of guidelines which were presented to the governor for his action. The following are some of the committee's recommendations, which can be used as a guide for other communities.

Policies

Written policies outlining the parameters of acceptable actions and behaviors are the vehicles propelling the educational process. Along with other protected categories, students (and staff) need protection in terms of actual or perceived "sexual orientation" in the areas of admissions and hiring; rights of teachers to discuss information relevant to the LesBiGay experience in the classroom; and rights of everyone in the school setting to be safe from harassment and violence. Clear procedures need to be developed outlining the consequences of any acts of homophobic harassment (as well as other forms of hate-related harassment) in school settings.

These policies should be clearly accessible to staff and students. They can be posted at strategic locations around campus and

---

[1] Advisors to the Education Committee of the Massachusetts Governor's Commission on Gay and Lesbian Youth include Warren J. Blumenfeld, Jessica Byers, Happie Byers, Todd Fry, Janet Fuchs, Kevin Jennings, Arthur Lipkin, Robert Parlin and Reggie Sellers.

published in appropriate school documents, such as student hand-books, hiring applications, and written advertisements for school positions. Other school policies and forms should be written in such a way as to be inclusive of all sexual orientations and family structures.

A number of school districts around the country have insti-tuted protections on the basis of sexual orientation in addition to other protected categories. Local districts in Wisconsin, Massa-chusetts and many other states have statutes outlining anti-harass-ment guidelines, and, in 1988, the National Education Association adopted a resolution calling for equal opportunities within the public education system, regardless of sexual orientation.[2]

Training

One of the first steps in an effective schoolwide homophobia-reduction effort is the training of staff, conducted either by profes-sional outside consultants or by school personnel who have been specially trained in anti-homophobia workshop facilitation.

Workshop components should include both affective (feelings) and cognitive (informational) activities. Participants should be allowed the opportunity to freely express their previously held beliefs and concerns without fear of censure, while creating a supportive environment for gay, lesbian and bisexual staff to be open about their sexual orientation. Programs should also provide factual information concerning LesBiGay life, the ways in which homophobia is related to other forms of oppression, and how

---

[2] Wisconsin Department of Public Instruction, Statute Section 118.13, P. O. Box 7841, Madison, WI. Cambridge Massachusetts Public Schools, Anti-Harassment Guidelines, 159 Thorndike Street, Cambridge, MA 02141. National Education Association, Resolution C-11, adopted by the NEA on July 7, 1988 at NEA convention, New Orleans.

homophobia hurts everyone regardless of sexual orientation. Handouts could include community resource lists and bibliographies for further study (Blumenfeld, 1992).

One or even a short series of workshops alone will not alleviate problems. Follow-up activities (including "all school" assemblies, panel discussions, guest speakers) and additional workshops over a period of months or years will continue the learning process while establishing the school's continuing commitment to the issue.

Services

School systems must identify, develop and advertise appropriate support services for LesBiGay and questioning youth. These services are essential in overcoming the isolation and low self-esteem many of these young people experience, which puts them at greater risk for dropping out of school and for self-destructive behaviors.

Counseling

Openly LesBiGay or "gay-positive" counselors should be hired, and all counselors and social workers currently employed should receive training from professionals in the field in how to deal with the unique needs of students struggling with issues of sexual orientation and identity. The availability of such counseling should be made known to all students by listing the service in student handbooks, discussing it each year during orientation week activities, and posting announcements throughout the school, including in the counseling center.

Referrals to appropriate community resources should be made for students whose needs cannot be met within the school setting. These resources include LesBiGay community youth groups, counseling centers and individual clinicians, as well as social, religious and political organizations. A national network of Parents and Friends of Lesbians and Gay (P-FLAG) chapters are available to support parents and other family members of LesBiGay people.

Groups

Since one of the most effective support systems is one in which students support one another, school staff could encourage students to coordinate on-campus "gay/straight alliances" to address the needs of students who identify as LesBiGay, those still questioning their sexuality and children of LesBiGay parents, as well as supportive heterosexual allies. Administrators can provide appropriate school facilities and urge a faculty member to act as group advisor.

Resources

Young people and their families need to have readily accessible resources both within the school environment and the larger community that provide accurate and up-to-date information and referral support services. Some schools have established "resource rooms" or "drop-in centers," which contain LesBiGay-positive books, videos, pamphlets, music and other materials for students, parents and staff to use at their convenience.

Also included are current guides (including the *Gayellow Pages* published by Renaissance House in New York City) listing community resources, telephone numbers for community LesBiGay hotlines, bookstores located in many cities throughout the country and local LesBiGay newspapers. A supportive staff member can be available at specified "office hours" to students who need additional information or simply someone with whom they can talk.[3]

---

[3]For more information contact the prototype "Project 10," Virginia Uribe, PhD, 7850 Melrose Avenue, Los Angeles, CA 90046.

Curriculum

Students spend most of their school day in the classroom. In an ideal world students would receive accurate, honest, up-to-date and age-appropriate information about LesBiGay people. This information would be integrated into the traditional curriculum and presented nonjudgmentally in many subject areas at every age level.

For young people who are or someday will be LesBiGay, such information could affirm that they are not alone or bad, and that others like themselves live happy and productive lives. For heterosexual youth, this information can provide the basis for appreciation of human diversity and help to counter homophobia.

Since students form impressions about LesBiGay people quite early in their lives, they should be given the opportunity to learn about these issues in an age- and developmentally appropriate way from the beginning of their schooling—from elementary through secondary school and into their college years.

At the elementary and middle school level, curriculum content should do the following:

- Acknowledge and support self-identified lesbian/gay families within the community.
- Counteract gender and sexuality-based stereotypes by providing opportunities for play, dress and behaviors that are authentic to the individual rather than conforming to gender role stereotypes.
- Identify and discuss stereotypes when they occur in student behavior, literature and other contexts.
- Present LesBiGay culture in contexts other than sexuality, for example, literature, the arts and family life.
- Make statements that reflect real-life situations and demonstrate the diversity of relationships, family structure and other contexts in which students will find themselves.

- Identify vocabulary and developmentally appropriate discussions when addressing issues of sexual orientation with younger children.
- Support appropriate expressions of same-sex and other-sex relationships.

At the secondary level, information would be integrated into every academic discipline including English, social studies, foreign languages, science, visual and performing arts, and vocational education.

In addition, school-based libraries would enlarge their holdings of LesBiGay-specific materials in the areas of health/sexuality; literature and poetry; nonfiction materials dealing with current events, history, sociology, philosophy, anthropology, education, religion, physical and natural sciences and psychology; and also include periodicals and newspapers. Multimedia centers could purchase posters, films, videos, compact discs and audio tapes on LesBiGay themes.

Realistically, incorporating this material into the sexuality and family life classroom is a good first step. Content could include discussions centered on the biological and psychological theories of causation of sexual orientation; opposing philosophical and religious viewpoints of sexuality in general, and homosexuality in particular; the concepts of "homophobia," "heterosexism," "heterosexual privilege," the "coming out" process, and the distinction between "gender identity" and "sexual orientation"; and the history of the LesBiGay social movement with discussion of some famous historical LesBiGay figures. Throughout these discussions, the educator should use inclusive, affirming, and/or gender-neutral language when referring to sexuality and human relationships. (An example of inclusive language: "During puberty a person begins to develop strong sexual and emotional attractions to people of the other sex and/or people of the same sex.")

Roadblocks and Responses

Teaching, especially teaching which has social change as one of its goals, provokes many questions from many different constituencies. Any time we begin to raise questions about deeply rooted assumptions, we are liable to encounter resistance and even hostility. While it is hoped that people will address LesBiGay topics in a totally supportive environment, to assume this would be naive and would underestimate the pervasiveness of homophobia. Resistance may come from a variety of quarters.[4]

Teachers

Many teachers are truly concerned about the needs of LesBiGay students and colleagues, but due to their lack of experience on the topic may not know how to respond. One strategy in beginning the process is to examine one's own assumptions and feelings about the issue of homophobia and homosexuality. Following are some questions teachers might ask themselves:

- How comfortable am I in talking about sexual matters?
- Do I have any lesbian, gay or bisexual friends?
- How do I respond to "fag" jokes?
- What was I taught about homosexuality?
- What would I do if I knew that one of my students was gay, lesbian or bisexual?

---

[4]I would like to thank Diane Raymond (my coauthor of *Looking at Gay and Lesbian Life* [Boston: Beacon Press, 1988, 1993]) for her assistance in developing the ideas for this section.

• How would I feel if I found out that one of my parents was gay? my child? my best friend?

No one is entirely free from the effects of homophobia; it is pervasive in our social fabric. Therefore, it is important to assess one's limitations realistically. It is rare, despite a relatively permissive attitude toward sex today, to find open, direct, nonjudgmental discussion of sexuality, homosexuality in particular. For information on the issues, educators can read some of the many books and periodicals accurately representing the LesBiGay experience and can attend cultural and other community events.

Even those educators who are comfortable with these topics will want to create support networks from the ranks of sympathetic colleagues and people in the community. In some states, community support groups have formed for LesBiGay educators and their allies. Within the school, an option to consider for the presentation of these topics is a team-teaching approach, which may help to alleviate possible feelings of isolation. It is often a good idea to invite guests from a local college or community-based LesBiGay speakers bureau, or graduates from the school, to address students as a way of personalizing the issue.

Administrators, School Boards and Other Staff

Some administrators, school board members and other staff have been true leaders in addressing issues of homophobia and homosexuality. Others, however, may not share this enthusiasm and may even be hostile to such efforts. They may automatically reject any proposed program or may need to be convinced of its merits. Many fail to appreciate the educational value of these topics; others simply fear the disapproval of the community or of monitoring bodies. Some do not see homophobia as a form of prejudice or are unaware of its existence. The following strategies can be useful in building support for programs:

- Invite speakers from local LesBiGay groups, members of Parents and Friends of Lesbians and Gays (P-FLAG), and teachers who have had success in addressing these issues in other communities to address faculty, administrators and school boards.
- Develop alliances with other staff members and prominent representatives from the community, including parents.
- Have available, whenever possible, evidence of the success of these programs in other schools around the country.
- Relate homophobia to other forms of oppression such as racism, classism, anti-Semitism and sexism.
- Make the administration and other staff aware of the possible legal repercussions of harassment of students who are perceived to be LesBiGay; provide statistical and anecdotal information related to harassment, violence, homelessness and increased risk for LesBiGay youth school dropout and suicide; and point out the probability of generally improved personal relations among students once these issues are addressed.
- Encourage the administration and other staff members to view a decision to tackle these issues as an indication of personal courage and compassion.
- Make clear that the learning derived from an inclusive curriculum can translate into benefits in other academic areas.

Students

Students—many of whom may be dealing with their own feelings about sex, love and identity—are likely to respond "energetically" to these issues. Many people tend to use the topic of homosexuality as a vehicle to ask all kinds of questions about sex, probably because there are few avenues available to them to explore this general issue safely.

There are always some students who express very strong homophobic feelings. Some of this springs from youthful energy as well as a bravado intended to impress or gain the support of peers. Other students probably feel the same way, but have been socialized to suppress outward expressions of prejudiced beliefs. In both cases, it is important for students to be able to vent a full range of emotions within acceptable parameters. Only by airing their gut reactions can they move on to a level of discussion that allows for change. It is also important to note that the absence of negative expressions and reactions does not necessarily indicate the absence of negative feelings.

Students might manifest their attitudes in a number of ways—defensiveness, yelling, name calling, obstructiveness, arguing and withdrawal. Such hostility can be a symptom of a host of deep emotions such as anger, fear—often a result of ignorance—or hurt. These issues may strike too close to home and elicit powerful emotional responses. Sometimes more sympathetic students will intervene, and a lively dialogue will then ensue. Sometimes the best thing an educator can do is just to listen.

Before beginning any discussion of homosexuality, however, the educator should set clearly defined limits or guidelines for discussion. These could include the following:

- All questions and opinions are appropriate to share.
- People need to respect all ideas, with no attacks or blame.
- Speak from personal knowledge; avoid generalizations; and do not attempt to speak for others. Use I-statements.
- Share air time. Take turns speaking; listen respectfully with no interruptions.
- Respect people's right not to participate in the discussion.

- Be open to change some of your assumptions or opinions on the topic.
- Anonymity must be respected. People can share information about this discussion with others outside the class only if class members' names are not used.

Parents and Other Members of the Community

Some parents and community members may genuinely support discussions related to homophobia and general issues of sexuality. However, a number of groups composed of parents, clergy and others have organized nationwide to obstruct these discussions on campus. Such organization has revolved around attempts to remove books and curricula from classrooms and school libraries, to restrict information and discussions about gay- or lesbian-headed households, and efforts to limit or eliminate sexuality education other than that focusing solely on (heterosexual) abstinence before marriage. There are, however, some strategies to help counter this resistance:

- School administrations can inform parents and other community residents about anti-homophobia programs sponsored by the school and provide clear explanations of and rationales for the need for such programs.
- If discussion about sensitive issues is planned for the classroom, some districts inform parents ahead of time by sending a letter home with students and then schedule meetings with parents to inform and educate them about the materials to be used.
- Some districts choose to get written permission from each student's parent(s) or guardian(s) before discussing the issue. In such cases, it might be productive to discuss with the students the reasons for this stipulation—that this issue, though very important to class discussion, is often controversial and

that, therefore, it is in everyone's best interests to lay the foundation for an open exchange of ideas before the actual discussions take place. Other districts send home a letter that outlines the entire course and puts the responsibility on parents or guardians to respond if they object. Districts that choose to teach such material without notifying parents or guardians beforehand should expect to handle phone calls or school visits.

• When talking with parents and guardians, do not act defensively. Instead, point out the benefits of discussions about LesBiGay issues. Also, assure parents that by teaching the topic, the school is not attempting to change or place judgment upon students' moral or ethical beliefs. Rather, a discussion of homophobia and homosexuality is presented to examine human diversity, and knowledge of this will help students function more productively in a changing world.

• Invite speakers from local LesBiGay groups, members of Parents and Friends of Lesbians and Gays (P-FLAG), and teachers who have had success with addressing the issues in other communities to address parent/teacher organizations.

When working with parents, educators must make it clear that they are available to discuss concerns. Some parents and guardians only need to air their concerns before allowing their children to participate.

Conclusion

Over a period of five days at four different sites, people from many walks of life (high school students, parents, educators and others) testified at public hearings sponsored by the Massachusetts Governor's Commission on Gay and Lesbian Youth. Before the television cameras and mainstream media, moderators read one mother's moving accounts of her daughter's suicide. Courageous young people told their stories of loneliness and despair, of substance use, of suicide attempts, of being driven from their homes by parents who either would not or could not understand, and of how they subconsciously put themselves at needless risk for HIV infection as a way of ending their unbearable pain and isolation.

This was the first occasion for some of these young people to publicly identify as lesbian, gay or bisexual. They spoke not only for themselves, but also for the countless others who have not yet found their voice; and they spoke for all those who left this world all too soon. Throughout the testimony, the assembled gathering was often moved to tears. One recurrent theme emerged in the course of these hearings: In general, educational institutions have yet to begin the journey of truly fulfilling their mandate to educate and to support students.

In her testimony presented at Boston's Massachusetts State House in November 1992, Adelaide Goetz, a 16-year-old high school junior, summed up this reality:

> [School] is a place I do not feel comfortable being gay, which means I cannot feel comfortable being myself.... School is a place I no longer want to be, mostly because of a lack of education about issues such as acceptance of diversity, but more so, homophobia. I have spent the last two years ignoring homophobic comments. I am positive a great majority of the students know I'm gay, but will the comments and jokes end?... I don't know, and that really scares me.

References

American Psychological Association. 1975. Minutes of the Council of Representatives. *American Psychologist* 30:633.

Bidwell, R. J. 1988. The gay and lesbian teen: A case of denied adolescence. *Journal of Pediatric Health Care* 2 (1): 3-8.

Blumenfeld, W. J. 1992. Conducting antiheterosexism workshops: A sample. In *Homophobia: How We All Pay the Price*, ed. W. J. Blumenfeld. Boston: Beacon Press.

Dressler, J. 1985. Survey of school principals regarding alleged homosexual teachers in the classroom: How likely (really) is a discharge? *University of Dayton Law Review* 10 (3): 599-620.

Finn, P., and T. McNeil. 1987. *The response of the criminal justice system to bias crime: An exploratory review.* Washington, DC: U.S. Department of Justice.

Fisher, T. 1982. A study of educators' attitudes toward homosexuality. Doctoral dissertation. University of Virginia, Charlottesville. (*Dissertation Abstracts International* 43, 10, 3294A).

Gibson, P. 1989. Gay male and lesbian youth suicide. *Report of the Secretary's Task Force on Youth Suicide.* Washington, DC: U.S. Department of Health and Human Services.

Griffin, P. 1992. From hiding out to coming out: Empowering lesbian and gay educators. *Journal of Homosexuality* 22 (3/4): 167-196.

National Gay and Lesbian Task Force. 1984. *National Anti-Gay/Lesbian Victimization Report.* New York.

Paroski, R. 1987. Health care delivery and the concerns of gay and lesbian adolescents. *Journal of Adolescent Health Care* 8 (2): 188-192.

Pollak, M. 1985. Male homosexuality. In *Western Sexuality*, ed. P. Aries and A. Bejin, 40-61. New York: Blackwell.

Price, J. 1982. High school students' attitudes toward homosexuality. *Journal of School Health* 52 (8): 469-474.

Remafedi, G. 1985. *Male homosexuality: The adolescent's perspective.* Adolescent Health Program, University of Minneapolis, Minnesota.

Sears, J. 1988. Attitudes, experiences, and feelings of guidance counselors about working with homosexual students. Paper presented at the American Educational Research Association, New Orleans. (ERIC Document No. 296210.)

Sears, J. 1989. Personal feelings and professional attitudes of prospective teachers toward homosexuality and homosexual students: Research findings and curriculum recommendations. Paper presented at the American Educational Research Association, San Francisco. (ERIC Document No. 312222.)

Sears, J. 1992. Educators, homosexuality and homosexual students: Are personal feelings related to professional beliefs? In *Coming out of the classroom closet: Gay and lesbian students, teachers and curricula,* ed. K. Harbeck, 39. New York: Haworth Press.

Smith, D. 1985. An ethnographic interview study of homosexual teachers' perspectives. Doctoral dissertation. State University of New York, Albany. (*Dissertation Abstracts International* 46, 1, 66A.)

Yates, G. L., R. MacKenzie and J. Pennbridge. 1988. A risk profile comparison of runaway and non-runaway youth. *American Journal of Public Health* 78 (7): 820-821.

Ziebold, T. 1979. Alcoholism and recovery: Gays helping gays. *Christopher Street* (January): 36-44.

Chapter 20

Special Education Students: Issues and Needs

Lynne Muccigrosso

S exuality education is critical to special education learners. Poor self-esteem, reduced skill in coping with stress, and lower reading levels limit special education students' access to accurate information and make them prey to myths and unreasonable fears. Their most available models for sexual behavior tend to come from television commercials and films (Kempton and Stiggall, 1989). This population is more vulnerable to sexual abuse than nondisabled individuals (Baladerian, 1991; Muccigrosso, 1991). Many special education students are raised in fairly sheltered or protected environments; families may be more resistant to allowing their special education son or daughter the ordinary community interactions most other young people have. This can result in the development of fewer community social skills.

Despite the critical need, the very thought of sexuality education for special education learners "renders many people inoperable," according to the late Warren Johnson (Johnson and Kempton,

1981). Accepting this idea is just as difficult for some people as accepting and coping with diversity in skin color or gender or sexual orientation. People with disabilities are another group who are not seen as whole, real people. And yet, whether we like it or not, people with disabilities are forcing us to acknowledge and accept the fact that *all* people are sexual and have a right to education about this part of their humanness.

Once stereotypical attitudes about persons with disabilities having a basically different—or nonexistent—sexuality than others are overcome, developing a sexuality education program for special education students is quite similar to developing such a program for other students.

Who Are Special Education Students?

In schools for students ages five to twenty-one, students with disabilities who need and qualify for individualized educational programming (IEP) as defined in Public Law 94-142 are in special education. These students come with a wide range of special conditions and needs, including vision or hearing impairment, mental retardation (mild to severe or profound), learning disability, orthopedic (mobility) impairments, emotional disturbance, autism and other developmental disabilities. Their learning styles vary and certain students may require special adaptations in teaching methods and materials.

Some special education students attend classes on segregated, self-contained campuses where all the students have similar disabilities and somewhat similar learning difficulties and needs. These students usually have more noticeable disabilities—ones that are obvious to any observer. The more severe the disability, the more likely a student will receive his or her education in settings like these. These programs are often run by the county office of education.

Special education students can also be integrated into mainstream campuses designed for students who don't have disabilities. (This is called called "inclusion.") These campuses may have only a sprinkling of special education students. Programs are usually run by the district and may serve special education students with disabilities that aren't immediately obvious to the casual observer. The current trend in special education is for total inclusion.

Education also continues beyond high school for students with disabilities. Community colleges, adult education programs and rehabilitation workshop programs often offer continuing education covering a range of subjects, including sexuality education.

Program Design

The particular school or agency placement dictates how sexuality education programs are designed. The segregated, self-contained site offers students classes with similarly disabled students (nonmainstreamed) and education from one or two special education teachers who usually know the student well. This setting allows a lengthy period of time to teach the topic; teachers generally are not restricted to only·one 50-minute period for instruction. There is time for reinforcement and maintenance of the lessons and for taking advantage of teachable moments.

The student who is mainstreamed into a regular sexuality education class is usually taught by a teacher who is not well known to the student, who will only see this student for one 50-minute period for x number of days or weeks, and who is not specifically skilled in instructing special education students. This is often the case when the special education student is mainstreamed into regular physical education or home economics classes, where sexuality education is frequently taught.

It is easier to teach sexuality education in the segregated setting, where the teacher knows the students and their learning styles and who has an established relationship with them. The homogeneity in learning styles makes the selection of teaching techniques and materials more manageable. However, it is advantageous from a social integration point of view for the special education student to mix and associate with nondisabled students as much as possible. Success at the mainstream site depends upon several factors:

- The particular type of sexuality education class being taught. Is it one where paper/pencil teaching assignments are emphasized, or is it primarily a discussion, small group work, visual aids or roleplay kind of class?
- The support the student has. Is an instructional aide from the Special Education Department able to attend the class with the student, to assist in interpreting complex material and in the follow-up communication with the special education teacher?
- Length of the course. It will probably take more time for the special education student to assimilate the material. The usual class period of 50 minutes may be too long for such students' attention span. Shorter instructional periods spread over a longer time period are optimum.

On a mainstream campus, it taxes even the most creative of teachers to come up with lessons that will meet the needs of the variety of students found in classes with special education students. It means finding more than one way to teach the same content and trying to speak to each student's learning level without singling out any one student. When the student's disability requires special communication assistance (e.g., interpreters, word boards, instructional aides), someone at school needs to work this out. This person is likely to be the homeroom special education teacher, or an ancillary staff person, like the school psychologist.

Needs of the Special Education Student

Regardless of where sexuality education instruction is given, special education students have needs that are similar to other students. Special education students need:

- good teachers, who are trained to offer sexuality education instruction objectively, with knowledge and skill
- positive social opportunities, where they can practice skills in communication, decision making, refusal and other personal and social skills
- acceptance in the whole social and political structure of the school or agency
- a program that concentrates on the critical elements of effective sexuality education (knowledge, social skills, influences, perceived personal risk), and that offers opportunities for reinforcement and maintenance of learned skills
- positive role models, who show disabled people as fully functioning, sexual adults just like other people
- social interactions, such as dances and parties, where special education students are honestly welcomed

There are also some differences in the needs of the special education student. In general it is likely that a longer teaching time will be required to cover the material with any effectiveness. Depending on the school setting (segregated or mainstream), students in special education can usually attend school until age 21. This means that the classes can be repeated each year, to maximize the likelihood of learning. While regular education students are often offered sexuality education in two- or three-week time blocks (inside a biology, P.E. or home economics class), special education students at a segregated site have the advantage of a lengthier time span for their lessons. The education can take place over a whole year and can be more comprehensive in topics covered.

Getting students to talk about sexuality is a challenge for any teacher. With special education students, it is particularly effective to use the teaching strategy of "drawing out" known information from the students. Ask open-ended questions—"Tell me how you can tell this person is a man or a woman" rather than saying "This is a man," or "This is a woman." Or, "Tell me what you see in this picture" rather than "In this picture, we are looking at...." This technique invites response from the student, and is a way to find out where the students are at any given time. "Drawing out" elicits information from the students and gives the teacher a valuable check-in on students' knowledge-base, which helps determine the need for more or less instruction. This technique also builds self-esteem in the students, because it involves the learner as a very important partner in the instruction.

Teaching materials will need to be more graphic and explicit to ensure student comprehension. Expectations regarding what is to be taught may also differ, depending on the level of disability and age of the students. There will be more discussion of this in the section on student assessment.

Family Involvement

In general, family involvement is more intense with the special education student. There are many reasons for this, but suffice it to say that these parents often have had to fight tooth and nail to have their son or daughter accepted in the school. Thus, they are very interested in what is being taught; they're likely to want to be more involved than parents of the nonspecial education students. Many teachers fear that parents will be opposed to a sexuality education program, but when the need for this education is presented thoughtfully, families welcome it with open arms. Parents are fearful of sexual exploitation of their special education child and may be self-conscious about the child's inappropriate social behaviors. These become topics to cover in a sexuality education class, and there is usually great support for it.

However, parents who are very protective of their special education sons and daughters may be suspicious or fear that such education will negatively influence their children with information that they would not otherwise receive. This is no different in special education than in regular education. Parents need to be reassured that the program will not interfere with their family values. This reassurance can be offered in the early description of the program and through using parent/child homework assignments.

When parents are invited to join in the planning of a sexuality education program, it is likely that more of them will respond than is usual in nonspecial education. Involved parents are more likely to be advocates for the program than parents whose sole involvement consists of receiving a notice about the course and a request for permission. Students will learn better if the lessons taught in school are supported in the home.

Why Sexuality Education?

Teachers need to be clear about why the sexuality education program is important and what its objectives are. This is true across all programs. For the special education student, motivators for developing and offering the program are much the same as they are for other students. The order of importance for certain topics may differ. For example, because special education students may be more vulnerable to sexual abuse, sexual abuse prevention is probably high on the family's list of priorities, with HIV/AIDS prevention a close second. Other than this, and the inclusion of an objective to increase appropriate public social behaviors (or decrease inappropriate behaviors), the goals of a good comprehensive sexuality education program for special education students are the same and include enhanced self-esteem; improved social skills, including communication/refusal skills; abstinence from early sexual involvement; and reduction of pregnancy, STD and HIV risk.

Parents may need assistance in understanding that sexuality education is not designed to put sexual ideas into their children's heads. Anyone watching or listening to TV is receiving many sexual messages. Part of a good sexuality education program is to help students sort out all the influences on their choices (including the media) and make good decisions about what's right for them.

The IEP Process

The IEP (individualized educational program) is a planning tool required for special education students in the United States. It is a process by which the teacher, the parent or guardian and the student sit together to bring up any issues that need to be dealt with educationally during the school year. This is a perfect backdrop for developing and initiating a sexuality education program. As appropriate, objectives can be written that are best met in a sexuality education class. The IEP process can serve as a sanction for the sexuality education program, documenting even stronger support than a positive parent permission slip (the common procedure in regular sexuality education).

Teacher Preparation

Preparation of teachers for special sexuality education classroom teaching is virtually the same as that of teachers of regular sexuality education students. Attributes important for teachers of sexuality education include a high degree of empathy and sensitivity, the ability to establish rapport with students and communicate effectively with young people, the understanding and restraint not to impose personal viewpoints and values on students, flexibility, a sense of humor, and a lack of embarrassment in discussing matters of sexuality (Dickman, 1982).

In addition, the special sexuality education teacher needs to have a strong commitment to the task. According to Winifred Kempton (1988):

To teach students with special needs takes patience, understanding, dedication and love; until sex education for them is accepted by more people, it will take an additional amount of emotional energy to teach this subject, for it requires courage, conviction and determination.

Training and staff development opportunities for learning how to teach this sensitive topic are very important. Training courses are not always easy to find and it is unlikely that teachers will have received training in special sexuality education in a teaching certificate program, as very few colleges and universities offer such training. The local family planning agency or rehabilitation agency may be able to offer suggestions. For teachers unable to find an appropriate training course, reading and engaging in the exercises offered in Winifred Kempton's two books, *A Teacher's Guide: Sex Education for Persons with Disabilities that Hinder Learning* and *Socialization and Sexuality: A Comprehensive Training Guide for Professionals Helping People with Disabilities that Hinder Learning* is highly recommended. (See References.)

Student Assessment

There is such a wide range in student understanding and comprehension that it is not possible to predict the level of knowledge by merely observing student behavior, or even by reading the volumes of student records usually available. The streetwise student who swaggers around, "knowing it all," and the innocent-looking younger student may have very similar learning deficits in this topic area. Assessment is critical. While it might be advantageous to have one-on-one interviews with each student prior to the sexuality education class, it usually is not practical from a time perspective.

Simple pretests can assist in assessment, but tests cause some students to freeze up, resulting in false readings of acquired knowledge. Attempting to administer pretests or use assessment tools to measure knowledge about human sexuality prior to the course, before trust and ease between teacher and students has been established, is not advised. Some assessment tools ask questions that seem very intrusive. It is important to only use assessment information that is appropriate and relevant to the development of a good sexuality education class (Leyin and Dicks, 1987). A Pre-Instruction Planning Assessment checklist is shown in Figure 1.

During precourse preparation, the teacher should find out as much as possible from other teachers, from families and from records. The first few class sessions can be used to draw out what the students know; this is an effective way to assess. During this ongoing assessment phase, it may be necessary to ask the same question in several different ways, as phrasing alone can be the trigger necessary to help students share what they know. The teacher must pay attention and check learning in all possible ways as she or he proceeds in teaching the course content. Students can recite back what they heard said, or can demonstrate (as in roleplay, dramatization, pantomime). All approaches necessary can be used, based on communication styles. This can include writing assignments for some students. Teachers must be flexible and try new approaches when it's clear that many students aren't moving along

Figure 1
Pre-Instruction Planning Assessment

Name _____ Age _____ Gender _____

Living with family or in group home? _____

Any special community needs? Describe. _____

_____

_____

Previous sex education? when? topics covered? _____

_____

_____

Describe the disability. _____

Family's expressed needs regarding sexuality education. _____

_____

_____

Student's behavior or expressed need regarding sexuality education. ___

_____

Former school/program. _____

Rate vulnerability to sexual abuse: high   medium   low

Describe. _____

_____

Known history of sexual abuse. _____

_____

Reading skills. Please describe. _____

_____

Figure 1 (continued)
Pre-Instruction Planning Assessment

Name _____ Age _____ Gender _____

Peer interaction.   good   OK   not good

Describe. _____

Attention span: about how long? _____

Instructional setting.   mainstream   self-contained

How many students will be in class? _____

Will instructional aide attend with student? _____

Is this instruction written in IEP? Describe. _____

_____

_____

Estimated number of sessions possible. _____

Topics planned to be covered. _____

_____

_____

General comments to assist in planning. _____

_____

_____

_____

_____

_____

_____

_____

at the expected pace. Rushed teaching makes for poor listening, and good teacher listening skills are critical for checking student learning.

Course Content

Student assessment can assist in selecting course content. While the teacher must be prepared with a general outline, allowing students to brainstorm all the topics they would like to know more about in the context of sexuality education works well and is empowering for students, enhancing their self-esteem. Content will also be influenced by the amount of time allowed to do the program. Diane Maksym (1990) defines sexuality education as having three components:
1. developing self-esteem
2. teaching social skills
3. giving information about our bodies and sexual feelings

While keeping in mind that families may be most motivated by the goal of self-protection, it must be clear that the goal of a good sexuality education program is a positive, broad one—that all students reach their highest potential and make good decisions about the expression of their sexuality by knowing as much as they can about the social, emotional and physical aspects of human sexuality.

A sample course outline might include the following topics:
- self-esteem
- identifying feelings
- gender identification
- decision making
- personal safety
- families

- communication skills
- friendships and social relationships
- appropriate private/public behaviors
- growth and development
- anatomy
- dating
- male and female roles
- laws about sexual activity
- reproduction/childbirth
- sexually transmitted disease
- HIV/AIDS
- male and female health care
- community resources
- date rape
- sexual abuse prevention

The teacher may logically start with a core set of expectations and previously published or developed lesson plans in hand. Whether the teacher will adhere to these plans or alter them depends upon student response. Teachers who prefer to use formal, written pretests to assess knowledge are advised to pretest for knowledge before each new topic, rather than pretesting for the entire course before beginning.

Teaching Materials and Methods

Established, published curriculum guides often rely on reading and writing skills for student assignments. The special education student is likely to learn more effectively with concrete learning strategies, roleplays, group discussion and visual aids. It's important to search for and discover materials which appropriately model people with disabilities. This may be a challenge, but the people depicted in the teaching materials should not all be body-perfect, nondisabled models; this limits effectiveness of instruction and inhibits student motivation. Many published materials for use in special education sexuality education *do* reflect diversity and show illustrations of people with disabilities. If a teacher is using non-special education materials (and adapting them to this learner group), such illustrations aren't as likely. Teachers may need to search through magazines and ads to find pictures that reflect this diversity. This is increasingly possible today, with the media's improved awareness of the need to have models of all sorts to appeal to all consumers.

We need to offer sexuality instruction in the modality of learning that works for each particular student. For example, if the student is visually impaired or severely retarded, instruction may need to be conducted by using explicit, tactile aids. This undoubtedly can lead to some teacher discomfort; these more graphic materials are not customarily used in a regular sexuality education course. (See the Resources at the end of this chapter for a list of teaching materials.)

Tips and Strategies

- Be sure to establish groundrules at the beginning of the class that make it clear that no put-downs will be allowed. Try to make it safe for all students to speak in the class; the special learners may need some extra drawing out and support to participate. Minimize their differences as much as possible.
- Use visual aids: overhead projectors, slides, videos, posters, collages, diagrams, film strips, models, dolls. Be sure these aids are age-appropriate, not infantilizing.
- Draw out what the students know (or think they know). This is important for correcting myths and misinformation. Draw out; don't pump in.

- Roleplay or dramatic play reinforces learning, and is fun. Students may need some help to get started with this—the teacher may have to model the procedure—but it is very effective for learning and for checking learning.
- Make the education practical. Decide on the critical pieces of information and translate them into relevant examples from the student's lives.
- Maximize the use of group discussions and cooperative learning groups. More limited readers can be paired with skilled readers.
- Be as concrete as possible. Demonstrate. Illustrate. Check learning to see if you need to find another way to teach. Use a variety of materials to teach the same concepts.
- Repeat and repeat, with dignity. Check learning by asking for feedback: "I'm not sure I described that clearly; could you tell me what you heard me say?"
- Be flexible and remember to take advantage of teachable moments.
- Reduce the number of paper/pencil assignments, if possible. At least offer alternative ways to complete assignments.

Remember that many special educators believe that students in special education are at higher than average risk for sexual abuse, teen pregnancy, HIV/AIDS and sexually transmitted disease. With this in mind, family life education for students with special needs should have the following goals (Kempton, 1988; Kempton and Stiggall, 1989):
- to protect students (from exploitation, sexual abuse, HIV/ AIDS, other sexually transmitted disease and drug use)
- to improve students' self-esteem and help students recognize that they are special and important
- to help students become more independent

- to help students make friends. A life goal for all people is to experience satisfying human relationships through friendships and family. This program should offer the special assistance necessary for these students to learn how to relate to others in a loving, respectful and appropriate manner

Resources

Curriculum Programs

Being with People, a social skills training program featuring videomodeling by the New Eticats, James Stanfield Publishing, P.O. Box 41058, Santa Barbara, CA 93140; 800-421-6534. A funny, very effective teaching aid for friendship and dating skills.

Changes in You, curriculum and booklets about puberty for girls and boys, P. Siegel, Family Life Education Associates, P.O. Box 7466, Richmond, VA 23221. Beautifully illustrated, simply worded explanations of the changes.

Circles I: Intimacy and Relationships; Circles II: Stop Abuse; Circles III: Safer Ways (communicable disease, including HIV/AIDS), L. Walker-Hirsch and M. Champagne, James Stanfield Publishing, P.O. Box 41058, Santa Barbara, CA 93140; 800-421-6534. Video or slide format.

Education for Adulthood, Elizabeth Pouch Center for Special People, 657 Castleton Ave., New York, NY 10301.

Entering Adolescence, ETR Associates, P.O. Box 1830, Santa Cruz, CA 95061-1830; 800-321-4407. Series of curriculum books, focussing on variety of family life topics for the middle school student.

Into Adulthood, ETR Associates, P.O. Box 1830, Santa Cruz, CA 95061-1830; 800-321-4407. Series of curriculum books, focussing on variety of family life topics for the older student.

Family Education Program Manual: A Curriculum and Training Manual for Teaching Sexuality, Self-Esteem and Abuse Prevention to Students with Developmental and Learning Disabilities, ed. K. Simpson, The Family Stress Center, 2086 Commerce Ave., Concord, CA 94520; 415-827-0212.

Family Life Education: Curriculum Guide (rev. ed.), ed. S. Bignell, ETR Associates, P.O. Box 1830, Santa Cruz, CA 95061-1830; 800-321-4407.

Family Life Education: Resources for the Elementary Classroom, L. DeSpelder and A. Strickland, ETR Associates, P.O. Box 1830, Santa Cruz, CA 95061-1830; 800-321-4407.

Family Life Education: Special Education, Virginia Department of Education, P.O. Box 6-Q, Richmond, VA 23216-2060. Breakdown of goals and objectives for all age groups of special education, divided by mildly to more severely handicapped students. Not matched with teaching activities or lesson plans.

Family Life/Health Education: A Special Education Curriculum for the Developmentally Delayed, L.A. County Office of Education, Rm. 104A, ECE, 9300 E. Imperial Highway, Downey, CA 90242, Attn: Ray Guillame; 213-923-2413.

5/6, 7/8, 9/10 FLASH: Family Life and Sexual Health. Seattle King County Department of Public Health, 110 Prefontaine Ave. S, #300, Seattle, WA 98104.

Human Sexuality: Values and Choices, The Search Institute, 122 W. Franklin, Suite 525, Minneapolis, MN 55404. Not for the special learner, but a good junior high program paired with video tapes—adaptable for many special groups.

Life Horizons I and II, W. Kempton, James Stanfield Publishing, P.O. Box 41058, Santa Barbara, CA 93140; 800-421-6534. Twelve parts with 1,000 slides to counsel and teach socialization and sexuality to students who are developmentally and learned disabled.

Life Facts: Sexuality; Abuse Prevention; and *AIDS,* James Stanfield Publishing, P.O. Box 41058, Santa Barbara, CA 93140; 800-421-6534. Curriculum and large black and white drawings, laminated.

Life Planning Education: A Youth Development Program, Center for Population Options, 1025 Vermont Ave. NW, Suite 210, Washington, DC 20005.

Living Your Life: A Sex Education and Personal Development Programme for Students with Severe Learning Difficulties, A. Craft, available from Living and Learning, 2195 Turnage St., Salem, OR 97304, 800-521-3218.

Positive Images, P. Brick and C. Cooperman, Planned Parenthood of Bergen County, New Jersey, available from ETR Associates, P.O. Box 1830 Santa Cruz, CA 95061-1830; 800-321-4407.

Socialization and Sex Education: The Life Horizons Curriculum Module, G. Rodriguez Rouse and C. Birch, James Stanfield Publishing, P.O. Box 41058, Santa Barbara, CA 93140; 800-421-6534.

Special Education: Secondary FLASH (Family Life and Sexual Health for grades 7-12). J. Stangle, Seattle-King Co. Department of Public Health Family Planning Publications, 110 Prefontaine Ave. S, Suite 300, Seattle, WA 98104.

SAFE, Stopping AIDS Through Functional Education, J. Hylton, CDRC Publications, CDR/OHSU, P.O. Box 574, Portland, OR 97207-0574. Includes lessons, video segments and more.

Sexual Abuse and Self Protection, Seattle Rape Relief Developmental Disabilities Project, 1825 S. Jackson, Suite 102, Seattle, WA 98144; 206-325-5531. Good curriculum with film and audiotape. Individual parts available.

Sexuality Education for Persons with Severe Developmental Disabilities, B. Brekke, James Stanfield Publishing, P.O. Box 41058, Santa Barbara, CA 93140; 800-421-6534. Slides and curriculum guide; very simple.

Take Charge of Your Life, The Salvation Army Booth Memorial Center, Available from ETR Associates, P.O. Box 1830, Santa Cruz, CA 95061-1830; 800-321-4407. A workbook for teens or young adults.

Visual Aids

Breast Self Exam (video), Kaiser Permanente, 1742 Franklin St., Oakland, CA 94612.

Jackson Pelvic Models, 33 Richards Ave., Cambridge, MA 02140; 617-864-9036.

Life-Sized Instructional Charts, Planned Parenthood of Minnesota, 1965 Ford Parkway, St. Paul, MN 55116.

Portfolio: Human Sexuality for the Mentally Retarded, Planned Parenthood of Seattle-King Co., 2211 E. Madison, Seattle, WA 98112. Large illustrations of 11 x 17 plate cards. The back of each card has suggestions for the educator.

Teach-a-Bodies, June Harnest, 3509 Acorn Run, Ft. Worth, TX 76109; 817-923-2380. Instructional dolls, whole families.

Victoria House Dolls, Victoria House, P.O. Box 663, Forestville, CA 95436. Anatomically correct dolls (more adult-like).

Videos Good for Use with Student Groups

Birth Control: Myths and Methods, Churchill Films, 622 N. Robertson Blvd. Los Angeles, CA 90069; 800-852-9818.

Boy Stuff, Churchill Films, 12210 Nebraska Ave., Los Angeles, CA 90025-9816; 800-852-9818. Hygiene and puberty concerns for boys. Uses humor, animation and live action.

First Things First. Bill Wadsworth Productions, Austin, TX 78731. Story of teenage couple deciding to wait, delaying sex until they are both ready. Good discussion for gender roles, communications and peer pressure.

He's No Hero, Intermedia, 1300 Dexter N, Seattle, WA 98109-9974. Young men's issues, snappy music.

Human Growth IV, adolescent development, Churchill Films, 12210 Nebraska Ave., Los Angeles, CA 90025-9816; 800-852-9818.

It Only Takes Once, Intermedia, 1300 Dexter N, Seattle, WA 98109-9974. Danitra Vance of "Saturday Night Live" is a positive Black role model. Real-life teen parents speak to how unplanned pregnancy alters life plans and dispel romantic myths about parenting.

Sexual Abstinence: Making the Right Choice, Human Relations Media, 175 Tompkins Ave., Pleasantville, NY 10570.

Teen AIDS in Focus, San Francisco Department of Public Health, AIDS Prevention Program, 25 Van Ness Ave., San Francisco, CA 94102; 415-554-9000.

3-2-1 Contact Special: I Have AIDS, Ryan White. Available from Santa Clara County Office of Education Media Center, 100 Skyport Dr., San Jose, CA 95115. Can be reproduced.

AIDS: The New Facts of Life, ETR Associates, P.O. Box 1830, Santa Cruz, CA 95061-1830.

My Self-Esteem, Pyramid Film and Video, Box 1048, Santa Monica, CA 90406.

Understanding Human Reproduction, Sunburst Communications, 101 Castleton St., Pleasantville, NY 10570.

Playing the Game, Intermedia, 1300 Dexter N, Seattle, WA 98109-9974.

Videos for Use with Parents or for Staff Development Programs

Board and Care, Pyramid Film and Video, Box 1048, Santa Monica, CA 90406. Academy award-winning documentary showing the romance with two people who have Down's Syndrome.

Learning to Talk About Sex When You'd Rather Not, Special Purpose Films, 416 Rio Del Mar, Aptos, CA 95003; 408-688-6320. Good for bringing up the topic with parents and staff.

Person to Person, Mary Ann Carmody, 6121 Nevada Ave. NW, Washington, DC 20015.

Street Safe and *You Have the Right to Say No,* Special Purpose Films, 416 Rio Del Mar, Aptos, CA 95003; 408-688-6320. Designed to help staff learn how to teach self-protection skills.

This Child Is Mine, W. Shumacher, University of California Extension, Media Center, 2176 Shattuck Ave., Berkeley, CA 94704. Documentary about mothers with mental retardation.

Who's In Control? Planned Parenthood of Sacramento Co., 1507 21st St., Sacramento, CA 95811; 916-446-0930. About socialized vulnerability.

Articles, Books and Reference Materials

AIDS Education for Individuals with Developmental, Learning or Mental Disabilities, L. Stiggall. In *The AIDS Challenge: Prevention Education for Young People*, ed. M. Quackenbush, M. Nelson and K. Clark, ETR Associates, P.O. Box 1830, Santa Cruz, CA 95061-1830; 800-321-4407.

Becoming Male and Female, E. Ames and L. Trucano, Comprehensive Health Education Foundation, 22323 Pacific Highway South, Seattle, WA 98198.

Building Self-Esteem in Persons with Developmental Disabilities, R. Frank and J. Edwards, Ednick Communications, Box 3612, Portland, OR 97208.

Changing Inappropriate Sexual Behavior, D. Griffiths, V. Quinsey and D. Hingsburger, 1989, Paul Brookes Publishing, P.O. Box 10624, Baltimore, MD 21285-0624.

Does AIDS Hurt? M. Quackenbush and S. Villarreal, ETR Associates, P.O. Box 1830, Santa Cruz, CA 95061-1830; 800-321-4407. Suggestions for teachers, parents and other care providers of children to age 10. Can be used for many older special education students.

Double Jeopardy: Pregnant and Parenting Youth in Special Education, L. Muccigrosso, M. L. Scavarda et al., Council for Exceptional Children, 1920 Association Dr., Reston, VA 22091-1589.

An Easy Guide to Loving Carefully, W. Kempton, L. McKee and L. Stiggall, ETR Associates, P.O. Box 1830, Santa Cruz, CA 95061-1830; 800-321-4407.

Family Life/Sex Education Guidelines, Publication Sales, P.O. Box 271, Sacramento, CA 95082-0271.

Family Life Education Curriculum Guidelines, The National Council on Family Relations, 3989 Central Ave. NE, Suite 550, Minneapolis, MN 55421.

Family Life Educator, ed. K. Clark, ETR Associates, P.O. Box 1830, Santa Cruz, CA 95061-1830; 800-321-4407. Quarterly publication that surveys and summarizes the latest information on family life content areas.

Growing Older: Facts and Feelings, ETR Associates, P.O. Box 1830, Santa Cruz, CA 95061-1830; 800-321-4407.

HIV Prevention and AIDS Education: Resources for Special Educators, Association for Advancement of Health Education, CEC, 1920 Association Dr., Reston, VA 22091-1589. Free.

I Contact: Sexuality and People with Developmental Disabilities, D. Hingsburger, Vida Publishing, P.O. Box 587, Mountville, PA 17554.

I to I...Self Concept and People with Developmental Disabilities, D. Hingsburger, Vida Publishing, P.O. Box 587, Mountville, PA 17554.

Making Love, Etc., Bloorview Children's Hospital, 25 Buchan Ct., Willowdale, Ontario M2J 4S9. A booklet for young people with physical disabilities.

Sex Education for Persons Who Are Mentally Handicapped, W. Kempton and L. Stiggall. In *Sexuality Education/Theory into Practice* 18 (3), College of Education, University of Ohio, 174 Arps Hall, 1945 N. High St., Columbus, OH 43210.

Sexual Abuse Prevention Strategies and Programs for Persons with Developmental Disabilities, L. Muccigrosso. In *Journal of Sexuality and Disability* 9 (3), Human Sciences Press, New York.

Sexuality and the Developmentally Handicapped, W. Row and S. Savage, Edwin Mellen Press, Box 450, Lewiston, NY 14092.

Sex Education and Counseling of Special Groups, W. Johnson and W. Kempton, Charles Thomas, 2600 S. 1st St., Springfield, IL 62717.

Sexual Assault: A Survivor's Handbook for People with Developmental Disabilities, Book I: for people who read best with few words; Book II: for people with disabilities and their advocates; and Book III: for family members, advocates and care providers; N. Baladerian, Mental Health Consultants, P.O. Box T, Culver City, CA 90230-1690; 213-391-2420.

Shared Feelings: A Parent Guide to Sexuality Education for Children, Teenagers and Young Adults Who Have a Mental Handicap: Discussion Guide to Shared Feelings, D. Maksym, G. Allan Roeher Institute, Kinsmon Bldg., York University, 4700 Keele St., Downsview, Ontario; 416-661-9611.

100 Ways to Enhance Self-Concept in the Classroom, J. Canfield and H. Wells, ETR Associates, P.O. Box 1830, Santa Cruz, CA 95061-1830; 800-321-4407.

Talking with Your Child About Sex, M. Calderone and J. Ramey, Random House, New York.

A Teachers' Guide: Sex Education for Persons with Disabilities that Hinder Learning, W. Kempton, James Stanfield Publishing, P.O. Box 41058, Santa Barbara, CA 93140; 800-421-6534.

Understanding and Expressing Sexuality: Responsible Choices for Individuals with Developmental Disabilities, R. Monat-Haller, Paul Brookes Publishing, P.O. Box 10624, Baltimore, MD 21285-0624.

The Universal Childbirth Picture Book, F. Hosken, Women's International Network News, 187 Grant St., Lexington, MA 02173.

Vulnerable: Sexual Abuse and People with an Intellectual Handicap, C. Senn, G. Allan Roeher Institute, Kinsman Bldg., York University, 4700 Keele St., Downsview, Ontario; 416-661-9611.

When Sex Is the Subject: Attitudes and Answers for Young Children, P. Wilson, ETR Associates, P.O. 1830, Santa Cruz, CA 95061-1830; 800-321-4407.

References

Baladerian, N. 1991. Sexual abuse of people with disabilities. *Journal of Sexuality and Disability* 9 (4): 323-335.

Dickman, I. R. 1982. *Winning the battle for sex education.* New York: Sex Information and Education Council of the United States.

Johnson, W., and W. Kempton. 1981. *Sex education and counseling of special groups.* Springfield, IL: Charles C. Thomas.

Kempton, W. 1988. *A teacher's guide: Sex education for persons with disabilities that hinder learning.* Santa Monica, CA: Stanfield.

Kempton, W., and L. Stiggall. 1989. Sex education for persons who are mentally handicapped. *Theory into Practice* 13 (3): 203-210.

Kempton, W., T. Davis and L. Muccigrosso. 1993. *Socialization and sexuality: A comprehensive training guide for professionals helping people with disabilities that hinder learning.* Haverford, PA: Winifred Kempton.

Leyin, A., and M. Dicks. 1987. Assessment and evaluation: Assessing what we are doing. In *Mental handicap and sexuality: Issues and perspectives*, ed. A. Craft, 139-157. Turnbridge Wells, Kent, UK: Costello.

Maksym, D. 1990. *Shared feelings: A parent guide to sexuality education for children, adolescents and adults who have a mental handicap.* North York, Ontario: The G. Allan Roeher Institute.

Muccigrosso, L. 1992. Course outline. Social relationships and human sexuality. Foothill College. Los Altos Hills, California.

Muccigrosso, L. 1991. Sexual abuse prevention strategies and programs for persons with developmental disabilities. *Journal of Sexuality and Disability* 9 (3): 261-271.

Muccigrosso, L., M. Scavarda et al. 1991. *Double jeopardy: Pregnant and parenting youth in special education.* Reston, VA: The Council for Exceptional Children.

Community Programs and Partnerships

Chapter 21

Sexuality Education Coalitions

Susan N. Wilson, MS

"Together we are strong!" is the rationale behind coalitions. Coalitions bring together diverse groups that may or may not share similar purposes, but agree to temporarily put aside their own agendas to focus on achieving a single, commonly-accepted goal. Achieving this goal indirectly or tangentially fits into the mission and activities of many of the organizations that join in the collaborative effort. Coalitions that work can remain in partnership to continue working collectively toward meeting other goals that members want to achieve. Successful coalitions prove that working in concert can effect change.

Coalitions are especially important in the area of sexuality education. Sexuality education remains a personally sensitive and politically controversial issue. Coalitions can help to reduce the sensitivity of sexuality issues, lessen the surrounding anxiety and embarrassment, and reassure policy-makers that overwhelming majorities strongly endorse sexuality education for young people. The voice of the small, intensely vocal minority that opposes sexuality education programs can be put in perspective when many different organizations and individuals join together in support of sexuality education.

Advocates of sexuality education programs during the 1960s and 1970s generally fought alone. Before 1980, only Maryland and the District of Columbia had mandates for teaching about human growth and development and sex education. During the 1980s, the number of states requiring sexuality education increased from two to 21, and the number of states requiring HIV/AIDS education rose from zero to 33 (deMauro, 1990). The creation of new coalitions, and sometimes unlikely partnerships, played an essential role in the progress of sexuality education.

Allies for Sexuality Education

Sexuality education gained new supporters as a direct result of increased public awareness about the high rates of adolescent pregnancy, births and abortions in the United States. Beginning in the 1970s and continuing through the 1980s, the Alan Guttmacher Institute published a series of reports that brought this information to attention of the nation. That one in ten American girls between the ages of 15 and 19 got pregnant—unintentionally—every year was a statistic that did not go ignored. The Guttmacher reports attracted the interest of independent researchers, departments of federal and state governments, national child advocacy organizations, state and local task forces, major private foundations and the media.[1]

---

[1] The National Urban League, the American Medical Association, the American College of Obstetricians and Gynecologists, the March of Dimes, the American Association of University Women, the YM/YWCAs, Planned Parenthood Federation of America, the National PTA and Girls' Inc. (formerly Girls Clubs of America) took up the issue of teenage pregnancy prevention or launched programs to help teen parents during the 1980s. When Marian

The adolescent pregnancy rate in the United States was two to seven times higher than the rates in Canada, England, France, the Netherlands and Sweden according to the Guttmacher Institute 1985 study, *Teenage Pregnancy in Developed Countries: Determinants and Policy Implications.* Teen birth and teen abortion rates in the United States were also much higher than in other western industrialized countries. A lack of sexuality education in American public schools was cited by the authors of the Guttmacher report as one of the principal reasons for the disparity (Jones, 1986).

The National Academy of Science 1987 report on teenage pregnancy, *Risking the Future*, attracted even more attention to the problem of adolescent pregnancy and the importance of sexuality education. This discourse about teenage pregnancy concluded that the causes of teen pregnancy were complex, and were rooted in the economic and social inequities of the society.

Sexuality education programs became one element of an overall strategy that included family planning services, reducing poverty, and enhancing young people's lives by providing improved public education, job training, health care, housing, mentoring and after-school programs. Sexuality education proponents now could make a better case for what the programs could and could not do with the support of the coalitions involved in preventing adolescent pregnancy.

The HIV epidemic further enlarged the circle of support for sexuality education. Surgeon General C. Everett Koop's call for sexuality education beginning in the third grade underscored the

---

Wright Edelman, president of the Children's Defense Fund learned that nearly half of all Black babies were born to single, teenage mothers, she led her child advocacy organization in a five-year national campaign to prevent "first births" among teenagers. Family life education, including sexuality education, was one of the adolescent pregnancy prevention strategies identified by the Children's Defense Fund.

need to teach about sexual behavior, sexual health and sexual responsibility. The federal government joined the coalition supporting sexuality education when the Centers for Disease Control provided some five billion dollars from 1985 to 1990 to the states with mandates for HIV education for teacher training and curriculum development as reported by ABC's Peter Jennings on "The AIDS Quarterly Report." Health care groups, state legislators, and gay and lesbian advocates joined to support sexuality education programs. The expanding coalition resulted in more state laws and administrative regulations requiring HIV prevention and sexuality education, more comprehensive programs, more funding, more teacher training and more curriculum development.

The 1980s war over abortion rights added more groups to the growing coalition for sexuality education. Pro-choice groups, women's rights organizations and women's health networks, promoted sexuality education along with the right to safe and legal abortion. The National Abortion Rights Action League, the National Organization for Women, and the Religious Coalition for Abortion Rights saw sexuality education, including information about contraception and family planning, as necessary to reducing unwanted and unintended pregnancies.

Forming a Sexuality Education Coalition

There can be no single or ideal model for a sexuality education coalition. Coalitions are formed when people sharing common concerns come together to fight for sexuality education or to fight the forces opposing it. More often than not, coalitions are born out of a threat from opposition forces. Most sexuality education coalitions operate on an ad hoc basis, then disband or lie dormant once the threat has passed or battle has been won. Some, however, like the New Jersey Network for Family Life Education, the North Carolina Coalition on Adolescent Pregnancy and the Virginia Family Life Education Network evolve into resource, education and and adolescent pregnancy prevention networks.

A sexuality education coalition is determined first by the issue that draws its members together—opposition to sexuality education in any form; pressure for an abstinence-only curriculum; controversy over condom distribution; or lessons that cover masturbation, homosexuality or contraception, to name a few. The focusing issue, at least initially, creates the coalition's agenda and defines what individuals and organizations come to the fore.

The makeup of the coalition—from individual personalities to organizational strengths, including financial resources, dedication, persuasiveness and creativity—is the second force that influences its workings. Which people or groups emerge as coalition leaders, how the coalition comes to consensus, and how tasks are assigned and accomplished varies according to the particular context and human mix. For example, a local or statewide sexuality education coalition might include individuals and organizations with expertise or interest in the fields of healthy child and adolescent development, child and youth advocacy, social services, education, health and women's rights. These are all logical participants in a community or a statewide coalition.

By nature, a coalition should be open to all organizations that support the basic purpose of the collaboration. In the case of coalitions, bigger is better and the more organizations that join, the merrier! Politicians in particular are impressed by a coalition's size and the number of people (i.e., voters) that it represents.

Coalitions are informal—some might say "ad hoc"—groups that do not wait for protocol. Often they are formed under pressure and the nicety of rules and regulations are waived until the collaboration is formalized. For example, the New Jersey

Network for Family Life Education grew out of a conference on public issues held at Rutgers University in 1979. One of the speakers talked about the recently passed statewide mandate for family life education and the need for proper implementation in local school districts. At the conference's end, some representatives of statewide organizations in the audience spoke to the chair of the conference about the need to set up an organization that would support the mandate's implementation and help to diminish potential controversy.

The chair then issued invitations to all organizations that had sent representatives to the conference to attend an informal working meeting to pursue this idea. Eighteen statewide organizations sent representatives to this meeting and the Network was born. This group decided to raise funds from private foundations in order to hire an executive coordinator to direct the Network's operations. The representatives of the original 18 organizations helped write the proposal for funds and developed a set of rules to govern the organization. A representative of one organization volunteered to send out notices of membership meetings; another offered to take and distribute minutes of meetings; and still another offered to chair a subcommittee to interview prospective candidates for the executive coordinator's position.

The "helping professions" are ideal allies in forming a local coalition because they are concerned with the well-being of children and youth. If we believe that family life and sexuality education protect children and youth from the dangers and risks of premature sexual activity, adolescent pregnancy and disease, then individuals and groups that work for and with children and youth are natural partners for a coalition that advocates this type of education in the public schools. Invitations could be issued to medical doctors, including pediatricians, neonatologists, obstetricians, gynecologists, family practitioners and nurses; social workers, personnel from recreational and other youth serving organizations, counselors, and representatives of groups concerned with juvenile justice, child abuse prevention, or developmental or physical disabilities; representatives from preschool through higher education; and women's groups, civic and civil rights groups, and agencies working with the poor and disadvantaged. Parents of children of different ages, parents whose children have recently graduated, and, if possible, recent graduates themselves should be included in the coalition. Representatives of legal and religious professions are also natural partners for sexuality education coalitions.

The organizing person or organization makes the initial decision about which organizations are natural partners for the coalition and should be invited to join. This person initially becomes the coalition's leader until another is chosen once the group is up and running. Usually, the leader leaves the choice of representatives to the coalition up to each organization. Some organizations send the same person to each coalition meeting, others rotate the position. However, usually an executive director of an organization testifies in person before a legislative committee.

The following organizations, with both statewide and local affiliates, should be considered in creating coalitions:

- Education organizations:
  — American Association of University Women
  — Parent Teacher Association
  — School Nurses Association
  — School Health Educators Association
  — School Boards Association
  — School guidance counselors
  — School social workers
  — Child care/nursery school organizations
- Health organizations:
  — American Academy of Pediatrics

— March of Dimes
— Planned Parenthood affiliates
— Health education councils
— HIV/AIDS advocacy, education and care groups
— Sexuality education organizations (ASSECT, SIECUS)
- Religious organizations:
— Council of Churches
— Council of Jewish Women
— Specific denominations
- Social service and youth-serving organizations:
— Association of Social Workers
— Family Service Agencies
— YWCAs and YMCAs; YMHAs and YWHAs
— Boys and Girls Clubs
— Girls Inc.
— Big Brothers/Big Sisters
- General advocacy, civic and women's rights groups:
— The Urban League
— The League of Women Voters
— The Associations of Junior Leagues
— ARCS (formerly Associations of Retarded Citizens)
— Associations of Business and Professional Women
— National Organization for Women (state affiliates)
— Battered women's organizations
— Homeless organizations
— Pro-choice, gay and lesbian organizations

Choosing an Agenda

The agenda for a state or local coalition for sexuality education can be as broad or narrow as its members choose. Coalition members might focus on an agenda for policy development, policy implementation or program development, or an agenda that includes a combination of the three. If a coalition chooses to become a formal organization able to receive funds from foundations and corporations to pay staff and implement programs, it needs to become a nonprofit organization and gain a 501 (c)3 status. In order to achieve this tax-exempt status, the coalition needs to follow federal and state regulations that include establishing a board of directors and drawing up a set of by-laws.

Gathering Data

The first step in creating an agenda is gathering data on the need for a sexuality education policy. Collecting accurate information about child and teenage health problems that a sexuality education program would address, and over time mitigate, is a fundamental task. Obtaining information from several sources ensures a more complete picture. A solid databank would include up-to-date information on the following topics:

- state or local rates of adolescent pregnancies, births and abortions
- state rates of child poverty
- costs of programs for adolescent mothers
- pre- and postnatal care costs for teenage births
- rates of adolescent sexually transmitted disease
- rates and modes of transmission of HIV/AIDS among adolescents and young adults
- numbers and cost of care of low-birth-weight babies
- infant mortality rates among babies born to adolescents
- incidence of child sexual abuse among babies born to teenagers
- child welfare costs and the proportion of AFDC funds expended on households consisting of single mothers and young children
- estimated remedial education costs for children of teen parents
- dropout data and causes for dropout of female teens

The coalition can use these statistics to make the point that prevention of problems is far cheaper and wiser than trying to remediate them. High quality sexuality education can diminish the problems of teenage pregnancy and sexually transmitted disease by helping youth postpone sexual intercourse or learn to use reliable forms of contraception when they have intercourse. As a society, we spend very little on prevention and have invested very little money in sexuality education and health education programs. But politicians and policy-makers do listen to economic arguments because they are always looking for ways to reduce public expenditures and save tax money.

Polling

The new coalition might take a strong second step by commissioning a statewide poll to show levels of public support for sexuality education programs. State universities, private research organizations, or the state's larger newspapers often conduct polls that ask citizens for their opinions on various issues. Frequently, polling organizations will add questions about interesting or potentially controversial issues at little cost. State legislators, in particular, would tend to look favorably at polling data that shows strong support for sexuality education programs among a high percentage of state residents.

A coalition could seek funds from private foundations, corporations and state department of government to finance the poll. Or some private polling organizations might be willing to run such a poll as a public service, particularly if the coalition gives them credit when the results are announced. Polling is costly, which is why obtaining a grant from a foundation or corporation often makes the most sense. A state department of government interested in learning more about public attitudes about sexuality education and teenage pregnancy prevention might also be willing to offer financial assistance for a polling project.

Polling data can indicate community opinions and support for local programs. For example, educators preparing to implement sexuality education might find it helpful to know that residents in their area of the state believe young people should learn about abstinence and chastity before marriage as well as about contraception and condoms. It is wise to ask questions geared to the future. Advocates commissioning a poll might ask how residents feel about condom availability plans in high schools, even though no school is yet planning to implement such a program. Even if poll results do not reveal widespread support for this program element at this time, a statewide poll can be helpful to policy-makers, proponents, and those who are undecided about their support of the issue.

Americans put a lot of faith in polls and polls often offer an accurate picture of citizens' views on issues. Most polls taken over the past few decades about sexuality education show very strong support for this instruction in the public schools. In New Jersey, for example, poll results in 1980 helped push a mandate through the State Board of Education and kept it from being revoked by the state legislature. At that time, 78 percent of New Jersey residents favored offering sex education programs in junior and senior high school; in 1992, when another poll was done, this number had increased to 87 percent. Policy-makers and educators thus can see that support for this instruction is widespread.

Making Policy

A policy-formation agenda requires coalition members to undertake numerous tasks: to seek political allies; to understand their opponents' arguments; to prepare responses to these arguments; to work constructively with the media and testify at public hearings and legislative committee meetings; and to handle controversy. Coalition members who want to influence policy development must possess or develop the ability to compromise, whether it be on legislation or administrative regulations issued by executive departments.

A 1993 incident in New Jersey shows a coalition at its best. Statewide organizations, under the direction of the New Jersey Network for Family Life Education organized rapidly to beat back an effort by right-wing and religious groups to pass a state law that would require all teachers to "stress abstinence" whenever any topic of sexuality was taught in any classroom and to use only materials that gave this message. This bill was introduced in 1988 and was opposed then by members of the New Jersey Network for Family Life Education; it resurfaced without any warning during the 1993 legislative session. The State Assembly voted 54 to 7 to have the bill become state law. Immediately after this vote, the Network's executive coordinator put together the Coalition to Support Comprehensive Family Life and Sexuality Education (including instruction about abstinence and contraception) to oppose the abstinence bill and prevent it from becoming a state law. Within two weeks, 34 statewide organizations and three departments of state government (Education, Health and Human Services) joined the coalition, including the Association for the Children of New Jersey, the New Jersey Federation of Business and Professional Women, the New Jersey State School Nurses Association, the League of Women Voters and the New Jersey School Boards Association. Together, these organizations represented thousands of citizens.

The organizations participated in a letter-writing campaign, writing to all the members of the Senate Education Committee, which had jurisdiction over the bill after it had passed the Assembly, to the president of the State Senate and to the governor. Each organization urged its members to write to their own local senators voicing opposition to the bill. On 27 May, 55 people from the coalition appeared at a meeting of the Senate Education Committee in Trenton, the state capital, to testify against the bill. The number of opponents surpassed the people who testified for the bill by a sizable margin.

Politicians were impressed with the long list of organizations that did not support the proposed legislation, and the press was able to report on the long list of organizations that had joined together in the space of two weeks to testify against the proposed law. At the end of the day-long session, the chairman announced that the senators "would take no action on the bill" and might hold further committee hearings on it. The Coalition members took pride in the day's outcome and felt that they had slowed, perhaps permanently, the bill's passage into law.

Proponents of comprehensive sexuality education programs are in a position to "compromise up" when they start out from a very strong position. They can then compromise without weakening the policy or program. In 1980, the New Jersey State Board of Education wanted to mandate kindergarten through twelfth grade family life education for all students in the public schools (except for those whose parents chose the excuse option). Opponents fought tenaciously to stop the policy in the state legislature. The State Board saved the curriculum mandate when it compromised with the legislators by changing "kindergarten through grade twelve" to language requiring only "elementary and secondary programs." Compromise on this and a few other minor changes defeated opponents' efforts.

Coalition members must prepare for the controversy that inevitably attends making policy about sexuality education. Some general principles apply when listening and responding to the opposition: hold public meetings; identify the opponents; know their arguments; make the facts work for you; plan a process for dealing constructively with the media; be respectful; and have courage.

Implementing Policy

Coalitions are helpful in implementing sexuality education policies after they have been passed by state legislatures or adopted by state boards of education. Coalition members who have expended a lot of energy in securing passage of the policy may be weary and eager to return to the activities to which they owe their first loyalty. It can be tempting for coalition members from other organizations to walk away from the implementation of sexuality education in the schools. The implementation phase tends to be slow, tedious, concerned with details, and as frustrating as the policy formation phase. Also the opposition to sexuality education does not dissipate; rather, opponents shift their efforts to blocking the policy's smooth implementation.

The implementation stage of policy development requires coalition members to change their focus from the broad framework of writing a policy to the smaller details of implementing it. Coalition members must focus on developing curriculum, training teachers, securing resources and serving as watchdog to ensure that opponents do not undermine the purpose of the policy. Coalitions working to implement policy might have many of the following goals:
- responding to requests from local school districts for clarification of the requirements of the policy
- forming a speakers' bureau to answer questions and clarify any misunderstandings among community groups

- appearing at school board meetings to comment on the curriculum as developed by professionals
- ensuring that policies are written and deadlines met
- serving on local advisory committees
- ensuring that there is adequate funding in the school budget for the new curriculum
- ensuring that the school board provides resources for teacher training
- ensuring that the school board budgets for current materials for the program
- responding to opponents who may want to undermine the program
- responding to inquiries from the press about program implementation

Coalitions working on the implementation of sexuality education policies and programs need to adopt the long view. Policy implementation is a slow, incremental process. School boards are political in nature and their members, like legislators, try to find middle ground between the majority and minority positions. Should only one or two members of a school board favor abstinence-only instruction, the majority will do its best to listen and implement some of their recommendations. People with political ambitions often begin their careers on school boards and are, therefore, unwilling to spoil their chances for higher office by taking controversial positions. A strong coalition of citizens willing to testify to why they think comprehensive family life and sexuality education programs are important is necessary to counter the "safe" path that school boards tend to take when left to their naturally conservative natures.

Local or statewide coalitions can further support sexuality education by providing or attracting resources. Such coalitions will need staff assistance, either through one of the coalition organizations, or by establishing and staffing a separate organization. Coalitions can provide many different types of support, including:

- publishing a newsletter for sexuality education teachers
- producing and selling videos to enhance instruction
- organizing statewide or local conferences and professional development workshops for teachers and parents
- planing an annual media fair for educators to sample the latest written and audiovisual materials
- offering mini-grants to strengthen teachers' skills and program development

Disadvantages and Advantages of Coalitions

No organization or individual should join a coalition without clearly understanding the possible barriers to success. In her doctoral dissertation, "Inter-Organizational Networking as a Community-Based Approach to Adolescent Pregnancy and Teen Parenting," Ann M. Wilson noted that, "Agencies have their own [problems]: Different constituencies, multiple sources of funding, various professional perspectives, and values, assorted definitions of the problem, lack of resources to satisfy need or demand—hence competition among agencies—and diverse levels of staffing and competency keep organizations separate and apart from each other."

Organizational self-interest, resistance to change and territoriality are particularly destructive to coalition building. "Burn-out" behavior and negative attitudes are serious impediments to effective collaboration. Wilson also notes how destructive coalition members with a hard-line or hidden agenda can be to the group as a whole when they arrive "with an established 'line'—and with fervor to match—and are quite intolerant of other points of view. Like those who can't abide by a group process, these are equally dismissive of the trust and mutual confidence that collaborative efforts need to be sustained."

The interdisciplinary nature of coalitions accentuates the differences in training, education, values, language, problem identification and definition that each organization brings to the table. While the members of the coalitions strive for equality, someone must assume leadership within the group in order to move the group forward. Once a leader emerges, resulting resentment and dissatisfaction may weaken dedication to the common cause. In spite of these very real disadvantages, however, coalitions committed to preventing adolescent pregnancy, preventing HIV/AIDS, and protecting reproductive rights have directly and indirectly advanced sexuality and family life education programs, and the advantages of organizations and individuals working together collaboratively for sexuality education far outweigh the disadvantages.

Coalitions working together to achieve commonly-held objectives can:

- bring disparate organizations together to focus on a temporary or long-term goal common goal
- convey a sense of power to politicians, foundations and the media
- share information, ideas, strategies, staff, funding, and political power
- reduce fragmentation and duplication of services, and enhance coordination of efforts
- attract special project-oriented funding from foundations and corporations by conserving tight financial resources
- emphasize the enrichment of sharing and mutual cooperation, particularly during difficult political and economic times

- offer members a chance to see a larger picture of the world than they would out of their own specific windows
- offer members new viewpoints on how to solve seemingly intractable problems
- enhance the universal values of hard work, trust, cooperation and mutual support
- diminish the very real human tendencies toward competition, jealousy and clinging to "turf"
- give members courage to take risks

Advancing Coalitions Within Schools

New models for the delivery of sexuality education suggest that untapped possibilities for promoting sexuality education exist within the educational system itself. For example, the time allotted to sexuality education might be increased by infusing the subject matter into other subjects in the school curriculum, or by offering students the option of sexual counseling and sexual health services. Either approach expands the mantle of sexuality education and builds support for adding groups of teachers not presently now involved in its delivery.

A 1992 study in New Jersey of the implementation of family life education after ten years revealed disparities in instruction along urban and suburban lines. The author of the study, *Family Life Education in New Jersey: Is Playing It Safe Unsafe?*, professor William Firestone of Rutgers University, observed:

> Remedial education and preparation to pass the high school graduation test are taking increasing amounts of time in poor districts, and the current effort to raise standards with a more challenging test will, if anything, increase that squeeze. Where dropout rates are

already high, it is not feasible to increase the school day significantly. Family life education must compete with other subject areas even though rates of teen pregnancy, AIDS and other results of unplanned sexual activity are most extreme in these very districts.

Firestone recommends efforts to make public schools centers for the delivery of integrated delivery of social services. Providing more extensive health counseling and health services will increase the number of professionals providing information (and contraceptive products) that extend and underscore the information provided in the few hours devoted to sexuality education in health classes. Marrying family life education to school-based youth-services programs or the school-based clinic program would allow health and sexuality educators to work cooperatively with youth-services and clinic staff.

Firestone also recommends infusing family life education content into other areas of the school curriculum. In particular, he suggests that sexuality education be incorporated in language and especially writing classes for middle and high school students, where drill and practice approaches are relatively ineffective. Firestone asks, "Why not use the time that is being spent to practice writing to learn and then write about sexuality?" If elementary classroom teachers, social studies teachers, language arts teachers, science and math teachers and guidance counselors were to integrate sexuality education into what they teach, students would not only benefit from increased hours devoted to the subject, but a new coalition of supporters would be formed within the school community.

Coalitions can advocate for good training for sexuality education teachers as well. The New Jersey Network for Family Life Education consistently advocates for more and better training and holds annual conferences and professional development work-shops, produces training videos and publishes a popular news-letter—all of which contribute to improving family life teaching and learning. In 1992, the Network raised grant money from foundations and corporations to underwrite a study of family life education from the perspective of teachers. The research recom-mended that local school districts offer more and better teacher training particularly for male, minority and urban teachers.

Extending Coalitions

Sexuality educators and advocates in the 1990s are in an excellent position. They can call upon the National Coalition to Support Sexuality Education recently created by the Sex Information and Education Council of the United States for the purpose of extend-ing sexuality education to all children and young people by the year 2000. Many of the sixty members of the new Coalition have statewide and local affiliates who can provide advice and support (see Appendix D). In addition, state and local affiliates of the American Medical Association, the American Home Economics Association, Girls, Inc., the National Network of Runaway and Youth Services and the National Urban League offer support to sexuality education advocates interested in lobbying for statewide mandates or increased resources for school programs or in finding members to serve on local curriculum advisory committees to revise curricula.

Sexuality educators can also reach out for new members during the next decade. New partners might include the business com-munity, health care reform advocates and environmentalists. Political and economic leaders agree that the overriding challenge in America for the next decade is to create good jobs at decent wages, control health care costs and reduce the deficit. There is a place for sexuality educators alongside the groups who advocate for change on these broad economic and social issues.

Support for new initiatives that reduce child and family poverty would assist sexuality educators' mission of keeping youth healthy and safe. Young people who grow up in poverty have little concept of a future that requires self-discipline and postponement of immediate gratification. For many, early sexual activity and parenthood provide their only feelings of success. Government initiatives such as job training programs, earned income tax credits and health care coverage can reduce poverty as well as problems associated with too-early sexual activity.

Environmental activists are concerned about the growth of world population. By adding population education to comprehensive sexuality education, sexuality educators could enlist the support of many large, dedicated and highly politicized groups. And, finally, when debate rages over sexuality education programs, students are nearly always left out of the process. Recent graduates, high school students and even middle school students, could become most effective advocates if given the opportunity. Coalition-builders might well benefit from student involvement and insight.

Working in enlarged coalitions as the year 2000 approaches, sexuality education advocates could achieve not only success for their own agendas, but could help accomplish goals that will change America, including reduced child and family poverty, a well-trained workforce, budget deficit cuts and universal health care coverage.

References

Archer, E., and M. Cahill. 1991. *Building life options: School-community collaborations for pregnancy prevention in the middle grades.* New York: Academy for Educational Development.

Brindis, C. D. 1991. *Adolescent pregnancy prevention: A guidebook for communities.* Palo Alto, CA: Stanford University, Health Promotion Resource Center.

deMauro, D. 1990. Sexuality education 1990: A review of state sexuality and AIDS education curricula. *SIECUS Report* 18 (2): 1-9.

Firestone, W. 1993. *Family life education in New Jersey: Is playing it safe unsafe?* New Brunswick, NJ: Rutgers University, The Center for Education Policy Analysis, Rutgers Graduate School of Education.

Haffner, D. W. 1990. Developing community support for school-based AIDS education. In *The AIDS Challenge,* ed. M. Quackenbush, M. Nelson and K. Clark, 93-103. Santa Cruz, CA: ETR Associates.

Haffner, D. W. 1990. *Sex education 2000: A call to action.* New York: Sex Information and Education Council of the United States.

Haffner, D. W., and D. deMauro. 1991. *Winning the battle.* New York: Sex Information and Education Council of the United States.

Jones, E., J. D. Forrest, N. Goldman, S. Henshaw, R. Lincoln, J. Rosoff, C. F. Westoff and D. Wulf. 1986. *Teenage pregnancy in developed countries: Determinants and policy implications.* New Haven, CT: Yale University Press.

Leo, J. 1986. Sex education: What should children know? When should they know it? *Time* 128 (21): 54-63.

National Guidelines Task Force. 1991. *Guidelines for comprehensive sexuality education: Kindergarten-12th grade.* New York: Sex Information and Education Council of the United States.

Network News. 1992. Newsletter of the Virginia Family Life Education Network. July. Richmond, VA.

Pittman, K. 1986. *Preventing adolescent pregnancy: What schools can do?* Washington, DC: Children's Defense Fund.

Rosensweig, J. 1988. Sexuality professionals: How we can influence public policy. *SIECUS Report* 16 (3): 10-12.

Wilson, A. M. 1990. Inter-organizational networking as a community-based approach to adolescent pregnancy and teen parenting. Doctoral dissertation. The City University of New York, New York.

Wilson, S. N. 1985. *Creating family life education programs in the public schools: A guide for state education policymakers.* Alexandria, VA: National Association of State Boards of Education.

Chapter 22

Partnerships Through Community Organizations

Ellen Wahl, MA

C ommunity youth organizations have a significant role to play in providing comprehensive sexuality education.[1] No small force, 17,000 community-based agencies serve school-age children, and the 15 largest alone serve well over 30 million young people.

But how much are these agencies actually doing? What are the issues and challenges they face? And what needs to be done to move this vast array of youth-serving institutions toward providing the ongoing, intensive services and advocacy necessary for young people to be sexually healthy now and in the future?

---

[1]In this chapter, I am using the SIECUS definition of sexuality education as "a lifelong process of acquiring information and forming attitudes, beliefs and values about identity, relationships and intimacy. It encompasses sexual development, reproductive health, interpersonal relationships, affection, intimacy, body image and gender roles. Sexuality education addresses the biological, sociocultural, psychological and spiritual dimensions of sexuality from (1) the cognitive domain, (2) the affective domain, and (3) the behavioral domain, including the skills to communicate effectively and make responsible decisions."

What's Unique About Youth Organizations?

The distinguishing feature of youth-serving organizations is their voluntary nature. They rely on the elective participation of young people. They depend on contributions and membership dues rather than tax levy funds. To attract young people, the activities offered must be compelling, engaging and fun. To attract public support, the programs must address issues of concern to the community. To attract financial support, the agencies must be responsive to donors and giving trends in the philanthropic community.

Their voluntary nature also means that community youth organizations are free to be creative, active and hands-on in their approaches. Since they are not dependent on tax levy funds, they, unlike schools, are not nearly so constrained by what they can or cannot "teach." The political disputes that currently threaten sexuality education in the schools make the role of community youth organizations even more critical.

Ideally, youth-serving organizations provide informal, flexible, enjoyable places for kids to be, with staff and/or volunteers who are caring, capable and skilled in group work, counseling or informal education, though not necessarily in sexuality education. Some are committed to social change, including change in availability of services related to adolescent health and sexuality. All believe they are engaged in "youth development," responding to the hierarchy of developmental needs and helping young people build their capacity to succeed as adults.

Most youth-serving agencies believe they have a role in helping young people avoid early pregnancy, substance use and HIV infection. Some include information about and access to contraceptive services as an explicit part of their programs, and a few are active advocates on these issues. Yet the emphasis for the past ten years has been on prevention—of pregnancy, intercourse and STD—rather than on promotion of healthy sexual development.

Some of the national youth organizations and many of the local agencies serve youth who get the least and need the most. They reach out to young people who live in poverty, who are faced with racism and sexism, and whose communities lack adequate health and educational services. They serve young people who may not be in school or who are not engaged when they are in school. Many go well beyond offering enriching, after-school care to providing the most basic services and support. Within this context, how youth organizations meet the needs of young people regarding sexuality education becomes an even more pressing question.

Programs

The range in scope and depth of community-based sexuality education is enormous. At one end of the spectrum is comprehensive sexuality education offered within comprehensive programs. This, however, is the exception rather than the rule. At the other end are fragmented, short-term, or dancing-around-the-topic programs that might be effective if they were part of a coordinated effort but in and of themselves don't go very far. In the middle are programs that are doing substantial parts of the agenda. Also in the middle are some of the national organizations that have clear policy statements on the issues, national curricula and some level of training and support, but spotty implementation at the local level.

Children's Aid Society
In New York City, the Adolescent Sexuality and Pregnancy Prevention Program of the Children's Aid Society, developed by health educator Michael Carrera, takes a holistic approach. Sexu-

ality education is one part of a program that includes academic enrichment, employment, medical and health services, parental involvement and counseling. Every young person is guaranteed a job while she or he participates and is guaranteed admission to Hunter College. On-site medical services are provided by doctors who carry their own malpractice insurance. This program is being replicated in New York City settlement houses and in a number of cities across the country (Carerra, 1993; Carerra et al., 1992; Carerra, 1984).

Girls Incorporated
For Girls Incorporated, a national organization dedicated to helping girls overcome the obstacles posed by gender discrimination, health and sexuality is one of six categories of programming deemed essential to meeting girls' needs. Based on research and addressing knowledge, attitudes and behavior, the four-component Preventing Adolescent Pregnancy Program includes parent/child communication; training in assertiveness, decision-making and refusal skills; life-skills training; and connections to health services, including contraceptive services. All components include age-appropriate, indepth sexuality education. Equally important is the overall emphasis on building girls' abilities to analyze gender roles, resist limiting gender stereotypes and develop skills to be competent, self-reliant and strong individuals, friends and partners (Cobbs, 1993; Houchin, 1993).

Association of Junior Leagues
The Association of Junior Leagues developed their Teen Outreach Program—a life-options program that includes community service, with a central goal of preventing pregnancy—to help young people explore how they make decisions and set goals. A

policy statement affirming the rights of young girls as well as adult women to full information about contraception supports this purpose. The program was based on the assumption that young people could learn to make good sexuality decisions, although the program was not created as a knowledge-based sexuality education program, and, in fact, evaluators noted that the curriculum units covering traditional sexuality education topics were covered less thoroughly by facilitators (Philliber and Allen, 1992, Herre, 1993).

YWCA

The YWCA of the U.S.A. has a long history of commitment to sexuality education. Like Girls Incorporated, they have national policy statements on both sex education and a woman's right to choose. Their PACT program is a peer education program in which the teen educators, both male and female, receive extensive training—somewhere between 60 and 140 hours—in sexuality education that is consistent with the SIECUS definition. Schools are a popular locus for program delivery, with collaborations forged by local YWCAs. Besides PACT, YWCAs also operate a number of other programs they term sexuality education; few are as comprehensive as PACT or as fully consistent with the SIECUS definition, though they do include typical components such as decision-making skills, use of outside speakers and leadership development, as well as services for pregnant and parenting teens (Mohamed, 1993; Sola, 1993).

Boys and Girls Clubs of America

Other national youth organizations also do some degree of sexuality education. Boys and Girls Clubs of America's policy statement on human sexuality makes clear that they consider the family the primary sexuality educator of children, take responsibility for a "supplemental role in sex education," and view human sexuality as part of the total human development of a young person. In SMART Moves, Boys and Girls Clubs of America's overall prevention program, staff are now considering ways to expand the sexuality education component, sensing more readiness on the part of affiliates. A social-skills, resistance-training curriculum, SMART Moves provides basic information about sexuality, strategies for looking at media messages, and activities that emphasize roleplaying and decision making. With the need for more intensive attention to sexuality education coming from the field, national program staff are seeking ways to expand the curriculum (Kavanaugh, 1993).

Big Brothers/Big Sisters

Big Brothers/Big Sisters of America does not yet have sexuality education on its national agenda, though such education is part of the training for adult volunteers. Their delivery system is different from most community youth organizations in that it uses a mentoring, one-to-one relationship rather than small groups. One of ten sessions for the training of adult volunteers is intended to help adult volunteers become more aware of their own sexuality and comfort level around sexuality issues so that they can help young people deal with the myths and realities that surround sexual development. The definition of sexuality is broad-based, and includes "gender, attractiveness, roles, dress, behavior, feelings, beliefs, relationships, homo-hetero-bisexuality, values" (Big Brothers/Big Sisters of America, 1991). The training does not include reference to contraception beyond suggesting in general terms that volunteers identify and refer young people to community resources (McGill, 1993).

Other National Organizations

The National Network for Runaway and Youth Services, the umbrella organization for runaway shelters, agencies serving incarcerated youth and others from particularly high-risk situations, has a strong and carefully developed HIV prevention program, which is currently being revised to include more sexuality education. Advocacy even more than program development is the major task of the National Network, and their public policy statements that form the basis for legislative and policy action are far-reaching. None targets comprehensive sexuality education directly, though statements do address HIV/AIDS, full access to health care, services for pregnant and parenting teens, reproductive freedom, and civil rights and program services for lesbians, gay males and bisexual youth (Darmstadter, 1993).

Teens in Camp Fire Boys and Girls chose HIV as their focus for programming over the next few years, and that effort will be teen-directed. Young people play a significant role in governance in Camp Fire, and meet to determine priorities for national program activities. Besides the teen-initiated work, the national organization has published a number of highly regarded works in such areas as leadership development, although they have not produced program materials on sexuality education (Coutelier, 1993).

The YMCA of the U.S.A., which serves nearly 6 million young people, does not have a national policy or programmatic focus on sexuality education. "Activities that improve personal health" fall within the youth development initiative that was adopted in 1989, but that is as direct as any reference to sexuality education gets. The limited activity among local YMCAs in this area focuses primarily on services for pregnant and parenting teens (Overby, 1993).

At the national level, Girl Scouts of the U.S.A. includes

programming emphasis on sexuality, but not birth control; although Girl Scouts is not a religious organization, a number of major churches are centrally involved in Girl Scouting. This national organization responds both to the institutional presence and to the broad diversity of background and belief of the 2.5 million girls they serve. They do, however, encourage adaptations at the local level, where Councils are free to make decisions consistent with community attitudes and parental concerns (Hussey, 1993).

Boy Scouts of America does relatively little sexuality education, although their handbook now addresses the issue, albeit in two pages, stressing responsibility and advising abstinence: "For the followers of most religions, sex should take place only between married couples. To do otherwise may cause feelings of guilt and loss. Abstinence until marriage is a very wise course of action" (Birkby, 1990). The handbook talks about healthy, supportive, equal relationships with girls and young women and about the burden that an unwanted pregnancy or child will cause.

The Door

In community youth organizations not affiliated with national organizations, the level of sexuality education ranges from none to fairly well-developed efforts. A number of these agencies are "one-stop" service models. In New York City, The Door, founded in 1972, offers health and medical care, mental health and drug treatment, social services, recreation, employment training, legal services and educational services to youth up to age 21. Sexuality education, counseling and services are an integral part of the program. In order to get a permanent membership card, young people must get a physical examination at the Adolescent Health Center within sixty days of entry. Part of the orientation process for the examination is participation in a "HEAL" group, Health

Education and Lifestyles. The group discusses making decisions about becoming sexually active, contraceptive methods, STD and HIV prevention, dealing with sexual feelings, and the importance of health maintenance. Each young person also has an individual intake interview as part of the case management process, which includes discussion of whether the young person is sexually active or planning to be and contraceptive information (White, 1993; U.S. Department of Health and Human Services, 1991).

Methods and Training

The case management approach is frequently used in freestanding agencies. At Lemmon Avenue Bridge in Dallas and Manhattan Valley Youth Program in New York City, for example, the sexuality education needs of a young person are assessed, often as part of a formal intake process and often involving the family. Staff abide by the family's values and expressed wishes regarding the services and information offered to the child, even if the staff believe that the child would benefit from different approaches. Those needs are then addressed as part of on-site programs or workshops, or through referrals. Lemmon Avenue maintains close relationships with other youth organizations in Dallas and uses curricula and program ideas from Girls Incorporated and the YWCA, among others (Glasgow-Mack, 1993; Thomas, 1993)

In programs that use the small group format, roleplaying, discussions and hands-on activities are standard fare. Practicing behaviors in simulated situations prepares young people to be assertive, clear and self-protecting when the real occasion arises. There appears to be fairly widespread acceptance that best practice includes some combination of information provision, life options, and skill building (Kirby, 1984; McAnarney, 1982; Allen, Hoggson and Philliber, 1990; Nicholson and Postrado, 1992; Philliber and Allen, 1992; Public/Private Ventures, 1987).

Resistance, assertiveness and communication skills—learning to say no to unwanted sexual activity, being positive about what one does want and making up one's own mind rather than succumbing to pressure from peer groups—are critical components of most programs. Understanding what constitutes a healthy relationship and how to identify and stop harassment, date rape and gender violence are gaining greater attention in programs, although there is disagreement about including these topics. Many believe such issues are better dealt with as part of violence prevention, so as not to condone the notion that they in any way constitute appropriate *sexual* behavior.

Practitioners also emphasize decision-making skills, though some scoff at the overly rational models that few adults, much less young people, can use effectively and consistently. Peer education is popular as well, used by the YWCA and Camp Fire programs, and in a number of local community youth organizations. Speakers are used frequently, especially in shorter-term programs.

Unfortunately, worksheets and vocabulary tests are used by some programs as a means of imparting knowledge; but these techniques are poorly suited to the out-of-school environment. More likely to engage young people are activities that take the embarrassment out and put the fun in. (For example, the Girls Incorporated Growing Together Program, for girls ages 9 to 11, has girls making "anatomy puzzles" and running balloon races in which one question is placed inside each balloon and teams compete to pop the balloons and answer the questions.) Probably the most common technique of all is a discussion format where young people meet regularly with an adult facilitator; the most successful sessions are usually those where the adult provides support and guidance and allows the young people to direct the conversation (Cahill, 1993; Canada, 1993).

One of the big problems in offering sexuality education is the critical need for staff training. Some sexuality educators believe that only professionals should be operating these programs, but others feel that high quality staff development can be effective preparation. In either case, the field of sexuality education is well developed, and there are many highly qualified sexuality educators and trainers available to conduct training or to assist in its development. It is clear, however, that youth leaders without background in sexuality education need help and practice in delivering accurate, nonjudgmental information and in discussing attitudes about sexuality.

Curricula

Despite the existence of high quality, and, in some cases, carefully evaluated curricula, many organizations develop their own. On the one hand, there is a common body of knowledge, approaches and activities that are widely acknowledged, and agencies theoretically can pick and choose, tailoring their programs to their populations. But, in reality, youth organization staff do not always have the time, resources or capacity to identify the best rather than the serviceable, or the theoretical and research base on which to make informed decisions. Moreover, many sexuality education curricula are purposefully designed with sequenced sessions, so the picking and choosing approach may undermine the effectiveness of the original program.

California's recent adoption and financial support of Marion Howard's *Postponing Sexual Involvement* (1990) has provided the impetus for organizations in that state to look at a national model and curriculum. But few agencies or affiliates use nationally tested curricula. Even nationally tested curricula can be distorted or misused, and so the ideal is for youth organizations to seek high quality curricula accompanied by high quality training that will enable them to adapt others' work responsibly and effectively to their own situations.

Collaboration

Many youth organizations have referral and collaborative relationships with health clinics, both for education and services. Connections to Planned Parenthood and, especially in the case of HIV education, the Red Cross, are fairly common. A few offer health and reproductive health services on site. The Girls Incorporated Health Bridge component was designed to link girls to health services, building an ongoing relationship with a clinic. Recognizing that knowledge of the existence of services does not necessarily guarantee use, structured visits and activities at both the clinic and the Girls Incorporated center help girls overcome the psychological and logistical barriers to using the services, as well as sensitize clinic staff to the issues facing adolescent girls.

Collaborations with schools are another link some community youth organizations have pursued to get their programs to more young people; this is especially successful when the program focuses on abstinence, postponement of sexual involvement, and resistance skills, but is less common when contraception and addressing the needs of sexually active youth are central.

Prevention or Promotion?

Most of the sexuality education programs developed at the national level were or are funded by a combination of foundation, corporate and government grants. During the Reagan and Bush administrations, some agencies decided not to take federal funding, since discussions of contraception were prohibited. During the 1980s, the goal of these monies was generally to prevent teen pregnancy; more recently, HIV-prevention funds have supported sexuality education, particularly at the local level. Also at the local level, agencies tend to receive funding from city and state monies and United Way allocations, as well as foundation and corporate contributions.

The emphasis on preventing problems—pregnancy, substance use, dropping out—dominated the funding and program development of the 1980s. Programs that incorporated sexuality education were generally termed pregnancy prevention, and the notion that healthy human development includes positive sexual development was hidden between the covers of the curriculum guides. For those organizations committed to effective sexuality education, the prevention focus was a fundraising strategy, although it also helped programs move beyond simply providing information toward developing more effective ways to help young people translate knowledge into behavior. On the other hand, the problem focus justified a negative approach to teen sexuality that was coupled with a conservative national agenda based on the ineffective abstinence-only, "just say no" approach.

In quite a few community youth organizations, services for pregnant and parenting teens are more common than either pregnancy prevention or comprehensive sexuality education programs. Part of the reason for this may have been the government funding pattern, which allocated the bulk of available funds to these services rather than to prevention or promotion. It may also be that the change in status from sexually active teenager to parent may make the discussion of sexuality seem more socially acceptable.

The question of whether the purpose of sexuality education is simply to postpone or prevent is salient regardless of the setting for the program, but it has special meaning to youth organizations because of the recent move toward "youth development." Community youth organizations are speaking out for a more positive philosophy, one that celebrates young people's potential and need for constructive support rather than one that condemns them as collections of problems to be fixed. Community youth organizations are now looking critically at whether prevention must be the only justifiable outcome, rather than the positive outcome of healthy relationships and sexuality.

Gaining Community Support

Even where prevention has been the primary and public purpose of a program, the inclusion of contraceptive information and access to or provision of health and contraceptive services has been viewed by many agencies as too controversial. Convincing the public that adolescent sexual development needs to be supported in and of itself is not easily done, especially in a society that has such ambivalence about sexuality in general and teen sexuality in particular.

Agencies worry that they will lose funding, clients or public goodwill. Some believe that their very survival would be endangered if they appeared to diverge too strongly from what they perceive as dominant community norms. Even among local affiliates of national organizations that have strong policy statements and programs, it is the rare agency that is forthright, outspoken and fearless in this area. All manage their public presentations carefully and strategically.

Yet executive directors who have taken risks have sometimes found that they had overestimated community resistance. One executive director whose program, including contraceptive access, was covered in the local paper worried needlessly about negative reaction. She received one critical letter and a great deal of positive press and response. The experience of Girls Incorporated is that parents often express relief that someone is providing life-saving HIV education, information about sexuality and help for their daughters to protect themselves—in all ways.

The Annie Casey Foundation has launched an initiative in five communities across the country to test the idea that community attitudes toward teen sexuality and contraceptive use can be changed, as the precursor to improving access to contraceptive information and services. In the Plain Talk model, community organizations serve as the lead agencies, building parental and community support toward a new consensus. Many parents and other adults know young people who are already sexually active or plan to be, and want to be able to give them effective guidance. The assumption of this program is that in most communities, the perception of resistance is much greater than the reality. The majority of parents support sexuality education, and represent a large untapped community force to be mobilized in support of sexuality education and expanded contraceptive/protective services for sexually active youth (Edwards, 1993).

Few adults feel comfortable with sexuality or sexuality education. Before we talk about what community-based organizations could be doing with young people, we need to address what they should be doing with adults. Changing adult attitudes and increasing public awareness of what young people reasonably need is one approach. When explaining The Adolescent Sexuality and Pregnancy Prevention Program to parents, Michael Carrera makes it clear that the issues of roles and relationships are critical and that sexuality education is not about plumbing or "genital obsession," but rather is part of a whole spectrum of completely reasonable needs (Carerra, 1993).

Conclusions and Recommendations

Should community youth organizations provide comprehensive sexuality education? The answer is a qualified yes. Any agency that has as part of its mission the healthy development of youth and goes beyond straight recreation or a single activity focus should be addressing these issues. On the other hand, providing non-judgmental, effective and accurate sexuality education is no easy task, and only agencies that will seriously commit resources and energy should be in this business. So what needs to be done to realize the potential of community-based sexuality education?

Community youth organizations should do the following:

- Clarify their positions, avoid euphemisms for sexuality education and make unambiguous decisions about their role in sexuality education.
- Form collaborative relationships with others in the community to provide direct services and education, identify and fill gaps in service, and improve coordination and access.
- Involve young people in determining what their needs are and what role the institutions in their lives might play in meeting these needs.
- Incorporate active, youth-centered methods, such as roleplaying and peer education that build skills, knowledge and positive attitudes.
- Systematically review existing curricula, programs and training opportunities and make careful decisions about whether to use, adapt or develop their own sexuality education programs.
- Develop and implement a systematic approach to staff training.

Funders and policy-makers should do the following:

- Support the compilation and review of curricula, programs and training opportunities through a central and accessible source.

- Support the adaptation of high quality programs, curricula and training, whether developed for school or out-of-school settings, to particular community youth organizations.
- Support the revision, updating and repackaging of prevention-based curricula so that they reflect more fully the SIECUS guidelines and positive approach to healthy sexual development.
- Support the training of youth development professionals to provide sexuality education.
- Support the provision of sexuality education in community youth organizations as a legitimate alternative and/or supplement to the role of schools, families and religious organizations.

Although few community organizations are doing all they could to provide comprehensive sexuality education to young people, they are well positioned to do so. With some work, they can offer appropriate environments and philosophies, sympathetic and supportive staff, evaluated curricula and activities, structured and high quality training, and access to or actual provision of health and contraceptive services. Given the desperate need for both prevention of negative outcomes and promotion of positive ones, and the abdication of responsibility by many other institutions, community youth organizations *must* accept the challenge.[2]

---

[2] The author would like to thank Heather Johnston Nicholson, PhD, Director, Girls, Incorporated, National Resource Center, for her assistance in preparing this manuscript.

References

Allen, J. P., N. Hoggson and S. Philliber. 1990. School-based prevention of teenage pregnancy and school dropout: Process evaluation of the national replication of the Teen Outreach Program. *American Journal of Community Psychology* 18 (4): 505-524.

Big Brothers/Big Sisters of America. 1991. *Volunteer education and development manual.* Philadelphia, PA.

Birkby, R. C. 1990. *Boy scout handbook.* 10th ed. Irving, TX: Boy Scouts of America.

Cahill, M. 1993. Interview with author, New York, 19 February.

Canada, G. 1993. Interview with author, New York, 23 February.

Carerra, M. A. 1984. *The primary pregnancy prevention program.* New York: Children's Aid Society.

Carerra, M. A. 1993. Interview with author, New York, 1 February.

Carerra, M. A., P. Dempsey, W. Philliber and S. Philliber. 1992. Evaluating a comprehensive pregnancy prevention program: Notes on the evolution of a process. *Family Life Educator* 11 (1): 4-9.

Carnegie Council on Adolescent Development. 1992. *A matter of time: Risk and opportunity in the non-school hours.* Washington, DC: Carnegie Corporation of New York.

Cobbs, J. 1993. Interview with author, New York, 8 January.

Cook, A. T., J. L. Sola and R. Pfeiffer. 1989. *Peer education in sexuality and health.* New York: YWCA of the U.S.A.

Coutelier, C. 1993. Interview with author, Washington, D. C., 11 February.

Darmstadter, M. 1993. Interview with author, New York, 21 January.

Edwards, S. L. 1993. Interview with author, New York, 12 January.

Girls Incorporated. 1988. *Growing together: A sexuality education program for girls ages 9-11.* Indianapolis, IN.

Girls Incorporated. 1988. *Health bridge: A collaborative model for delivering health services to young women ages 12-18.* Indianapolis, IN.

Girls Incorporated. 1988. *Taking care of business: A sexuality and career exploration program for young women ages 15-18.* Indianapolis, IN.

Girls Incorporated. 1988. *Will power/won't power: A sexuality education program for girls ages 12-14.* Indianapolis, IN.

Girls Incorporated. 1991. *Truth, trust and technology: New research on preventing adolescent pregnancy.* Indianapolis, IN.

Girls Incorporated. 1992. *Past the pink and blue predicament: Freeing the next generation from sex stereotypes.* Indianapolis, IN.

Glasgow-Mack, D. 1993. Interview with author, New York, 19 February.

Herre, K. 1993. Interview with author, New York, 11 January.

Houchin, S. 1993. Interview with author, New York, 20 January.

Howard, M., and M. Mitchell. 1990. *Postponing sexual involvement: An educational series for young teens.* Atlanta, GA: Emory/Grady Teen Services Program.

Hussey, S. W. 1993. Interview with author, New York, 8 January.

Kavanaugh, G. B. 1993. Interview with author, New York, 26 January.

Kirby, D. 1984. *Sexuality education: An evaluation of programs and their effects.* Atlanta, GA: U.S. Department of Health and Human Services.

McAnarney, E. R. 1982. *Report on adolescent pregnancy to the William T. Grant Foundation.* New York: William T. Grant Foundation.

McGill, D. E. 1993. Interview with author, New York, 8 January.

Mohamed, I. 1993. Interview with author, New York, 8 January.

National Guidelines Task Force. 1991. *Guidelines for comprehensive sexuality education: Kindergarten-12th grade.* New York: Sex Information and Education Council of the United States.

Nicholson, H. J., and L. T. Postrado. 1992. A comprehensive age-based approach: Girls Incorporated. In *Preventing adolescent pregnancy,* ed. B. C. Miller, J. J. Card, R. L. Paikoff and J. L. Peterson, 110-138. Newbury Park, CA: Sage.

Overby, L. 1993. Interview with author, New York, 21 June.

Philliber, S., and J. P. Allen. 1992. Life options and community service: Teen Outreach Program. In *Preventing adolescent pregnancy,* ed. B. C. Miller, J. J. Card, R. L. Paikoff and J. L. Peterson, 139-155. Newbury Park, CA: Sage.

Public/Private Ventures. 1987. STEP: Cohort II finishes strong. *Public/Private Ventures News:* 1-2.

Sola, J. 1993. Interview with author, New York, 15 January.

Thomas, T. 1993. Interview with author, New York, 23 February.

U.S. Department of Health and Human Services. 1991. *Adolescent health, volume 3: Cross-cutting issues in the delivery of health and related services.* Washington, DC.

White, M. 1993. Interview with author, New York, 21 June.

Chapter 23

The Role of Religious Organizations in Sexuality Education

Elma Phillipson Cole

Τ he family and the church are two social systems with the potential to have a great impact on personal beliefs and behaviors. It is in the home that we first learn who we are and how to relate to others. Unfortunately, as reflected in the history of sexuality education in the United States today, neither families nor religious bodies are answering many of the questions young people are asking about sexual matters and how to deal with them (Clapp, 1985; Dean and Yost, 1991; Gordon, Scales and Everly, 1979; Blume, 1986; Thornton and Camburn, 1989; Johnson, 1986).

Because sexuality permeates all aspects of our lives, it is a major determinant in life choices and opportunities. Our sexuality includes emotional and physical components of our being and enables us to move into loving, complementary relationships with others.

Religious bodies universally recognize human sexuality as a gift from God, to be received with thanksgiving and to be used with reverence and joy for the enrichment of life and the potential creation of new life. How we respond to this gift depends on our acceptance or rejection of moral values that basically derive from a religious system. For young people, particularly adolescents, blind acceptance of moral values is not enough. They want to know what and why. Acting responsibly depends on knowing the facts and applying this knowledge—as true in sexual behavior as it is in business. As controversy rages over who should teach what about sexuality, and when and where it should be taught, our inquiring young people are left vulnerable due to a lack of formal guidance.

National religious organizations recognize this and most have, in one way or another, tried to address the need. Many have developed sexuality education programs based in Scripture and the doctrine of the individual organization. These programs are usually available for local use, but use is not mandated and is therefore spotty. Included in most programs are suggestions for how to identify barriers to local use and ways to overcome them. "Resources and an intentional guiding vision" are the basic need, with committed adult leadership the most essential ingredient (Dean and Yost, 1991).

In this chapter, the term "religious organization" is used to include religious bodies, denominational groups, synagogues and mosques. The illustrations are drawn from Judeo-Christian programs, as these represent the major population of the United States (Kosmin and Lachman, 1991).

Young People, Sex and Religion

Surveys of the impact of religion on sexual activity give a general picture rather than provide hard data. Periods covered, age ranges and questions asked vary among researchers. There is also a reluctance on the part of many young people to respond honestly to questions on so personal a matter as sexual behavior and religious beliefs. In the surveys cited, young people called on religious organizations to help them understand themselves and to guide them in moral behavior.

A 1985 report covers young people ages 13 to 18 who come from 48 congregations, including Protestant, Evangelical, Jewish and Catholic (Clapp, 1985). Fifty-nine percent of the males and 42 percent of the females had experienced sexual intercourse. Ninety-five percent said they believed in God, but just 22 percent said that their religious beliefs were the most important factor in their lives.

A 1987 survey of the sexual behavior of teenagers ages 12 to 18 in eight Evangelical churches combines the male and female data (McDowell, 1987). The report states that 65 percent of these young people had engaged in some form of sexual behavior (e.g., fondling breasts and genitalia) and 43 percent had engaged in sexual intercourse and did not consider this to be unacceptable behavior. Eighty-five percent said that becoming a better Christian was important to them, and 82 percent attended church regularly.

Studies of young people's sexual behavior offer interesting data regarding the impact of their religion on behavior. Young people say they believe in God, but few say that their religious beliefs are the most important factors in their lives (Dean and Yost, 1991; Clapp, 1985; McDowell, 1987). Those who attend organized religious activities frequently have a less permissive attitude about sexual activities; while those who are sexually permissive are less apt to take part in religious activities. The 1991 report prepared for the Carnegie Council on Adolescent Development notes that "religious affiliation...while moderately predictive of lower sexual activity, does not provide 'insurance' for a young person's chastity" (Dean and Yost, 1991).

The levels of sexual activity for nondenominationally identified young people cover the same range as for those who take part in religious activities. A 1979 report notes that 54 percent of the males and 42 percent of the females had experienced sexual intercourse by age 18 (Hass, 1979). A 1992 report from the Alan Guttmacher Institute on teens ages 15 to 19 shows 60 percent of the males and 50 percent of the females as sexually active. Researchers note that an increasing percentage of teenagers are sexually active and that the age of the first experience is going down.

Most of the girls in the surveys cited reported that their sexual experience was disappointing and a cause of worry, although some said it was a warm and beautiful experience when the males seemed to genuinely care for them. The boys were on the whole more enthusiastic, but many of them also said "it wasn't that great."

Three other areas were included in the 1985 report: masturbation, homosexuality and sexual abuse. Masturbation topped the list of sexual activities for both boys and girls ages 13 to 15—85 and 62 percent—and for ages 16 to 18—87 percent and 74 percent. Same-sex contact between the ages of 10 and 18 was reported by 45 percent of the males and 25 percent of the females. Unwanted sexual contact by age 18 was reported by 20 percent of the males and 52 percent of the females. Forty-nine percent of those 13 to 15 and 72 percent of those 16 to 18 knew someone who had been sexually abused by parents. These young people felt that their religious organization gave them little or no help with issues of sexuality, dating or marriage preparation, and half of them would not seek a minister's help if they had a serious problem (Clapp, 1985).

The religious organization and the family together can help young people see that sexuality is a gift from God, meant for true union with another, and, for some, procreation. Clearly young people want information and personal resources to help them form their moral values and translate these values into behavior. Instead they often hear they should say no to anything involving sex but are given little help in understanding why.

Sexuality Education Programs of Selected Religious Organizations

National bodies of most religious organizations offer help to local units in developing and presenting sexuality education programs. The overall goal is for young people to "own a religious identity and to grow into healthy, functioning adults in their communities." This means developing solid values to govern behavior and to avoid those activities that place them at risk (Dean and Yost, 1991).

Program materials are available through many denominational bodies. They include ideas for dealing with sexuality education, along with doctrinal and Scripture support for the content. For successful results, parents and adult caregivers must be involved in planning the program, and must have personally gone through the content (Emphasis, 1986). Structured programs can be supplemented through discussing religious rituals, such as weddings or baptisms, a family event, such as a sweet-sixteen birthday party, or TV programs or news events.

The programs vary among the denominations with some offering a comprehensive array of materials starting at birth. Other programs are targeted to specific age groups, with the majority centering on adolescents. A local congregation will want to examine the program guides issued by the national body and then determine what, if any, modifications are needed for those who will take part. This is particularly important when several denominations are working together on a program. The sponsoring group will know from reading the entire program guide and the research material what will best suit the local purpose. Doctrine and interpretation of Scripture may differ among congregations. These differences can be discussed and consensus reached; they should not preclude doing the program.

Unitarian Universalist Association

The Unitarian Universalist Association's program, *About Your Sexuality*, for adolescents ages 12 to 14, is complete and explicit. The package includes background material, guides for orientation sessions, videos and resources for participants. Units deal with anatomy, masturbation, dating relationships, conception and birth, same-sex friendships, birth control and abortion, sexual minorities, sexually transmitted disease, femininity and masculinity, and heterosexual, bisexual and homosexual lovemaking. For adults and parents of participants, there is a two-and-one-half hour overview of the content.

Disciples of Christ

The Christian Church Disciples of Christ offers local congregations annotated bibliographies on sexuality subjects and assists local units in finding speakers and leaders. Some local units emphasize physiology, some spirituality, some do both. Local congregations function independently in developing their programs. Local concerns are expressed through a regional structure and proposed to the national body, but there is no national mandate on the local church.

United Church of Christ

The United Church of Christ Board for Homeland Ministries has prepared *Created in God's Image: A Human Sexuality Program for Ministry and Mission* to help local congregations incorporate issues of human sexuality into the church's ongoing activities. Human sexuality is explored from Biblical, theological and ethical perspectives. The ten-session program covers what has shaped our understanding of human sexuality, early learning, personal feelings, intimacy and loneliness, contradictions and myths about gender identity, sexual health, sexual violence, public policy implications and advocacy, evaluation and feedback. The national board has trained leadership teams who will train teams from local congregations that elect to do the program.

The need for this content and approach was established by a nationwide survey of clergy and local church members. There was strong support for church involvement in sexuality-related issues in the church's educational program. The majority of the respondents felt that the church should offer guidelines rather than rules about sexual behavior (Johnson, 1986).

United Methodist Church

The United Methodist Church has a series of age-specific guides:
- *Before They Ask: Talking About Sex from a Christian Perspective*, for parents and teachers of children from birth through age 12, is designed to help adults answer children's questions and to help children develop concepts of masculinity and femininity.
- *Created by God: About Human Sexuality for Older Boys and Girls*, is a program for children in fifth and sixth grades and their parents. Included are discussions of the growing, changing body; maleness and femaleness; love, marriage and procreation; and being responsible for how God's gift is used.
- *Our Sexuality: God's Good Gift* is a program for young people ages 12 to 15. It is designed to equip participants with facts, provide a Christian understanding of sexuality, assist in building communication skills, and help young people make informed choices about their sexual values and behaviors.

- *Male and Female: Blessed by God* is a program for ages 16 to 18. It is designed to help older teens make Biblically based, right choices for them.
- *Sexuality: Stewards of God's Gift* is a study guide for adults. The focus is on an honest, caring approach to sexuality.

Lutheran Church-Missouri Synod

The Lutheran Church-Missouri Synod offers *Learning About Sex: A Series for the Christian Family.* These include age-specific guides that begin with age three and extend to adults as parents. Each volume is graded for vocabulary and information and includes typical questions and possible answers. The books for the various age groups are designed for parents and children to use together. The books for the early years have simple text and pictures. The book for adolescents is a simply written presentation of information about physiology, feelings and responsible decision making. It includes a special questions section covering pornography, masturbation, sexual experimentation, contraception, unmarried pregnancy, sexually transmitted disease, homosexuality and dealing with guilt feelings. The guide for adults, *How to Talk Confidently with Your Child About Sex*, is designed to help adults deal with their own sexuality along with practical tips on how to be wise sexuality educators at home. A video cassette showing sexual development and ways to help children develop healthy, Christian attitudes about their sexuality is also available for adult use.

Episcopal Church

The Episcopal Church and the National Association of Episcopal Schools jointly prepared *Sexuality, A Divine Gift: A Sacramental Approach to Human Sexuality and Family Life.* Five basic premises underlie the program:

1. The history of the Church's teaching reveals change, conflict and confusion, requiring each individual to evaluate what is truly sound religious guidance.
2. There is a lack of communication about sexual matters and a need for a shared vocabulary.
3. Traditional theological systems have emphasized sinfulness and morality rather than God's loving gift.
4. Dialogue with barrier-free exploration is needed.
5. All family patterns and lifestyles should be free of the labeling that sets up barriers to all people belonging to one family in Christ.

The content covers values, sex roles, sexual behavior, options open to Christians, decision making, and sexuality education at home and in the parish.

Presbyterian Church

The Presbyterian Church (USA) and the Reformed Church in America jointly prepared *God's Gift of Sexuality*. Scriptures and church doctrine, along with a range of activities, are designed to help young people put sexuality in a Christian perspective through four-day weekend retreats, with follow-up retreats for the older young people. Guides are provided for parent orientation sessions and for teacher training.

Subjects covered for the junior high age group include anatomy and physiology, puberty, relationships and intimacy, crises related to sex, values and decisions, and parent/youth communication. For the senior high group, subjects include sensuality, intimacy, sexual identity, good health habits, reproduction and contraception, sexually transmitted disease, parenthood, decision making, and how to handle situations that could mean trouble.

Jewish Congregations

Jewish teaching draws on the Torah, the Bible and the Talmud. Matters of sexuality education differ among the denominations: Orthodox, Conservative, Reformed and Reconstructionist. *Love, Sex and Marriage: A Jewish View,* a program from the Union of American Hebrew Congregations (UAHC), is a basic guide to sexuality education. Local congregations supplement this for use in religious schools and with youth groups. UAHC also issues a guide, *Looking at Sexuality: Educating for Lifestyle Choices.* The guide includes a glossary of Jewish values, a discussion of sexuality education in religious schools, guidelines for parents and teachers in talking with children, sections on building self-esteem, homosexuality and child abuse, and a suggested sexuality education program for teenagers. The sessions cover assertiveness training, including Judaism's view of sexuality as a gift from God to be used responsibly as part of a caring and committed relationship; moral and practical issues of birth control; a field trip to a Planned Parenthood clinic; and a discussion of HIV/AIDS.

The New York Federation of Reform Synagogues has developed a human sexuality program for use in religious schools, youth groups and camps. Leaders for the eight sessions are to be specialists who can deal with values, myths and fallacies, sex stereotyping and sex roles, ways to express sexuality, birth control, the number of children to bear, and building a strong Jewish life structure.

Catholic Church

The United States Catholic Conference publication, *Human Sexuality: A Catholic Perspective for Lifelong Learning,* discusses the basic principles of the Church, then offers a framework for sexuality education for different age levels from early childhood to adulthood. *Parents Talk Love: The Catholic Family Handbook about Sexuality* from the Paulist Press covers the myths and the realities of human sexuality and offers guides for parents to teach their children from early childhood on. Some dioceses, Albany, New York, for example, have developed detailed curricula for use in both Catholic schools and parish education programs. Other dioceses buy their sexuality education curricula from Catholic publishers.

Baptist Church

The Baptist Sunday School Board has recently issued a sexuality education program for four age levels: young child, middle child, preadolescent and adolescent. There is also a program for married adults and a guide for leaders and parents. The materials are for parents to use at home, with church leaders providing two to three hours of orientation. The program includes physical aspects of sexuality, responsibility for one's body, moral values and a theological base for sexual decision making and stresses abstinence, chastity, self-discipline and self-respect. Contraception is included in the parent orientation, and parents are encouraged to share with their children their own values on this subject.

Salvation Army

The Salvation Army, along with six other youth-serving organizations, has developed a series of education for parenthood programs designed to help teenagers understand what it means to become a parent. The goal is to encourage young people ages 12 to 18 to delay sexual activity until they are physically, emotionally and socially prepared to become parents. *Bridging the Gap Between Youth and Community Services: A Life Skills Education Program*, is based on the premise that young people will make good decisions about their lives if they have the help needed to do so. The program centers on the skills youth need to reach their goals and the behaviors to avoid that might preclude them from reaching their goals.

Getting to Know You, a cross-age peer education program, has older teens helping younger teens understand relationships. Favorite activities, what to look for in friends, where to turn for help, dating, sexual behavior, marriage and children are included.

There are common elements in the programs discussed. Each emphasizes that human sexuality is a gift from God, to be used with joy; each has a Biblical and doctrinal base; each offers sufficient content, description, facts and resources to provide an effective program. Participants, time frames and settings vary in keeping with local identified need and the willingness to meet that need. The national bodies have solid program materials and do what they can to encourage local use. However, although all stress the imperative of skilled leadership, few have systematic, ongoing training programs for leaders, and little training is offered in the seminaries. Without a mandate, these excellent program materials are not sufficiently used to help parents and young people deal with the issues.

Barriers

It is ironic that young people are part of religious organizations that have available sexuality education programs and that these same young people say that the church or synagogue offers them little or no help in this major area of their development.

Why is this so? There are many possible underlying reasons. There is a widespread belief within many religious organizations that decent people don't talk about sex. A sexuality education program might split the church and leave it without members or funds. Some congregants consider sexuality education programs to be pornography. Some feel that sexuality education belongs in the school, home or physician's office.

Underlying these excuses is the fact that adults may be uncomfortable talking about their own sexuality, and therefore cannot deal openly with young people on this subject. This leads to the greatest barrier to using existing programs: the lack of skilled persons to implement the programs.

There are other critical issues that divide both local congregations and the national bodies. High on the list are homosexuality, contraception, abortion, masturbation and sexual intercourse outside marriage. Some of the programs deal directly with these issues while others gloss over or totally ignore them. Some stress that these matters are things individuals must decide for themselves, while others give definite rules. For all, dealing with facts appears to be more comfortable than providing guidance on individual behavior. It may well be that the denomination itself is not clear on its position or fears the controversy that clarification could bring. Yet these are behaviors that concern young people and about which they seek help.

For example, homosexuality is a generally unresolved area. Opinions vary about the origins of sexual orientation. Religious groups, with some exceptions, frown on same-sex sexual behavior; some recognize that homosexual persons may be celibate or may have lifetime commitments to another. Congregations seem to find it difficult to separate orientation and behavior for homosexuals in the same way that they separate heterosexual orientation and behavior. The dichotomy troubles young people who are taught that we are each made in the image of God and that nothing can separate us from God's love. The controversy over whether to ordain gay or lesbian members is disillusioning and can lead young people to challenge the authenticity of all religious teaching. When the issue cannot be resolved within the denomination, many local groups have split away and formed a separate body (Cook, 1988).

Overcoming Barriers

Two roads can lead to overcoming the barriers religious congregations face in pursuing sexuality education for young people. One is in the training of leaders. The second is in working together with other experts in the community.

An effective program always depends on the quality of the leader, who must be comfortable with self, informed, and willing to share with and support young people no matter their behavior. Such a person can come from the congregation, from the community or from the clergy. Seminaries must recognize the importance of training students to help local congregations implement sexuality education programs. Little or no such training is currently offered. The Center for Population Options (CPO) has successfully trained young people as peer educators for work in public schools. One such CPO program is *AIDS Ministries Program: A Peer Education Program*. Why not adapt this training for clergy and young people who work in religious settings?

Networking with other groups in the community can be rewarding. Often such collaboration can cross denominational lines. Many local church bodies are small, with a limited number of staff. One minister or priest or rabbi cannot be all things to all people. Bringing congregations together can diffuse tensions and enrich the mix of leaders and participants. The broader base also lends validity to the program.

Other community groups can provide the needed and experienced teachers: the board of education, the health department, a university or college, the library, or a health or service organization. Planned Parenthood has led the way in working together with local religious groups. *Partners in Diversity*, a manual produced by Planned Parenthood of Southwest Virginia in partnership with religious congregations of the area, is a detailed practical guide for how organizations and religious congregations can work together. *Project Plain Talk: Sexuality and Faith* was produced by Planned Parenthood Centers of West Michigan, in cooperation with local churches in Muskegon County. The manual details three phases: clergy/youth leader training, parent session overview, and youth retreat. There are ample resources for the leader and solid activities for participant use.

Nationally both the Sex Information and Education Council of the United States (SIECUS) and the Center for Population Options provide detailed program guides suitable for use in religious organizations, and each offers leadership training. *Guidelines for Comprehensive Sexuality: Kindergarten-12th Grade* (National Guidelines Task Force, 1991), prepared by a SIECUS task force, is based on six concepts: human development, relationships, personal skills, sexual behavior, sexual health, and society and culture. A unit on sexuality and religion is included.

CPO has developed a program, *When I Am Grown,* for K–2, 3–4 and 5–6, a three-volume curriculum to help these ages answer the questions: Who am I? Where am I going? and, How do I get there? Sexuality education is included in the total framework. CPO's program, *Life Planning Education,* for grades 7 through 12 covers these same questions.

Before a sexuality education program is undertaken by a religious organization there must be an assessment of where the congregants stand on the need for the program, and agreement about the leadership and content. For the program to be successful, parents and caregivers must be included in the orientation and must be aware of the content. Ample time is needed for leaders and parents to absorb the language and the messages. Ample time also must be allotted to the program itself; one or two hours or a weekend is a good start but is only the beginning. The group and the leader together should decide the meeting schedule and over how long a period they wish to meet.

Participants need time to build group identity feeling and trust. Meeting weekly can deepen this process and can add momentum to the discussion. Four-day weekend retreats work well for some groups, enabling members to fully concentrate on the subject, free from home, work or school distractions. Retreats can also be a time for fun. For other groups, weekly sessions of sixty to ninety minutes are effective, spread out over three to six months. A refresher course a year later can crystallize learning and be the chance for further exploration.

Why Religious Organizations Must Offer Sexuality Education

Religious systems are universally recognized as key shapers and preservers of the moral values that underlie society. Together with the family, religious bodies are the first determinants in what kind of a person an individual will become. Religious teaching includes respect for self, respect for others, and being stewards of what God has given us. These are also the major ingredients in sexuality education, making religious organizations an ideal source for learning about one's sexual self. Religious organizations are family centered and in the neighborhood. They can offer increasingly responsible activities that engage young people and give them the opportunity to learn about themselves and how to get along with others. The community relies on the church to carry forward its traditional role of leadership on moral values (Leonard, 1983).

Sexuality education encompasses facts, but, equally important, it includes respect for oneself, responsibility for one's actions and concern for how those actions affect others. Family and church together can help young people recognize why it is wise to delay sexual intimacy until they are physically and emotionally ready to make a lifetime commitment. A religious program can be effective in helping young people translate knowledge into behavior. Other community organizations teach values, but, appropriately, do not include the spiritual element that imbues the church with its power.

Four critical issues that challenge the church today also offer a golden opportunity for providing moral leadership for individuals and the community. Each is related to our sexuality and to our understanding of self:

1. Sexual permissiveness pervades the mass media; the message is that everyone is doing it so it must be OK for me to do it too.
2. Homophobia extends into churches, educational institutions and political actions, thereby shutting out too large a percentage of the population from acceptance.
3. Sexual abuse and domestic violence are on the upswing, a misuse of power that sexuality education can help diminish.
4. HIV/AIDS has opened the way for religious organizations to provide education to prevent HIV infection and to place sexual intimacy in a moral framework.

True understanding of human sexuality can forestall problems that arise in the denomination, in the community and at home. Strong marriages will result in homes where children have a safe passage into responsible adulthood. The changing roles of men and women can be understood so that each person can be free to reach his or her full potential. Coming to understand the uses of power can prevent domestic and intimate violence, including the sexual abuse of children. And, finally, the community looks to religious organizations for leadership in moral values—the foundation on which this country was built.

Resources

About Your Sexuality. Revised 1983. D. Calderwood. Pamphlets and videotapes on ten topics, resources and orientation guide. Unitarian Universalist Association, Boston, MA 02108.

Before They Ask: Talking About Sex from a Christian Perspective. For parents and teachers, for ages birth through twelve. Cokesbury, Division of the United Methodist Publishing House, P.O. Box 801, Nashville, TN 37202-0801. Includes:
  * *Created by God: About Human Sexuality for Older Boys and Girls.* D. B. Glass and J. H. Ritchie, Jr. Includes a leader's guide.
  * *Our Sexuality: God's Good Gift.* J. Miles. For ages 12-15.
  * *Male and Female: Blessed by God.* (no author). For ages 16-18.
  * *Sexuality: Stewards of God's Gift.* (no author). For adults.

Bridging the Gap Between Youth and Community Services. A Life Skills Education Program. Revised 1988. Leader's guide for a ten-unit program for adolescents. The Salvation Army, P.O. Box C-635, West Nyack, NY 10994-0635.

Christian Approach to Human Sexuality: A Curriculum for Catholic Elementary Schools. 1987. A Curriculum for Catholic Parish Elementary Religious Education Programs. 1987. A Curriculum for Catholic High School and Parish Religious Education Programs for 9-12 grade levels. 1990. Roman Catholic Diocese of Albany, P.O. Box 6480, Albany, NY 12206.

Christian Sex Education Set. 1993. Baptist Sunday School Board, an agency of the Southern Baptist Convention, 127 Ninth Ave. North, Nashville, TN 37234. Includes:
  * *Boys and Girls Alike and Different.* E. Chambers. For young children.
  * *My Body and Me.* N. Stevens. For older children.
  * *Sex! What's That?* S. Lanford. For preadolescents.
  * *Sexuality: God's Gift.* A. Cannon. For adolescents.
  * *Celebrating Sex in Your Marriage.* D. McGee and S. McGee. For married couples.
  * *Christian Sex Education.* J. Hester. For parents and church leaders.

Course on Human Sexuality for Adolescents in Religious Schools, Youth Groups and Camps. 1981. A. Daum and B. Strongin. Union of American Hebrew Congregations, 838 Fifth Ave., New York, NY 10021.

Created in God's Image: A Human Sexuality Program for Ministry and Mission. 1993. United Church Board for Homeland Ministries, 700 Prospect Ave., Cleveland, OH 44115.

Getting to Know You: Personal Relationships with the Opposite Sex. 1988. For older teens. Corps Cadet Leadership Training Activities, pages 143-150.

Leadership Guide pages 125-136. The Salvation Army, P.O. Box 269, Alexandria, VA 22313.

God's Gift of Sexuality: A Study for Young People in the Reformed Tradition in the Presbyterian Church in America. M. L. Talbot, ed. 1989. Presbyterian Publishing House, 100 Witherspoon St., Louisville, KY 40202.

Learning About Sex: A Series for the Christian Family. 1989. Concordia Publishing House, 3558 Jefferson Ave., St. Louis, MO 63118. Includes:

- *Why Boys and Girls Are Different.* C. Greene. For ages 3-5 and parents.
- *Where Do Babies Come From?* R. Hummel. For ages 6-8 and parents.
- *How Are You Changing?* J. Graver. For ages 8-11 and parents.
- *Sex and the New You.* R. Bimler. For ages 11-14 and parents.
- *Love, Sex and God.* B. Ameiss and J. Graver. For ages 14 and older.
- *How to Talk Confidently with Your Child About Sex.* L. Buth. Parents' guide.

Life Planning Education. 1989. For grades 7-12. *When I'm Grown.* 1993. For grades K-2, 2-4, 5-6. Center for Population Options, 1025 Vermont Ave., Washington, DC 20005.

Partners in Diversity. 1988. Planned Parenthood of Southwest Virginia, 2708 Liberty Rd., Roanoke, VA 24012.

Project Plain Talk: Sexuality and Faith. 1985. Planned Parenthood Centers of West Michigan, 425 Cherry SE, Grand Rapids, MI 49509.

Sexuality, a Divine Gift: A Sacramental Approach to Human Sexuality and Family Life. 1987. Prepared by the Task Force on Human Sexuality and Family Life in cooperation with the National Association of Episcopal Schools. The Episcopal Church Center, 815 Second Ave., New York, NY 10017.

References

Alan Guttmacher Institute. 1992. *Facts in brief: Teenage sexual and reproductive behavior.* New York.

Blume, J. 1986. *What kids wish they could tell you: Letters to Judy.* New York: Simon and Schuster.

Clapp, S. 1985. *Teenage sexuality: Local church and Christian home program guide.* Peoria, IL: Kolbe Publishing Company.

Cook, A. T. 1988. *And God loved each one: A resource for dialogue about the church and homosexuality.* Nashville, TN: Reconciling Congregation Program.

Dean, K. C., and P. R. Yost. 1991. *A synthesis of the research on, and a descriptive overview of Protestant, Catholic, and Jewish religious programs in the United States.* Unpublished manuscript prepared for the Carnegie Council on Adolescent Development. New York.

Eisenberg, R. L., and M. E. Singer. 1988. What does Judaism have to say about sex and sexuality? *Compass* 11 (1): 18-20. (Special issue: Looking at sexuality: Educating for life style choices.)

Emphasis. 1986. *Religion and sexuality: Current perspectives.* New York: Planned Parenthood Federation of America.

Gittelsohn, R. B. 1986. *Love sex and marriage: A Jewish view.* New York: Union of American Hebrew Congregations.

Gordon, S., P. Scales and K. Everly. 1979. *The sexual adolescent: Communicating with teenagers about sex.* 2d ed. Belmont, CA: Duxbury Press.

Hass, A. 1979. *Teenage sexuality: A survey of teenage sexual behavior.* New York: Macmillan.

Johnson, F. (Chairperson of working group.) 1986. *Ask the churches about faith and sexuality: A UCC survey of needs for program development.* Cleveland, OH: United Church Board of Homeland Ministries.

Kosmin, B. A., and S. P. Lachman. 1991. *The national survey of religious identification 1989-90.* New York: City University of New York.

Leonard, J. H., Jr. 1983. Close-up: A conversation with Rev. Joe Leonard. In *Religion: A key foundation for family life education.* New York: Planned Parenthood Federation of America.

McDowell, J. 1987. *Teen sexual survey in the Evangelical Church.* Manuscript. Dallas, TX: Josh McDowell Ministry.

McDowell, J. 1988. *What I wish my parents knew about my sexuality.* San Bernardino, CA: Here's Life Publishers.

Ku, L. C., F. L. Sonenestein and J. H. Pleck. 1992. The association of AIDS education and sex education with sexual behavior and condom use among teenage men. *Family Planning Perspectives* 24 (3): 100-106.

Miller, B. C., and K. Moore. 1990. Adolescent sexual behavior, pregnancy, and parenting: Research through the 1980's. *Journal of Marriage and the Family* 52 (4): 1025-1044.

National Guidelines Task Force. 1991. *Guidelines for comprehensive sexuality education: Kindergarten–12th grade.* New York: Sex Information and Education Council of the United States.

Sullivan, S. K., and M. A. Kawiak. 1985. *Parents talk love: The Catholic handbook about sexuality.* Mahwah, NJ: Paulist Press.

Thornton, A., and D. Camburn. 1989. Religious participation and adolescent sexual behavior and attitudes. *Journal of Marriage and the Family* 51 (3): 641-653.

United States Catholic Conference, Committee on Education. 1990. *Human sexuality: A Catholic perspective for education and lifelong learning.* Washington, DC: United States Catholic Conference.

Chapter 24

Sexuality Education
in Conservative
Communities

Michael Young, PhD

M any times people say, "You have to understand, we have a very conservative community. That just wouldn't be accepted here." The fact is that some communities really are conservative and almost all communities have conservative elements. In some communities, a strong, conservative element seems to pervade the entire community. Sometimes this conservatism takes the form of extreme religious opposition to sexuality education. In other communities religion seems to have little to do with it. Even in most "enlightened" communities there are parents who are opposed to their children receiving instruction about sexuality at school. Sometimes there are parents and other community members who are opposed to providing sexuality for any students.

Does this mean that the young people in these communities do not need sexuality education? Does it mean that sexuality education advocates should give in to those who would prefer not to have a program? No. It does mean, however, that successful program advocates will carefully examine a number of issues. These include the following:

1. What type of program will receive strong support from the community and provide the most benefit for students?
2. Will those people who have influence in the community enthusiastically endorse the program that has been identified or developed? Will this result in strong support throughout the community?
3. Who will teach the program?
4. How will the class be conducted (or how will order be maintained)?
5. How will the teacher address controversial issues and answer student questions?
6. How will support for the program be maintained?

The material in this chapter will address each of these issues. The suggestions included should be particularly relevant to persons working in conservative communities, but are also of value to anyone who has responsibilities related to sexuality education.

Programs with an Abstinence Focus

Most parents, teachers, school administrators and board members, even in many conservative communities, have come to the conclusion that sexuality education for young people must be a part of the school program. At the same time, they would prefer a conservative approach to such education. They want an approach that provides young people with the information they need, but which also provides guidance. Such communities should consider a program that emphasizes abstinence.

There are those who argue that a program for young people that promotes abstinence is not realistic. If, however, one recognizes that our country leads the industrialized world in adolescent pregnancies, accepts the fact that HIV/AIDS poses a deadly threat to all persons in nonmonogamous sexual relationships (not just homosexuals and drug users), realizes that adolescents are notoriously poor contraceptors, and understands the other negative consequences that often accompany early sexual involvement, one cannot help but conclude that abstinence is a positive choice for young people. It is a choice with which young people should be presented. It can form the basis of a program that is of benefit to young people and that receives strong parent and community support.

Several abstinence curricula have been developed in recent years in an attempt to provide a conservative approach to sexuality education. But often the message presented is a negative one— "Sex is bad, don't do it. Don't even think about it. Not now. Maybe not ever." One successful program manages to avoid this negative philosophy, yet still provides an effective conservative approach to sexuality education.

In 1987 the University of Arkansas at Fayetteville was funded by a grant from the U.S. Department of Health and Human Services, Office of Adolescent Pregnancy Programs (OAPP) to develop and field test two sexuality education curricula—one for junior high and one for high school. The curricula had to "unequivocally promote sexual abstinence." No lessons concerning contraception were to be allowed. Before the curricula could be field tested they would have to be reviewed and approved by OAPP's ultraconservative reviewers.

This presented project staff with a difficult situation. How could a real-world curriculum be developed, a curriculum that would truly benefit young people yet still gain OAPP approval? It seemed like an impossible task. After much work, including several revisions, the *Living Smart* curricula were developed (Core-

Gebhart, Hart and Young, 1991). In 1993 they were revised again under the title *Sex Can Wait* (Core-Gebhart, Hart and Young, 1994). At this time, a curriculum for upper elementary school was also developed and added to the program (Young and Young, 1994). These curricula present sexuality as a positive part of the human experience, represent sexual thoughts and feelings as healthy and normal, emphasize the building of basic skills, and promote abstinence as a positive choice for young people. They view adolescent abstinence as an instrumental value (a means to a successful future) rather than an ultimate value (an end in and of itself).

The junior high curriculum includes three sections. The first unit, Knowing Myself, addresses the topics of self-esteem, puberty, and values and decision making. The second section, Relating to Others, offers activities that address communication, family, friends, dating and sexual decision making. The third section, Planning My Future, focuses on goal setting and life planning. The high school curriculum includes three sections with the same titles, Knowing Myself, Relating to Others and Planning My Future, but also includes a fourth section, Understanding Sexuality. Topics for this unit are gender roles, male and female reproductive anatomy and physiology, pregnancy and childbirth, sexually transmitted disease, and parental readiness. The emphasis of both curricula is on the development of life skills, an emphasis that should be an important part of any sexuality education program. Research has demonstrated that there is a relationship between the development of these life skills and the postponement of early sexual involvement and avoidance of teen pregnancy.

Planned presentations that include information about contraception are not a part of these materials. Teachers are encouraged to acknowledge and help their students to understand that (1) most people at some point in their lives do move into a relationship that involves sexual intercourse, (2) for a number of reasons, a relationship involves sexual intercourse is not the best choice for teens, and (3) for people who are involved in a sexual relationship, decisions about birth control are important.

Many people believe that this type of program is far too conservative. They want specific units that deal not only with contraception, but with topics such as homosexuality, abortion rights and sexual pleasure. The question to ask them is, "Could your local school board be persuaded to adopt your program?" The answer almost always is, "No." The response is then, "Wouldn't you rather have a program that is conservative but promotes a positive view of sexuality than have a negative program or no program at all?" Generally, people concede that while it may not have everything that they want, a program like this is preferable to the alternatives.

There are parents who are opposed to their children participating in any type of sexuality education. When they clearly understand a conservative, abstinence-based program, however, they are generally willing to, as they put it, "take a chance on it."

Building Support

Regardless of the type of program developed or selected, for a program to be successfully implemented, it must have community support. Program planners may wish to visit with community leaders/decision-makers to obtain a feel for the support that does exist for the type of program being proposed. An advisory committee composed of educators, health workers, community leaders (including representation from the local ministerial alliance), parents and students could be asked to review possible programs and to make recommendations to the school board. At least one board member should also be part of the advisory committee.

Program planners may need to spend time with individual board members to be sure that they understand the program. Board members should also understand that when their support is solicited, they have been asked to not only vote for the initiation of a program, but also to support its continued implementation, even when faced with individuals who oppose it.

Open debate, involving all who wish to participate, concerning the relative merits of implementing a particular program is not an effective way to gain support or to decide upon a particular program. Open community meetings in the form of "parent preview nights" should occur *after* the advisory committee has reviewed curricula and made a recommendation to the board and the board has adopted a specific program. The approach is not "let's vote to decide whether our school will offer a program," but "we feel sure you will be interested in knowing about a program in which your young person will be participating. Please come to find out about the program, review materials, meet teachers and have your questions answered."

Parent preview nights attract parents who are supportive of the program, those who have questions and concerns, and those who are opposed to it. Several key factors can increase the likelihood of a successful meeting and build support for the program:

- a program that is conservative, educationally sound, and that promotes a positive view of sexuality
- a presentation that clearly explains the goals of the program and gives a clear outline of lessons
- an opportunity for parents to review materials
- a clear question and answer period in which all expressed concerns are addressed
- a mechanism for parents to exclude their child from the program

Parent preview nights can be an effective way to build support. Building support for your program is important regardless of the community in which you live. It is especially important in conservative communities.

The Teacher

A major concern of parents is who will be teaching the program. They want to know about the teacher's preparation and how the material will be handled. Many times they are concerned about a host of other factors not related to quality of instruction. Regardless of the program that is adopted, the teacher is the key element. A program that benefits students and receives support from parents will not neglect teacher selection. It is vital that the person teaching the program be well prepared in the content, possess good teaching skills, feel comfortable addressing sexual concerns and have a desire not only to teach the subject matter but to implement the program that has been adopted.

In one large school district, administrators felt the issue of "who will teach?" to be so important that they limited the teaching of sexuality education to two teachers who had received specialized training in sexuality education and in whom they had complete confidence. These teachers rotated from school to school providing students at all 13 of the district's junior high schools with a five-week sexuality education program. This policy eliminated the need for administrators to monitor the presentations of dozens of different teachers. Administrators, board members and parents all knew that the teachers "knew their stuff" and that they would follow the program that had been adopted.

Maintaining Order

Beyond the curriculum to be used and the selection of a teacher, many people are concerned with maintaining order, restraint and respect. They believe that sex is a serious subject and should be treated seriously. Especially in conservative communities, classroom discussions that get "out of hand" have the potential to incite the wrath of parents and endanger both the program and the teacher's contract. However, while it is true that "free-for-alls" should be avoided, it is also true that sexuality education should be fun—for the students and for the instructor. The appropriate use of humor, nonjudgmental attitudes and active student participation go a long way toward creating a comfortable learning environment. Take special note of the phrase, "appropriate use of humor." Humor is sensitive and can be misused, particularly in the sexuality education classroom.

To facilitate a comfortable learning environment, the establishment of class groundrules is important. These can be generated by the instructor and students and might include the following:
- Respect others.
- There is no such thing as a dumb question.
- Everyone has the right to pass.
- No personal questions.
- Use dictionary terminology.
- No private conversations during class time—listen and participate.

The groundrules that students help to develop can be used to maintain order. The teacher can remind students when they are violating groundrules and provide positive reinforcement for following the groundrules. While some people still have the idea that students should always be quiet, with heads in their books or listening to their teacher, such an approach is not compatible with good education, and certainly not good sexuality education. In a "good" sexuality education classroom there will be much student talk. There will be laughter. There will be respect. And there will be learning.

Controversial Issues and Student Questions

Many parents (and not just parents in conservative communities) have concerns about how teachers will deal with controversial issues and answer student questions. This is a legitimate concern. Teachers should be encouraged to create a classroom environment in which students feel comfortable asking questions. For many teachers the problem is not in getting students to ask questions, but in how to answer these questions. For example, how should a teacher respond to a student who says, "My mother said abortion is murder. Is she right?" Inappropriate answers to sensitive questions have the potential to cause major problems for the teacher and the program. To best serve students and to avoid problems, the following model is suggested to address value-laden questions dealing with controversial issues (using abortion as an example):

Define terms. "Abortion is the termination or ending of a pregnancy. Abortion may be spontaneous (as a miscarriage) or induced. Generally, when someone speaks of abortion they are referring to an induced abortion."

Provide factual information. "Abortion is a legal option in this country, but not everyone considers it a moral option. It is one of the most controversial social issues of our time. In its 1973 *Roe vs. Wade* decision, the Supreme Court returned the matter of abortion to the conscience of the individual." Depending upon the group the teacher may wish to provide specifics of the court decision and to also indicate that more recent decisions and state legislative actions have placed some restrictions on access to abortions in some states. Indicate the situation in your state.

Provide a range of values. "There are basically four positions relative to abortion. At one extreme are those who feel that abortion, for whatever reason, is murder. This is an extreme position. At the other extreme are people who feel that abortion is a woman's right and should be available on demand at any time for any reason with no restrictions whatsoever, and that there is no reason to consider fetal rights at any time. Again this is an extreme position. The vast majority of people in this country support one of the two remaining positions: either opposition to abortion with provisions to allow it under some circumstances, or support of safe and legal access to abortion with opposition to its use as a form of birth control."

Refer students to parents, clergy and other trusted adults. "If you haven't thought much about the issue of abortion, it may be important for you to do so. Read, listen to news reports, and be sure to discuss the issue with your parents. If you are part of a youth group at church, scouts or another organization, you may want to discuss it with your adult leaders."

Give your personal opinion only when you feel it is appropriate to do so. This will be the exception rather than the rule. (The following answer is in response to, "But what do you think?") "I know how I feel about abortion, but reaching a position that I could feel comfortable with wasn't easy. I read a lot. I talked to lots of people. I spent a lot of time thinking about it. That's what you need to do. I'm not sure that sharing my opinion with you will help you reach your own decision. If you think I'm going to make this easy for you, you're wrong. You need to do the same thing I did and reach your own decision on this matter."

Teachers who follow this model will be of great help to their students. They will provide students with information, but will challenge them to seek out information on their own and to consider all viewpoints before making their own thoughtful, considered decisions. Teachers can help students communicate with parents and other adults about important issues. By following the model, teachers can do all this without revealing to students how they personally feel about these issues. After all, the teacher's position on these issues is not really the important point. What is important to young people are the decisions they make.

There may be instances in which a teacher feels that it is important to share a personal opinion relative to a controversial issue. If that is the case consider the following approach: (Spoken while standing at the front of the room) "As your instructor I'm not sure that it is appropriate that I share my opinion with you." (Then move out into the classroom and sit at a desk with the students.) "But as someone who does have an opinion, an opinion that is just as important, but not more important, than any one else's, here's how I feel." (Briefly, give your opinion.) "Remember, this is my opinion. You may agree with it, or you may hold a completely different opinion, that's up to you."

Many questions don't fit the above model but do fall into one (or more) of the following four categories (ETR Associates Training Staff, 1983):

Informational. These are questions in which the student is simply seeking information. Answer questions as clearly and directly as possible. In answering, remember the phrase, "that's a good question," and use it often. Many times, when a student asks what others clearly perceive to be a dumb question, the teacher's role will be not just to provide information, but to also help the student save face.

Permission seeking. These questions are often prefaced with "How old do you have to be to...," "Is it okay to...," "When you were our age did you...." Remember in most cases it is not up to you to give permission. You might ask the class what they think. Almost always it is appropriate to refer the students to parents or guardians.

Am I normal? These questions sometimes are prefaced with "Is it normal to...?" or "Do most...?" Remember and frequently use the phrase, "many young people have that concern." In answering these type of questions the teacher's main job is to provide reassurance.

Shock questions. These are the questions that have the potential, either by accident or design, to blow teacher and program out of the water. Sometimes a student is sincerely seeking information, other times he or she is testing limits. In many cases the best way to handle these questions is to simply answer them. At other times the teacher may need to say, "I'm not comfortable discussing this in class; if you really want to know, I'll be happy to discuss it with you later." Personal questions in this category may be handled by reminding students of the groundrules, which should include "No personal questions."

To the greatest extent possible, the teacher should treat all questions as "legitimate" and do her or his best to answer them, knowing when to deviate somewhat from the plans for the day and when to stay on track, but always attempting to provide students with the information they need and want.

Maintaining Support

The number-one rule to follow in maintaining support for a program is, "Don't ever take support for granted." Program advocates must continue to do the things they did to initially build support. They must continually review the program to be sure that it is current, meets the needs of the students and is acceptable to parents. Planners must be willing to make revisions in the program when needed. The advisory committee should be maintained and review the program periodically, especially any changes that are planned. A mechanism must also be in place for addressing parent concerns.

The program must continue to insist on competent, well-trained teachers, who follow the adopted program and can address controversial issues and answer student questions. Teachers should be encouraged to participate in workshops and other continuing education programs to enhance their knowledge and skill. Programs must be continually evaluated. Is the program doing what planners hoped it would do? Programs that can do these things should have no problem in maintaining support.

Summary

This chapter provides suggestions for implementing sexuality education in conservative communities. The suggestions made here can actually be applied to any community:

1. Adopt or develop a curriculum that is conservative, gives a positive view of sexuality and provides young people with the information they need.
2. Build support through contact with community leaders, advisory committees and parent preview nights.
3. Hire teachers who are well prepared, who want to teach sexuality education, and who feel comfortable addressing students' sexual concerns.
4. Use groundrules to promote student learning and to maintain classroom order.
5. Effectively deal with controversial issues and provide answers to student questions.
6. Work to maintain program support. Never take it for granted.

Suppose that you live in a conservative community and you want your young people to have sexuality education. If you follow these suggestions will your program be guaranteed to have no problems, no difficulties, no opposition? No. But if you wait for such guarantees before you act, you will be waiting a long time. There are sure to be some problems, some difficulties and, except in rare situations, at least some opposition. These guidelines, however, can help bring the problems, difficulties and opposition down to a manageable size.

References

Core-Gebhart, P., S. J. Hart and M. Young. 1991. *Living smart: Understanding sexuality in the teen years.* Fayetteville, AR: The University of Arkansas Press.

Core-Gebhart, P., S. J. Hart and M. Young. 1991. *Living Smart: Understanding sexuality into adulthood.* Fayetteville, AR: The University of Arkansas Press.

Core-Gebhart, P., S. J. Hart and M. Young. 1994. *Sex can wait: An abstinence-based sexuality education curriculum for high school.* Santa Cruz, CA: ETR Associates.

Core-Gebhart, P., S. J. Hart and M. Young. 1994. *Sex can wait: An abstinence-based sexuality education curriculum for middle school.* Santa Cruz, CA: ETR Associates.

ETR Training Associates Staff. 1983. *Beyond reproduction: Tips and techniques for teaching sensitive family life education issues.* Santa Cruz, CA: ETR Associates.

Young, M., and T. Young. 1994. *Sex can wait: An abstinence-based sexuality curriculum for upper elementary school.* Santa Cruz, CA: ETR Associates.

Chapter 25

Sexuality Education in High-Risk Populations

Susan A. Yeres, EdD, and Betsy Crane, MA

Youth at high risk for problems in the area of sexuality can be reached and helped but it takes extra effort, commitment and a willingness to risk discomfort. It means breaking through denial that some youth are gay, that those with physical disabilities have sexual desires, that many teens have had sex since childhood due to abuse, and that racism, classism and other societal oppressions can make the usual message of sexuality educators seem irrelevant.

The information in this chapter is based on two assumptions: One is that successful work with any community or population must take place in a partnership, considering the needs and values of the group being "taught." Sexuality education does not take place in a value-free context. It is important to acknowledge one's own values and goals and strive to find alignment where possible with those of the students and the community.

The second assumption is the belief that in a diverse society, "the good life" has many forms. The life choices made by those in the community in which you are working may be different than those you might make. For example, a young woman who chooses to have a baby at 15, although statistically at high risk for future poverty, may use the pregnancy as a central organizing principle in her life, gain special help and attention, and do very well both as a parent and vocationally. In some communities, young people may put family needs before their own needs, even when such choices may jeopardize their future career decisions. To be a successful sexuality educator, you will need to be aware of the basic cultural values of the group with whom you are working.

Who Are the High-Risk Youth?

We see high-risk youth as the population of adolescents who lack equal access to information and choices, which thus inhibits their ability to have healthy relationships and make good (i.e., thoughtful) sexual and reproductive decisions. In this context, "information" means knowledge about one's body and its sexual and reproductive functioning, about healthy relationships and about protecting oneself from sexual abuse, unintended pregnancy, HIV/AIDS and other sexually transmitted disease. "Choices" means the ability to use this information. Choices can be inhibited by not having access to condoms or contraceptives or health care, lack of social time to spend with appropriate partners (e.g., youth with a developmental disability whose days are planned for them), or being forced into sexual behavior against one's will. On a broader level, choices are inhibited if, due to poverty or discrimination, a person cannot fulfill his or her potential vocationally and thus falls into sexual or reproductive situations because of hopelessness about the future.

High-risk youth, then, are the young people who are "out of the loop." Categorizing or labeling is not simple. Young people at high risk may fall into or identify with several of the following subgroups.

Young people who experience discrimination, based on class, ethnicity, gender, religion, sexual orientation, disability, size or even subgroup affiliation (e.g., skin heads, punks or gang members). Young people on the "target group" end of these oppressions may be excluded because of ignorance or prejudice and not be allowed or accepted into informal and formal settings where sexuality education is provided. The education they do receive may not be culturally appropriate.

These young people may be given different messages about sexuality than other groups of teens. Educators may assume youth are already sexually active or experienced because they look tough. Youth with disabilities may be told directly or indirectly that they will not have a sexual life and be left out of classes on sexuality education. Derogatory statements about low-income populations and childbearing send strong messages to young people about classism and sexuality. These youth may exclude themselves from sexuality education settings, feeling that they do not "fit in."

Young people with personal limitations/differences including those who are physically challenged; those who have learning problems; those who do not speak or read English well because of a learning disorder or teaching deficit or because it is not their native language; and those with emotional problems or psychiatric disorders. Young people in these groups may be excluded because the system believes they are not or should not be sexual and cannot handle information or access services. These youth may have difficulty understanding, absorbing or using information the way it is traditionally given. They may need more explicit instruction about sexual behaviors, e.g., how to have sex in a way that is pleasurable and "safe." To provide such instruction may seem "politically impossible" and appropriate materials are hard to find.

Young people with social and environmental limitations including those living in poverty, including the working poor; youth isolated in rural areas or living under violent urban conditions; those who have been abused physically, sexually or psychologically or who have witnessed family abuse; and youth in the foster care system. Also at risk are dropouts and delinquents—those who have removed themselves from the system or chosen to fight it. Youth in these groups may exclude themselves because they do not believe sexuality education information is for them. They may feel hopeless and may have given up. They may be forcibly kept from the information or services or have no knowledge that it exists. They may turn to risky sexual behavior for stability, to feel loved or as a way of connecting with others.

Special Issues

The many young people who are "out of the loop" have diverse needs, interests and values. What they have in common is that "doing the same old thing" in terms of sexuality education doesn't work with them. They are a complex group, as are the issues involved in working with them. Some issues are theirs; some are ours as sexuality educators.

Norms or Realities

Sexual behavior for many high-risk youth is influenced by social networks. Early childbearing and denial of the need to practice safer sex may be expected, encouraged, forced, learned or a part of the "rites of passage" for a particular group.

For example, young men in some groups believe that fathering a child is the first "rite" to becoming a man. This may not include raising a child, but simply having fathered one (sometimes in large numbers). When young people feel hopeless and can't envision a promising future they want to find a way to guarantee they leave a mark or make a difference. Early sexual activity can be perceived as affirming and reassuring, proving that someone notices them and cares. Having a child can mean that they have created a part of themselves for the future and have gained a sense of purpose for the years ahead.

Hierarchy of Needs

There may be life or death issues that stand in the way of youth's openness to sexuality education messages. Maslow's Hierarchy of Needs suggests that we will be successful in addressing higher needs only after basic survival needs are met (Maslow, 1970). Young people who are dealing with life-threatening issues may not care whether they have good communication skills. Maslow's model is an excellent reference for understanding where attention may be focused—on food, shelter and safety, not self-esteem or quality of relationships. Yet that is what many of our prevention education and interventions are geared toward promoting.

Some young people may be so focused on survival that they don't see a meaningful future for themselves and therefore don't plan for that future. In those situations, initial work may need to address those needs and concerns. A young man who carries a gun to school to feel safe may not be thinking about the outcome of his sexual behavior. Prostitutes may need money more than they need to practice safer sex.

Oppression

Societal oppression or "isms," can be defined generically as "prejudice plus power." The many spokes of the "wheel of oppression" include sexism, racism, ableism, classism, heterosexism, anti-Semitism and ethnocentrism. Those who are in the target groups of various "isms" (e.g., girls and women facing sexism and people of color dealing with racism) lack access to power as a group and have to deal with the misinformation about them held by the rest of society. Those in the target group know much more about the dominant group than vice versa.

While the "underdog" needs to study and understand those in power in order to survive, there is no similar incentive for those in the dominant group. Young people in target groups often find themselves in educational settings where the teacher has no idea of the reality of their lives. Given this, it is unlikely that sexuality education, which is so personal and so related to lifestyle issues and pressures, will be relevant and usable for the student.

Paradigms

The concept of the "paradigm," originally used in physical science, has entered the realm of social sciences as a way of describing models, theory, perception and frame of reference—how we "see the world." Thinking about paradigms can help us examine the way we approach high-risk populations and the way we perceive the issues and solutions.

Applying the concept of paradigms to sexuality education as a product, we need to ask whether we are using the same old solutions, when we may not yet have clearly seen the problems. What are the real barriers to a particular population of young people having or using information and services? Is your program addressing these barriers or merely pouring more water through a leaky bucket? If parental or community norms support early childbearing for girls, or fathering a child for boys, will your lessons on birth control be heeded? Attention may need to be focused on involving parents or community norm setters such as gang leaders in program planning, implementation and evaluation. While difficult and time-consuming, such approaches lead to the kind of paradigm shift which is often necessary for sexuality education messages to reach the target group.

Values

Nontraditional programs structured to meet needs of high-risk youth (e.g., safer sex programs for gay youth) may meet opposition. They may be seen as amoral, rather than a way of representing and responding to different values and needs.

Because of the emphasis in many curricula on self-esteem and decision making, sexuality educators may be accused of turning teens away from their families, or inculcating them with secular humanism or individualism. When working with young people from varying backgrounds and cultures, it is wise to acknowledge your values and work to find common ground. For example, if parents of teens with severe developmental disabilities are frightened about sexual exploitation or inappropriate behavior, their first reaction may be to withhold any sexual information and demand that programs restrict their son or daughter's access to teens of the other gender. By showing empathy and responding that you too fear such outcomes, you may be able to help them see that information about sex, not ignorance, is the better protection. Programs which teach about appropriate kinds of touching and assuage curiosity about body parts of the other gender can reduce sexually unwise behavior.

Denial

Even as the HIV epidemic and crack cocaine problem have spread throughout this country, various communities insist that, "It's not a problem here," or "It won't affect us." In many communities there is a pervasive denial of the problems of teen pregnancy, STD and HIV. If a community does not admit to having a problem and does not take responsibility for sexuality education, it is certainly not going to address the youth outside the loop who are often invisible or hard to reach. Similarly, there may be denial of the sexuality of youth with disabilities, or around the sexual orientation of gay, lesbian or bisexual youth.

Shame

In a society where most references to sex are negative, shame, confusion and embarrassment around sexuality can extend to feelings about sexual values, particularly if our values are more sex-positive than the prevailing "just say no" messages. At all levels and in all settings, positive affirmation of sexuality is absent. Educators, social workers, health care workers, community advocates and parents all carry their own barriers to dealing with sexuality issues. Thus, addressing these issues is hard to do, whether speaking with parents at a PTA meeting or talking with young people. We are fighting against an entire cultural "prime directive" at the same time as we must fight through the many barriers that keep us from reaching out to high-risk populations.

No Quick Fix

Many want to believe that one curriculum, program or one-year grant will meet the needs of high-risk populations. Such perceptions create problems when seeking funding from sources that expect quantifiable, fast results when the results of meaningful efforts may be long in coming. There is no quick fix to the problems of high-risk youth. A more integrated and comprehensive approach may be needed that first addresses "ancillary" issues that affect sexual behavior and teen pregnancy. There is no one approach that will reach an entire group of this population, and the means to reach them, being staff intensive and nontraditional, will often be expensive.

Arenas for Action

Although there are many issues that may impede effectively reaching these young people, there are steps that can be taken to overcome the barriers. Being allies for youth in high-risk situations can involve action on several fronts: advocating for better public policies, dealing with systems issues around design and operation of programs, and the way we ourselves act as sexuality educators for these populations.

Public Policy

We are emerging from a period of public policy that did not support making information and choices available to young people in the area of sexuality. Instead, federal policies advocated by right-wing religious groups were based on the assumption that restricting access to information and services would result in less sexual activity and lower rates of teen pregnancy and STD. Legislation termed the Chastity Bill funded programs for pregnancy prevention that use abstinence-only curricula. There is no scientifically reliable evidence that such curricula, which often use scare tactics and present negative messages about sex, are effective (Donahue, 1987; Trudell and Whatley, 1991). A more rational and effective approach seems to be a combination of helping young people avoid unwanted sexual involvement and teaching about contraceptives and where to get them if needed.

Experience in other countries, including those in Scandinavia, has proven that positive-based sexuality education policy can produce much better results in terms of preventing teenage pregnancy, HIV and STD (Jones et al., 1985). In societies where sexuality education is mandatory and birth control is free and available, the message to young people is not "Don't have sex," but "Don't get pregnant before you can support a child" and "Don't get or pass on a sexually transmitted disease." Interestingly, the rates of teen sexual activity are no higher in those countries than they are here (Jones et al., 1985). Young people who are going to have sex do so, whether or not they have information or access to contraceptives.

In the United States, over 2,000 federally funded family planning clinics provide education, health care and contraceptives to teens in both inner-city and rural areas, but funding has been cut in the past 12 years, and many teens do not live in areas where such clinics are present or accessible. Despite changes at the national level, the influence of the religious right remains at the state and local level. The Christian Coalition promotes a strategy of "stealth" candidates, using get-out-the-vote drives in fundamentalist churches. Such candidates win local school board positions as write-in candidates without ever declaring their candidacy. Or they may run openly as candidates but not reveal their anti-sexuality-education agenda until elected. The Catholic Conference is also a major political player, pressuring for abstinence-only curricula and arguing against access to condoms and funding for family planning centers.

The abstinence-only position has inhibited state education departments, school districts and youth-serving agencies from meeting the needs of youth because of fear of opposition from a minority of parents and religious institutions. The majority of parents who want sex education for youth *can* be mobilized to speak out, but they need support. In our sex-negative society, many people experience anxiety or shame if they talk about sex at a public forum. Those who would advocate for more information and access to services for youth are often people who were themselves "out of the loop" as youth and may not feel empowered to take action.

Advocates for high-risk youth must make advocacy for rational public policies a priority and help the communities with whom they work organize to effect change and support reality-based sexuality education. To help high-risk youth, leaders on the federal, state and local level must counter opponents who say that no knowledge and pat answers are the way to help youth and their families.

Lobbying and Advocacy

Lobbying and advocacy can include letters, phone calls, faxes and visits with state and federal legislators, as well as petitions, rallies, letters to the editor and presentations at "meet the candidate nights" or school board meetings. The public policy issues that need support include:

- Grants to schools and community organizations for special programs to reach high-risk youth.
- Funding for curricula, films and educational materials that address the realities of diverse youth populations.
- State mandates for comprehensive sexuality education in the schools. Only 13 states now have such legislation. State curricula should be amended as needed for at-risk youth.
- Access to free or low-cost reproductive health care for teens as part of universal health care.
- Increased funding for family planning clinics, especially for education and outreach.
- Laws which support access to reproductive health care for minors on their own consent.
- Laws mandating parental involvement in minor's abortion decisions often strike high-risk youth hardest. Parental involvement should be encouraged and supported but not mandated by law.

Programs for High-Risk Youth

In approaching the challenge of designing and operating programs to meet the sexuality education needs of high-risk youth, there are several caveats to keep in mind.

Work in coalitions. Join coalitions with people in high-risk communities to address pressing needs as *they* see them (e.g., housing, jobs). Work with community leaders on their issues and enlist their involvement in determining what type of sexuality education is appropriate and most useful in their community or with their youth.

Work toward consensus or alignment. To build bridges and scale the walls that divide, advocates can work together to find consensus based on basic survival issues and a morality that transcends differences. Common goals and agendas on sexuality, even with "conservative" parents, many emerge around the following messages:

- Don't get pregnant at 13. Have children when you are ready to care for them.
- Don't get HIV or other sexually transmitted disease. Stay healthy, you can't afford to be ill. It is the only way to help your family and to stay alive.
- Don't allow yourself to be exploited or abused.
- Be in relationships with and only have sex with people who treat you well.

Find allies. If issues of sexuality education are highly charged politically in your school or agency, don't try to go it alone. Though things will move more slowly if you take time to organize, you'll have more chance of success in the long run. Find other teachers, youth workers or parents, as well as youth, who recognize the need for greater access to information and choices for the population you serve.

Strategize. Gather data about the need, determine what or who the barriers are, decide what your message is, and strategize how to proceed—how to "market" your message.

Involve parents. Remember that most parents support sexuality education, (Louis Harris and Associates, 1988) but they may not know how to influence the system. They themselves may have had bad experiences as youth with schools, agencies or churches and may not come to PTA meetings or want to confront administrators. Find low-key or nonthreatening ways to involve them with your program, through home visits, potluck dinners, awards nights for youth, etc. to gradually start to build the trust they need to help advocate for better sexuality education.

Help parents in their role as sexuality educators. Parents are playing this role, consciously or not, by the subtle messages they are giving about bodies, how to act as males or females, relationships and how to behave sexually. Yet many parents feel insecure in this role. They are not sure what they want to communicate, given the differences between the values they were taught and what they know about the real world. They feel caught between what they think they *should* be telling their kids and what they'd really like to say if they thought it was all right. Informal conversations, or group discussions for those who will come to a meeting or workshop can help parents feel more comfortable with sexuality issues.

Involve youth in planning. Reach out and listen to youth themselves in planning and evaluating programs. This may mean going out to find teens in nontraditional ways—in homeless shelters, on basketball courts, or through youth workers who serve youth at risk. Ask these youth to be in a focus group. Such groups, used frequently in marketing, pay members of target audiences to meet and respond to ideas about products. Run ideas for a new program by such a group and determine interest or barriers before you spend a lot of time and money developing the program. Invite young people to be on youth advisory groups where they can be critics of the curriculum or educational materials. They can provide feedback and feel empowered and involved as well.

Train youth to be peer educators. This could happen either in formal settings, where they supplement what is being taught by sharing their own experiences (e.g., teen mothers), or by being available as informal educators or referral sources. One family planning program recruited and trained African-American youth for a Youth Ambassadors Program (YAP). The teens designed and wore YAP T-shirts. When other young people asked what YAP meant, they had an opportunity to talk about it with them. The number of African-American teens who sought family planning services increased in the year the program was initiated.

Choose educators who can relate to youth. Select those who will teach or do training carefully. Whenever possible choose educators or trainers who are members of the group to be served, or who are very sensitive to the lifestyle and cultural issues of that group. Particularly in the area of sexuality, teachers can be role models for youth, demonstrating how sensitive issues can be discussed and resolved in the context of one's own life and culture. For example:

- For immigrant youth, an educator who is from or understands their culture (and speaks their language) can assist with the culture shock of growing up sexually in a land where the expectations and pressures may be very different.

- Gay, lesbian, bisexual or "questioning" youth can have their self-esteem enhanced and may be more likely to listen to messages about sexuality from an adult who identifies as gay, lesbian or bisexual.

- Youth with a physical disability (e.g., paralysis) can benefit from the life experiences of an educator or counselor who retains and acts on her or his sexuality despite limitations in sensation and movement. If such educators are not available, seek out members of the community who would be willing to share their experiences.

Being an Effective Educator

This is complex work and there are no simple solutions. However if you are working with high-risk youth around issues of their sexuality, it may help to consider the following:

Start where they are. Remembering the "hierarchy of needs," look for ways to find out what the important issues are for the youth you are working with and start there. For example, find out what they see as important to family life. This beginning point may help you realize that a particular youth is worrying about whether there will be food on the table. You can then relate the discussion to choices related to providing for children and a family.

Teach about relationships. One of the areas where youth want help is relationships—how to get one and how to get out of one, without getting hurt or hurting the other person. Instead of starting sexuality education classes with anatomy and physiology or prevention of STD and pregnancy, start closer to where youth live, to what matters to them on a day to day basis—"Will anyone ever like me?" and "What do I do if someone does?" Discussions on these issues may be easier because they are less sexually explicit, and they can tell you a lot about where these young people are.

Be aware of sensitive issues. As you address topics of sexuality, relationships and family life, be aware that there are likely to be youth in your group who have been sexually abused as children or raped as teens; who are gay, lesbian, bisexual or questioning; who don't have homes or parents; or who never knew their fathers. Such youth may feel ashamed or "different," yet are so used to trying to appear "normal" that you may never know who they are. Acknowledge realities and encourage individual conversations if youth don't want to talk about some things in the group. Promising confidentiality (for everything but ongoing abuse) is critical.

Be prepared to be tested. Acting out in class, laughing at sexual references, acting bored and trying to steal attention from the teacher all can be ploys to stop conversation on topics that youth find difficult or anxiety provoking. It helps to be nonpunitive, encourage laughter (afterall, sex can be pretty funny) as long as it is not at anyone's expense, set clear ground rules, let things be light and take your time. In any group, individuals need to understand how they are expected to participate. When a topic is sensitive, the ground rules are even more critical to establish a safe climate for learning and make clear how the group is to treat each other. The important rules are to agree to listen to everyone; to laugh *with*, not *at* anyone; that one person talks at a time, no interrupting; that everyone has a right to his or her own opinion; that there are no wrong feelings and the group can agree to disagree.

Be patient. Many youth at risk have given up on adults. They have been let down so many times they aren't going to let anyone become important to them. Sex as a topic offers plenty of fuel for the youth who is trying to drive you out or wear you down, so you will fulfill his or her script—that you don't really care anyway. Be persistent but don't allow yourself to be abused. Often troublemakers are the ones who need our help the most. Reach out to the young people you most want to push away or ignore.

The process is important. In sexuality education, the process of talking about the issues is as important as the information being transmitted. Use films, activities, roleplays, dyads and small group discussions to engage youth in thinking and talking about the issues. With some high-risk populations, process—an opportunity to talk and sort out feelings—is even more important than content.

Don't assume knowledge. The "cool" kids who act the most bored may be the ones with the least knowledge. Since part of the traditional male role is to be sexually informed and experienced, it is particularly hard for boys to reveal how little they know. But boys often have less information about their bodies, sexual development and pregnancy prevention than girls, who at least may have seen a film on menstruation when they were going through puberty. Few males have seen a similar film on wet dreams. So keep the information coming, even when youth look bored or act "too cool to care."

Be aware of literacy levels and English language skills. You may not be able to count on pamphlets or books to transmit the information. If reading skills are poor, present the information directly or with films. Teachers of English as a Second Language (ESL) may have tips for you on alternative teaching methods to use with students new to English.

Use roleplaying to explain a concept or issue and to start discussion. Films and audio tapes help to engage everyone and don't rely on the students' capacity to read. Read material aloud or ask for volunteers to read to protect youth who would feel embarrassed by low literacy skills. Check that individuals have the needed information and understand by asking for explanations in their own words—don't take knowledge and understanding for granted on any topic.

Use young people as peer educators. Youth may be more ready and able to hear about these topics from another young person. Young people who can be resources can be found in a variety of ways:
- Your community may have a teen theater program that does interactive skits on sexuality related issues.
- A family planning center, HIV/AIDS program, or teen parents program in your area may have young people who work as peer counselors or educators who could speak to your class or do a workshop at your community center.

- Ask a high school health teacher to have some students do a panel for younger students, talking about sexuality-related issues and what they wish they had known when they were younger.

Conclusion

It is our responsibility to address the sexuality education needs of young people who are out of the loop. Reexamining paradigms and listening to young people's realities is a critical step. Identify these young people at risk and make efforts to get to know them. Ask them what they need. Examine the barriers that can stand in your way and find allies to help you overcome them and stretch beyond your limits. Pick your arena(s) and know the issues before you embark on your strategic plan of action. Be creative, have fun and empower the young people and families you want to reach.

References

Donahue, M. J. 1987. Promoting abstinence: Is it viable? In N. Cabaniss (moderator) session, Postponing Sexual Involvement: What are we finding? Office of Adolescent Pregnancy Programs. Technical Assistance Workshop for OAPP project directors and evaluators. September 28-29. Washington, DC.

Howard, M., and J. B. McCabe. 1990. Helping teenagers postpone sexual involvement. *Family Planning Perspectives* 22 (1): 21-26.

Jones, E., J. D. Forrest, N. Goldman, S. K. Henshaw, R. Lincoln, J. I. Rosoff, C. F. Westoff and D. Wulf. 1985. Teenage pregnancy in developed countries: Determinants and policy implications. *Family Planning Perspectives* 17 (2): 53-63.

Louis Harris and Associates. 1988. *Public attitudes towards teenage pregnancy, sex education and birth control.* New York: Planned Parenthood Federation of America.

Maslow, A. H. 1970. *Motivation and personality.* 2d ed. New York: Harper and Row.

Trudell, B., and M. Whatley. 1991. *Sex respect:* A problematic public school sexuality curriculum. *Journal of Sexuality Education and Therapy* 17 (2): 125-140.

Chapter 26

Parents and Caregivers as Educators, Partners and Advocates in Sexuality Education

Lynn Leight, RN, PhD

Envision this scene: A family is engaged in a lively dinner-table discussion. The parent asks a child about his or her day at school. The child enthusiastically relays a point of interest discussed in the sexuality education class. The parent responds in one of five ways:

1. Blushes with embarrassment, coughs or clears throat and evades the child's comment by introducing a new subject.
2. Nervously laughs, snickers, avoids eye contact and diverts conversation in a flip humorous vein, offering a joke or a sarcastic comment.
3. Becomes stiff-necked, conveying disgust for the subject of sexuality, especially during the dinner hour; silence reigns.
4. Ruffles brow in a confused or disapproving manner, questioning the teacher's right to divulge moral values in the classroom.
5. Smiles receptively, utilizing the moment as a "golden opportunity" to share with the child, in a trusting and loving environment, the joy of discovering newfound sexual knowledge.

The manner in which this scenario unfolds is probably the most influential predictor of the success or failure of any given sexuality curriculum. While many variables affect the outcome of sexuality programs, parents and caregivers may be the single most important factor in successfully designing, implementing and processing the core curriculum.

It is the parent or caregiver who affirms or denies the importance of formal sexuality education and its appropriateness in influencing the child's sexual socialization. The classroom is an institutional laboratory for dispensing knowledge. The teacher is an instrument of the institution, assigned the task of skillfully conveying knowledge without overstepping boundaries and usurping the parents' role. The home and the family are the living laboratory that tests, and accepts or rejects, the classroom theories.

Without partnership with and/or advocacy from the home, children will continue to question, doubt and devalue the importance and relevancy of the sexuality curriculum. Children's receptivity to learning will be colored by their parents' or caregivers' perception of the curriculum, whether they see that curriculum as a threat to the moral fiber of the family, an embarrassment, a waste of time, or an important life-enhancing component of a rich comprehensive education.

For better or worse, parents are the covert and overt sexuality educators of their children. From the moment of birth, the parent models the child's perception of trust, intimacy, power, control, assertiveness, self-esteem and the manner of expressing affection and mutual respect. Sexuality education is an ongoing process dependent upon the time and space the parent or caregiver occupies in the child's life. It is within the family structure that the basic values, beliefs and attitudes for sexual socialization are established. Through inflection, observation or active dialogue, the child senses and learns which issues are open for discussion and which are off-bounds. Early in life, children learn to recognize those family members who are "askable" and available.

In tracking teenage sexual behavior, a wealth of data shows that, "Where parents were the main source of sex-education, the children tended to follow more traditional (chastity) norms in their premarital sexuality relationship" (Lewis, 1973). These findings have been replicated many times in studies affirming that sex information provided primarily by parents, specifically the mother, appears to curtail rather than stimulate premarital sexual behavior (Spanier, 1977).

Parents continue to recognize the importance of conveying sexual knowledge to their children and express their desire to act as their children's primary sexuality educators. In 1986, Yankolvich, Clancy and Shulman conducted a poll for *Time* magazine in which 69 percent of the 1,015 Americans interviewed said that, "Parents are not doing as much as they should to educate their children about sex." Thirty-nine percent of the parents polled had had a "frank and open" discussion about sex with their teenager only "a few times" or "not at all" (Leo, 1986).

While teens may prefer their parents to be their primary sexuality educators, they frequently turned to other resources for information. Many teens felt that their parents weren't sexually literate, and that they expressed disapproval of the teen's behavior if and when they sought information. Teens also felt that their parents appeared embarrassed and evasive and were unable or unwilling to accept their teen's emerging sexual maturity (Couch, 1967).

With the disparity among what parents should, would and comfortably could do as their children's primary provider of sexuality education, especially in this era of HIV/AIDS, it may come as no surprise that the *Time* poll reported that 86 percent of the respondents favored sex education being taught in the schools; 89

percent wanted courses for children from age 12 on to deal with birth control; and about three-quarters recommended that homo-sexuality and abortion be included in the curriculum as well (Leo, 1986).

With this apparent clash of desires, intentions and realities, there emerges a theoretical problem: If a majority of parents want their children to participate in a sexuality education program, and if teens adopt a more responsible approach toward sexual behavior when parents do actively communicate sexuality information, then why does the parent majority not join with the public schools to provide at-home sexuality education that parallels the information and concepts presented in the sexuality education classroom?

Barriers to Parents as Educators

While many parents earnestly strive to talk comfortably with their children about sexual issues, they may be intimidated by their own perceived lack of knowledge. They may fear exposing their igno-rance and losing their children's respect. Assuming or choosing to believe that children are wiser and more sexually sophisticated than they are, by virtue of exposure to the media and formal programs of sexuality education, provides a legitimate excuse for withdrawing from dialogue.

Then there are those parents who struggle with their own sexual socialization. While they yearn to resolve their ambivalent sexual values and beliefs, they may feel so disabled by their per-sonal fears that they surrender their role as their children's primary educators, hoping their children will not learn "the wrong things." These parents are in a constant state of internal conflict.

Their concept of "the wrong thing" can range from a style of kissing to masturbation; it almost always includes premarital intercourse. Of course, the "wrong thing" is defined by an assortment of parameters, including the parent's gender, place of residence, religion, ethnocultural and socioeconomic status along with the political climate.

Parents from more conservative communities may believe that their children are either too young or too vulnerable to be exposed to such sensitive information. Parents who believe that what their children don't know won't hurt them represent the strongest challenge to a parent/school partnership. Laboring under the misconception that information and knowledge encourages promiscuity, they do not realize that silence speaks more loudly than words.

Any subject that is shrouded in silence is loaded with negative overtones. The inference is that the subject is either too vulgar, too violent or too blasphemous to discuss. To speak of it, to think of it, or worse yet, to consider *doing* it would be sinful and rightfully fear- or guilt-producing. Given a home environment of silence and a social and cultural milieu saturated with sexual innuendoes and blatant sexual messages, children are left with few resources to help them separate fact from fiction. Too often these naturally curious children seek answers from the wrong resources, such as peers who are equally ill-informed or persons who exploit their naiveté in abusive and self-serving ways. The sad reality is that these children usually mature into adults who again perpetuate the legacy of silence.

Seventy-three percent of the parents polled by Yankolvich, Clancy and Shulman stated that they had been, "only somewhat informed" or "poorly informed" about sexuality when they themselves were in their teens (Leo, 1986). Most of the parents polled recalled no trusted adult from their youth whose comforting sexuality communication style they could now emulate. They may have learned by example how to bake a cake, repair a tire or seed a garden, but none remembered a fireside chat concerning their evolving sexuality, dating, intimacy, love or sexual activities. These parents now feel ill-equipped and ill-informed to actively assume the role of sexuality educator for their children, although both child and parent wish this could be the case.

Ambivalent Partners

With few other recourses, parents may look to the schools as a convenient yet threatening conveyor of sexual knowledge. In abdicating their role, parents fear exposing their children to instructors whose teaching skills, personalities, values and maturity may be in conflict with their own, and to a curriculum that may stretch their boundaries of propriety. Because of such founded or unfounded fears, sexuality education in the school is often perceived as undermining the parental role and damaging the parent/child relationship.

Parents' defensiveness about their own perceived sexual illiteracy may fuel their lack of confidence, control and authority. Feeling threatened and defensive, these parents frequently resist expanding the school curriculum into the home setting. An important task in developing a successful sexuality education program for children is to first educate the parents. It has been said that, "An educated consumer is our best customer." The better educated the parent, the greater the chances that the school and parent will become closer and more trusting partners and advocates of sexuality education. Peter Scales (1981) points to parental involvement as the one consistent factor in exemplary models of sexuality education. Our mission is clear: We must direct our energies, public policies and resources toward promoting parental inclusion in sexuality education programs.

Connecting Parents, Schools and Teens: The Dade County Model

How do we begin the process? A variety of successful parent/school corroborating initiatives exist throughout the country from the rural area of Colusa County in Northern California (Family Life Education Project) to the New Jersey Network for Family Life Education and the exemplary parent program collaborative of St. Paul the Apostle School in Los Angeles (Lindsay and Rodin, 1989).

In 1974, under the auspices of the Sex Health Education (SHE) Center in Dade County, Florida, sexuality seminars for parents were promoted in a variety of settings. The SHE Center, established in 1973 as a private, nonprofit counseling and gynecological care center for clients of all ages, was grounded in the theory that sexuality information, provided in a professional yet informal, nonclinical, easily accessible setting and preceding every medical examination, would both humanize and internalize the learning process.

> The SHE Center established a reputation as a place where factual information on sexual matters could be obtained, where effective counseling and education programs were ongoing, and where medical services could be received in a manner that met client requirements for competence and discretion. As such, almost akin to an underground movement, the Center soon became a much-used resource for students, teachers, counselors and parents. It received a daily stream of open and anonymous inquires, usually related to sexually transmitted disease, unplanned pregnancies, or just plain lack of adequate information about sexual matters. (Leight, 1993)

The Center's personnel volunteered to supplement the schools' sexuality classes at the request of individual teachers and with the permission of parents. A significant number of school teachers, many of whom were uncomfortable with the subject matter or felt that they were somewhat less competent to teach the sexuality education unit, responded enthusiastically to the Center's offer of assistance. When the Center's personnel found that they were unable to meet the demands of the individual schools, they initiated communitywide parent/teen seminars on sexuality to parallel and/or supplement the efforts of teachers in the public schools. For the next two years, the SHE Center worked effectively, if unofficially, with public school teachers.

In 1972, the Dade School Board had "quietly" adopted a policy requiring both boys and girls in Dade's 63 junior and senior high schools to take at least one year of study in a course related to family living. But, without a state or county mandate for sexuality education, classes were included or excluded depending upon the particular school's principal, administrative staff and teachers' willingness to include the sexuality unit within the curriculum. The Dade County School Board really had no policy or regulation regarding how any given school might go about teaching sexuality courses.

With the advent of the birth control pill, the 1972 passage of the *Roe v. Wade* decision legalizing abortion, and the increase in teen pregnancies, STD rates and student dropout, there was a groundswell from concerned parents and teachers to promote sexual literacy. Seizing the moment, the SHE Center became a liaison between the home and the school and a catalyst in encouraging community resources to follow suit.

Parent Seminars

Breakfast seminars were sponsored by the PTA/PTSA, the student council, and various social, civic and religious organizations such as Junior League, Mental Health Association, Girl Scouts of America, Big Sisters/Big Brothers, the United Methodist Church, the Synagogue Council of America and the Unitarian Universalist Association. Lunchtime programs were provided in libraries, hospitals and workplace sites. A local television station promoted a lunchtime seminar on sexuality for its employees.

In addition, the SHE Center conducted a four- to six-week evening "seminar on sexuality" series for parents in the clinic setting and at a condominium location. By utilizing the resources of the public and private sector and strategizing the time schedule to meet the needs of participants, the SHE Center reached a broad segment of the population. To contact the vital but often neglected population of single parents, the Center initiated a lunchtime and a Sunday brunch seminar for fraternal organizations, county commissions and Parents Without Partners.

The seminars were informal. Invitations requested that participants bring with them one unsigned query about sexuality for the question box. The format dealt with defining the difference between sex and sexuality, the influences that affect one's perspective of sexuality and the interpretation of normal and abnormal sexual behavior. Humor, humanism and respect were the primary ingredients in the success of the series. The most popular segment of the program was the facilitators' response to the anonymous questions. The activity gave participants an opportunity to hear the most private and personal concerns of others and measure them against their own. The single-parent groups not only attracted people who sought advice for communicating with their children but encouraged friendships with others of the same or other gender to facilitate communication where gaps were perceived in the parent/child relationship.

Facilitators were chosen for their comfort, knowledge, professionalism, askability and humor in presenting a comprehensive view of sexuality. Preference was accorded to persons certified or trained by the American Association of Sex Educators, Counselors and Therapists (AASECT) and people who had been sensitized to accept, without judgment, the variety of ways by which consenting adults responsibly and ethically express their sexuality. Facilitators were chosen who clearly communicated, verbally and nonverbally, that expressing one's sexuality was natural and healthy and held the potential for physical satisfaction, emotional pleasure, increased personal knowledge and self-esteem, and renewed energy.

Parent/Teen Symposiums

In 1976, the SHE Center became the Florida state coordinator for National Family Sex Education Week (NFSEW), an innovative concept developed by Sol Gordon of the Institute for Family Research and Education at Syracuse University. The SHE Center, along with Dade Schools, and public and private agencies, donated their energies in creating a week of sexuality education activities (October 15 through 21, 1976) designed to open doors for communication about sexuality between children and parents, teachers and students, health professionals and clients. Health professional facilitators conducted a talent search for teen and adult "sexperts" to conjointly facilitate workshops dealing with appropriate ways of teaching young people about sexuality. The Center auditioned teens to stage vignettes at school assemblies related to dating and interpersonal relationships and blitzed the media, emphasizing the need for a uniform mandated sexuality education program for all Dade County children from kindergarten through twelfth grade, validating the need with startling statistics. The newsprint, radio and television stations provided public service announcements, editorial comment and interviews in advance of an all-day parent/teen seminar on sexuality that was the culminating event of the week's activities.

The seminar was held at a major synagogue in a centrally located downtown area of Miami. More than one hundred people attended ten different workshops that ranged from "How to Feel Comfortable as a Maturing Adult" to "Body Language and How the Body Works" to "Sex, Ready or Not?" The evaluations were favorable and the heightened community awareness was evidenced by the amount of newsprint devoted to the success and content of this first community coalition.

During the ensuing year, more invitations from radio and television talk shows, along with requests from teachers and parents for educational literature and classes, were evidenced. By 1977, the SHE Center had developed a teen sexuality hotline that kept the Center's team of educators busy from 9:00 a.m. to 9:00 p.m. Increasing sectors of the Dade community requested another symposium. The second all-day seminar expanded, with student service clubs volunteering as hosts. Art students decorated the seminar site; clergy offered to facilitate workshops; a supermarket and private caterer donated brown-bag lunches; department stores set up a model nursery illustrating the cost involved in preparing for a baby; community organizations provided literature and health-related services (e.g., blood pressure checks); and pharmaceutical companies supplied an array of health-related gift packs. School buses transported more than three hundred teens and teachers to the event, where most teens were met by their parents. The seminar included dialogue groups, films, experiential workshops, stand-up lectures, roleplaying activities, and inspirational songs. New avenues of communication were opened, myths were dispelled and "sensitive" subjects were addressed from a professional point of view.

Each year the event attracted a larger audience of people ranging from those who endorsed the event to those who were disgusted and outraged. In 1978, out of a barrage of controversy promoted by the Concerned Christian Mothers of Miami, National Family Sex Education Week became the daily headline grabber for weeks preceding the scheduled event. The Concerned Christian Mothers demanded that the event be boycotted and that all Dade County School approved absences be rescinded. Parents from all segments of the community were roused to comment in favor of or in opposition to sexuality education as it was being presented at the symposium.

Letters to the editor favoring the sexuality seminar appeared in the *Miami Herald*. High schools conducted parent/student polls for their school newspapers. The PTA and the Sex Health Education Center sponsored a poster and essay contest related to the need for sexuality education in the schools. A panel of parents who acted as judges selected the poster "You Better Let Them Know Before You Let Them Go" as the theme for the conference.

The event did take place. Attendance exceeded eight hundred parents and teens. Utilizing the groundswell as a "golden opportunity," participants were asked to respond to a petition stating: "If you believe that sex education begins and belongs in the home but you support that it be taught in the schools as well, please sign this petition." On October 16, 1978, more than 1,000 students attended the symposium on sexuality. Adults and students squeezed into the 21 workshops, sitting on the floor or standing when chairs were unavailable. The attendees furnished their own transportation; many came on school buses obtained through student/parent donations. Nearly 1,000 people had signed the petition.

On October 18, 1978 a delegation of Dade County public school students presented the school board with the signed petition calling for sexuality education in the schools. The school board approved the petition and unanimously passed a measure calling for sexuality education in Dade schools. A committee representing parents, teachers, clergy and community leaders was charged with establishing a curriculum. For nearly a year, the committee was embroiled in conflict with a mother representing the Concerned Christian Community who clung to the belief that sexual literacy causes overstimulation and promiscuity. Citizens Against Unacceptable Sex Education (CAUSE) joined forces with singer activist Anita Bryant in heading a fight to stop sexuality education.

In March 1979, at a public hearing before the Dade County Ad Hoc Committee on Sexuality Education, forty citizens presented sharply divided options. Some favored sexuality education with morals, others favored morally neutral sexuality education, and still others favored no sexuality education at all. At the May school board meeting "parents booed and waved Bibles," but after a three-hour public hearing at which 61 persons received one-and--a-half minutes each in which to make their presentation, the school board voted six to one to put sexuality in the county's classrooms (Young, 1979). School Board Agenda Item 23-2 authorized that the program of Human Growth and Development (HGD) be implemented for the 1979/80 school year.

Parents were invited to participate in day/evening orientation programs and review all support materials to be used within the program. Teachers were to be "trained, experienced professionals who are mature and have the ability to relate to children and adults comfortably when discussing these topics. They must be sensitive to their own values and guard against imposing them on the students. The school principal is responsible for selecting the most appropriate staff member(s)..." A resource person from each school was to attend an orientation workshop for implementing the program. Inservice for teachers was to be provided "to correct any misconceptions held by teachers and to prepare them to respond appropriately to children's questions" (Journal 40, p. 15, entry 28363-28365, Dade County School Board minutes).

The Curriculum

From the inception, the school board wisely included a broad representation of the professional and parent community in the curriculum planning. After the two previous years of nonproductive attempts at initiating a sexuality program, the heated curriculum advisory council meetings finally concluded, and the community was presented with the curriculum. Parents had the option to submit a written refusal for their children to participate. School and district meetings were called so that parents could inspect the curriculum content. Curriculum advisors attended the meetings and responded to parental concerns and comments. The message to the parents was, "We want to be partners with you in this life-enhancing endeavor. In doing so, we invite you to examine and question any area of the curriculum that makes you feel uncomfortable."

Parents began to relax when they discovered that the early grade curriculum dealt with feeling and interfamily relationships. They felt reassured that their interest and participation in their children's early curriculum studies would enhance their knowledge and ultimate participation in their children's later years of formal study and sexuality inquiry. As the alliance between the parents and schools increased, the sense of competition and the perceived threat to family values decreased.

Conclusion

In 1990, the SHE Center examined the status of the HGD program. How had the implemented curriculum fared since its inception in September of 1979? Informally, many secondary school teachers reported that the program was less than successful. Certain contributing factors were identified:

- the resistance of teachers who were compelled by principals to teach the sexuality education unit despite their discomfort with the subject matter

- the lack of effective inservice programs on human sexuality for affected teachers
- overemphasis on the technical aspect of the unit, leaving students bored and confused
- restrictions imposed by school administrators on course content, pedagogical practice, the students' right to know and teacher academic freedom due to fear of community opposition and perceived threat to administrators' own job security
- political vacillation of school board members
- budgetary constraints

But, above all other factors, the singlemost important obstacle was real opposition from parents and activist groups opposed to sexuality education.

It became clear that simply because a school district is mandated to teach HGD, one cannot assume that the unit is being taught in its entirety. A vocal minority, even one or two activists with no children of their own enrolled in school, may have a greater impact upon students' right to learn, teachers' right to teach, parents' permission for their children to participate, and, in many instances, even the law, if there is no ongoing ad hoc sexuality education committee to protect the integrity of the curriculum.

A closer observation of the Dade County School HGD program in 1992 and 1993 reaffirmed that the problem in transmitting sexual knowledge to the younger generation lies not with youth, but with the adult community. The mechanism to successfully sustain a long-term, quality, mandated sexuality program is multifaceted and is addressed from a variety of perspectives throughout this book. But recognizing and appreciating the value of partnerships with parents and caregivers may be the single most important component to meeting children's sexuality education needs.

Looking to the past successes, certain variables remain constant and provide a springboard for strategy building. Recommendations include the following:

- Create a grassroots coalition of parental support for sexuality education through small and large, informal and formal discussion groups.
- Provide parents with local statistics as well as national data, media reports, anecdotes to which they can personally relate, and opportunities to partake in experiential, interactive workshops.
- Invite the media to press conferences providing local hard data (teen pregnancy, STD, HIV/AIDS, school dropout, reproductive health-related cost to taxpayers, dysfunctional sequelae) directed towards parental consumption.
- Form a speakers' bureau of professional health educators and publicize their availability through public service announcements on radio and television and in the press.
- Network with PTA/PTSA, girls and boys clubs, Parents Without Partners, Planned Parenthood, health-related community agencies, churches, synagogues, the YWCA, the Red Cross, childcare centers, libraries, social and fraternal clubs, women's organizations, universities, hospitals and clinics to provide settings and/or expertise for parent and caregiver sexuality communication workshops.
- Include students and parents in school policy planning and decision making related to the sexuality curriculum.
- Encourage parents and caregivers to act upon their right and responsibility to address the school board, write letters to the editor and speak out on behalf of sexual literacy.

- Empower fearful, timid and intimidated parents with educational resources (books, handouts, videos, audio tapes) and communication strategies that reinforce their rightful place as their children's primary sexuality educators.
- Provide awards, certification and other means of recognition for parents who attend sexuality programs.
- Create and maintain an ongoing, broad-based citizens' ad hoc sexuality education curriculum advisory council prior to the initiation of the program.
- Orient parents and caregivers to the curriculum through school-coordinated meetings held in a variety of settings, geographically accessible to all segments of the community, and at various times to meet the schedules of working parents and homeworkers.
- Send home to parents and caregivers an outline of the course curriculum with a return parental signature tearsheet to ensure its receipt. Also require a written refusal response from parents who do not allow their children to participate.
- Establish an ongoing, ad hoc community-based advisory commission of parents, as well as a lawyer, teacher union representative, community relations specialist, equity and gender specialist, and religious leaders, including a fundamentalist, to hear teacher, student and parent grievances as they arise in relation to curriculum content, teaching methodologies and other issues related to the consistency and integrity of the program.
- Encourage teachers to maintain an interactive relationship with parents by way of take home fact sheets designed specifically for parents.
- Help generate sexuality communication between parents and students with homework assignments requiring that parents and family members be polled on specific issues and inter-

viewed about their childhood history, dating and adolescent experiences.

- Establish, through funded community mental health organizations, a task force of trained volunteers to listen to teens' sexual concerns and to act as a liaison to parents through the school setting.

In Dade County, the process of renewing the 1979 partnership with parents and caregivers as sexuality educators, in the context of today's society has begun. The SHE Center again is spearheading NFSEW in alliance with its original advocacy cosponsors. The newer entities in Dade county, such as foster-care homes, childcare centers, runaway houses and violence and abuse shelters established during the past ten years, are joining the program initiative. The energy emerging from the community effort is positive and will spark an awareness of the value of creating a legacy of sexual literacy—a legacy that is perpetuated when parents and caregivers become partners in and advocates of sexuality education.

References

Couch, G. B. 1967. Youth looks at sex. *Adolescence* 2 (6): 255-266.

Dade County School Board minutes. Journal 40, p. 15, entry 28363-28365.

Gibbus, N. 1993. How should we teach our children about sex? *Time* (May 24): 60-66.

Leight, L. 1993. A noble project flawed: The challenge and disruption (by Christian fundamentalist activists) of the original doctoral theses to measure the sexual knowledge, behavior and attitudes of secondary students at specific Dade County schools. Doctoral dissertation. Institute for Advanced Study of Human Sexuality.

Leo, J. 1986. Education: Sex and schools. *Time* (November 24): 54-63.

Lewis, R. A. 1973. Parents and peers: Socialization agents in the coital behavior of young adults. *Journal of Sex Research* 9 (2): 156-170.

Lindsay, J., and S. Rodin. 1989. *Teen pregnancy challenge.* Buena Park, CA: Morning Glory Press.

Mater, D. 1978. School board backs sex ed. *The Miami News,* 19 October.

Melton, E. 1978. Sex class "satanic" to foes, "long overdue" for fans. *Miami Herald,* 24 March.

Scales, P. 1981. Sex education in the 70s and 80s: Accomplishments, obstacles and emerging issues. *Family Relations* 30 (4): 557-566.

Spanier, G. B. 1977. Sources of sex information and premarital sexual behavior. *Journal of Sex Research* 13 (2): 73-88.

Young, E. 1979. Students say they need sex ed; board agrees. *The Miami News.* 10 May.

Chapter 27

School-Based Clinics and School Health Care

Barbara A. Rienzo, PhD, CHES, FASHA

The first school-based clinic (SBC) was opened in West Dallas, Texas, in 1970 by the Department of Pediatrics, University of Houston Health Science Center. The first SBC to offer reproductive health services was established in 1973 in St. Paul, Minnesota. Viewed as a "grassroots movement" (Kirby and Lovick, 1989), the number of SBCs doubled every two years, and by 1991 the Center for Population Options' Support Center for School-Based Clinics (from here on referred to as the Support Center) reported that 306 school-based and school-linked clinics were scattered throughout 33 states, many sponsored by national foundations, perhaps most notably by the Robert Wood Johnson Foundation (Hechinger, 1992).

According to the Support Center (1988), school-based clinics are "comprehensive, primary health care facilities located within or on the grounds of middle, junior or senior high schools [that] vary in size and organizational structure." Usually staffed by a multidisciplinary group of professionals with expertise in youth health issues, SBCs operate with a mix of public and private funds and are generally administered by hospitals, private and nonprofit organizations, or community health centers. School-linked clinics offer health services nearby school grounds, while the school-linked services initiative is part of a larger movement for integration of education, health and social services for children and their families through collaborative arrangements among those agencies.

Health services provided through these models include treatment of illness and injuries; routine and sports physicals; laboratory tests, including tests for sexually transmitted disease; counseling services for nutrition, mental health and substance use; immunizations; pregnancy testing and referral for or provision of prenatal care; counseling on, and less frequently, prescription or dispensing of birth control; and, occasionally, daycare and dental care (Waszak and Neidell, 1992).

Providing health and social services to youth addresses increasing concerns about their health-related problems. Teenage pregnancy and substance use affect adolescents' ability to perform well academically (Alexander, 1990; Elders, 1992; Penning, 1992; Advisory Council on Social Security, 1991; Lear et al., 1991; U.S. Congress Office of Technology Assessment, 1991; Fox, Wicks and Lipson, 1992; Hechinger, 1992). Poor school performance results in increased societal costs, such as public benefit expenditures, lost productivity, and erosion of national productivity, international competitiveness and standard of living (Center for the Future of Children staff, 1992; Morrill, 1992; Levy and Shepardson, 1992).

Establishing schools as the central institution in these efforts is based on their (mandated) accessibility to most children and their families, their durability as a dominant institution within the community, and their possession of an administrative structure with the capacity to deliver the necessary services (Chaskin and Richman, 1992; Millstein, 1988; Elders, 1992; Advisory Council on Social Security, 1991; Lear et al., 1991).

Chaskin and Richman (1992) caution that schools may not be the best location for providing these services in light of institutional distrust among the disenfranchised, schools' inherent bureaucratic structural problems, and school authorities' reluctance to become responsible for nonacademic problems. Proponents assert that provision of services can increase trust and comfort with the school among users and that collaborative methods allow for effective health and social service agency partnerships (Levy and Shepardson, 1992; Morrill, 1992). All concur that schools should not attempt to address these issues without receiving necessary resources, expertise and the cooperation of community agencies (Center for the Future of Children staff, 1992).

Finally, as noted by Hechinger (1992) and Elders (1992), health centers can provide a connection between their medically oriented function and the contemporary educational mission whereby schools include human biology as the core of science instruction. Providing instruction within the school's comprehensive health or sexuality education program, developing posters and other visual materials for placement throughout the school, writing a column in the school newspaper, and participating in school assemblies are several suggested methods for outreach efforts to integrate health services within the school health program (Donovan and Waszak, 1989).

Joycelyn Elders (1992) describes the potential impact of school-based health services as part of a much more integrated approach for the future:

As schools prepare for the 21st century, they will grow beyond their academic role to serve as a community's center for the integration of social, health, mental health, and support services for children and families. (Elders, 1992)

Support and Barriers

Support for these services is clear at all levels of society. A wide range of national organizations support the establishment of school-based or school-linked health care[1] (Support Center for School-Based Clinics, 1988). At least 15 national foundations fund projects related to school-linked or integrated services for children (Center for the Future of Children staff, 1992). States that have funded schools' large-scale efforts to provide health and social services include New York, New Jersey and Kentucky.

Nonprofit organizations that focus on, and sometimes promote integrated services for children include the Institute for Educational Leadership (Washington, D.C.), the Center for the Study of Social Policy (Washington, D.C.), the Family Resource Coalition (Chicago), and the Youth Law Center (San Francisco). Research and policy groups exploring approaches to integrated

---

[1]American Academy of Child and Adolescent Psychiatry, American Academy of Pediatrics, American Association of University Women, American College of Obstetricians and Gynecologists, American Jewish Congress, American Medical Association, American Public Health Association, American School Health Association, Central Conference of American Rabbis, Child Welfare League of America, Commission on the Future of the South, National Academy of Sciences (National Research Council), National Association of School Nurses, National Conference of State Legislatures, National Education Association, National Governors' Association, National Organization of Women, National Parent-Teachers Association, Society for Adolescent Medicine and the United Church Board for Homeland Ministries

services for children include Bush Center for Child Policy (Yale University), the Chapin Hall Center for Children (University of Chicago), and the California Policy Council. Perhaps most important is the level of local support demonstrated where school-based/linked services are established, especially by parents and students (Lear et al., 1991; Hechinger, 1992; Levy and Shepardson, 1992).

Despite all this support, however, development of school-based or school-linked services has been hindered by their association with reproductive health care and sexuality-related services for youth. Among the most pressing health problems contemporary adolescents face are those related to premature and unsafe sexual behavior. Initial clinics provided reproductive health services to address teenage pregnancy and sexually transmitted disease rates and demonstrated early success in addressing these issues (Kirby, 1992; Lear et al., 1991). However, a vocal, albeit minority, of opposition forces have focused their objections to SBCs almost solely on basis of their provision of these services (McCormick, 1989; AMA Council on Scientific Affairs, 1989; Gardner, 1992; Hechinger, 1992; Alexander, 1990; Saba, 1991; Elders, 1992; Fox, Wicks and Lipson, 1992; Lear et al., 1991; Rienzo, in review; Rienzo and Button, 1993).

Opponents assert (inaccurately) that SBCs increase teens' sexual activity and promote abortion. Clinics' support, growth and ability to offer reproduction health care have been seriously undermined by this opposition (Brindis, 1990; McCormick, 1989; AMA Council on Scientific Affairs, 1989; Fox, Wicks and Lipson, 1992; Elders, 1992; Rienzo, in review; Rienzo and Button, 1993).

Other factors that impair the development of such clinics include organizational problems, such as attempting to operate without adequate space and not being able to arrange sufficient medical backup or strong linkages to community health and social support resources. Without these assets, student access to comprehensive services cannot be increased. Obtaining and maintaining stable funding is another significant barrier (Fox, Wicks and Lipson, 1992).

Effectiveness

Studies have shown that clinics are associated with decreasing teenage pregnancy or birth rates (Dryfoos, 1985; Vincent, Cleary and Schluchter, 1987; Zabin et al., 1988); delay in initiating sexual intercourse (Zabin et al., 1988); reduced delay time for first-time family planners and increased use of school-based clinics for pregnancy prevention by teens prior to or beginning sexual intercourse (Bar-Cohen, Lia-Hoagberg and Edwards, 1990); and improved birth outcomes for teens (Dryfoos, 1985). Therefore, experts continue to contend that school-based/linked clinics should offer reproductive health services (Donovan and Waszak, 1989; Lear et al., 1991; Elders, 1992). Polls indicate that the public concurs—64 percent of Americans endorse condom distribution through health clinics in high schools (Hechinger, 1992).

Researchers claim, however, that definitive assertions regarding the effectiveness of school-based services to realize these sexuality and reproduction risk reduction goals are premature and that more longitudinal, large-scale data assessment is necessary. Furthermore, methodological issues have made evaluation of effectiveness difficult (U.S. Congress Office of Technology Assessment, 1991; Gomby and Larson, 1992; Hechinger, 1992; Kirby, 1992).

For these reasons, whether reproductive health services offered through these models affect teen pregnancy, birth and abortion rates is less than clear. Kirby's (1992) review of the data on SBCs indicated that while early efforts showed very promising reductions in these outcomes, later evaluation revealed less evidence that clinics decreased birth rates and that there were varying effects on contraceptive use. He also notes, however, that more promising effects result when SBC efforts are combined with more comprehensive approaches that focus on pregnancy and HIV/AIDS prevention. Gomby and Larson (1992) in their review of research, echo Kirby's assessment, concluding: "It is very hard to change behavior, but the most promising opportunities to do so may involve school-wide and community-wide mobilizations."

There is, nonetheless, clear documentation to substantiate claims that school-based and school-linked services improve access to those services that adolescents need (Dryfoos, 1985; U.S. Congress Office of Technology Assessment, 1991; Lear et al., 1991; Gomby and Larson, 1992) and reduce many of the health care barriers that children and adolescents face: lack of transportation, inconvenient hours of service, little or no health insurance protection for needed services, and concern over confidentiality (Schlitt, 1991; U.S. Congress Office of Technology Assessment, 1991). Research also verifies that school-based centers neither encourage nor increase students' sexual activity, even when they dispense or prescribe contraceptives (Gomby and Larson, 1992; Kirby, 1992).

Leadership and Community Support

Successfully planning school-based or school-linked services involves several important processes, beginning with the active support of key community leaders. An articulate coordinator, typically with expertise in adolescent health and fundraising, often heads a planning committee of approximately six to twelve committed supporters. Members of this group, many of whom are health care providers and school administrators, are primarily motivated by their awareness of the health care needs of their community's youth (Rienzo and Button, 1993). Major functions of this planning group are to document these needs, increase community awareness of and concern about them, and build community support for meeting them through school-based services (Rienzo, in review).

These school administrators (district superintendent, board of education, principals) must plan in a collaborative fashion with community agency executives. This sharing of responsibility for planning and for committing resources (required for successful collaborative efforts) often is a different working relationship than these leaders' have utilized previously (Jehl and Kirst, 1992). Leaders often have not worked together previously or have worked within a hierarchical (rather than a partnership) leadership model, and tend to have a history of competing for community resources (Jehl and Kirst, 1992).

Broad community support is also crucial to implementing school-based services. Proactively building support serves both to ensure that services meet community-defined needs and to counter potential opposition (Millstein, 1988; Elders, 1992; Rienzo and Button, 1993). Therefore, planners should establish a community advisory board to further cultivate representative supporters who can assist with fundraising and vocal endorsement. This fifteen-to twenty-member board is comprised of parents, teachers, community leaders, students, physicians, and, sometimes, religious leaders, school board members and elected officials. The board later advises clinic staff and monitors programs and services. The planning committee and the advisory board often require training for public advocacy and for handling organized opposition (Hadley, Lovick and Kirby, 1986; Rienzo, in review).

Parent/caretaker involvement is essential for the implementation of school-based or school-linked services. Most require parental permission for students to access services, except where state law allows for minors to give informed consent (Levy and Shepardson, 1992). Parents' interaction with school personnel often increases as a result of school health service implementation, with concomitant elevations in trust and services to the family (AMA Council on Scientific Affairs, 1989; Jehl and Kirst, 1992; Elders, 1992). Providers at the school site are able to identify needs and community-based services to meet these needs as well as barriers to health services for the youth and their families (Jehl and Kirst, 1992).

Documentation

Preparing a program justification and setting program goals and objectives are essential to instituting school-based or school-linked services. Both should reflect a local needs assessment of youth health problems, existing services provided by community agencies, and parents' support for these services (Rienzo, in review; Rienzo and Button, 1993; Fox, Wicks and Lipson, 1992: Levy and Shepardson, 1992; Jehl and Kirst, 1992).

Assessment results can be used to determine the scope, recipients, expected outcomes and financing of services to be provided (Jehl and Kirst, 1992). Funding for school-based or school-linked services is provided by state, federal Title V block grants, Medicaid and foundations (Elders, 1992). Local support—typically in the form of in-kind services, space and renewal of space contracts, maintenance and utility costs and renovation responsibilities—is vital for their maintenance (Rienzo, in review).

Additionally, information should be compiled about national youth health issues and about school-based services in general, which can be used for public relations efforts (Rienzo, in review).

Instruments for assessment efforts for process and outcome evaluation should be discussed and prepared at the initial stages as well (Gomby and Larson, 1992).

Public Relations

Effectively building and maintaining support for school-based services requires adept public relations skills (Rienzo and Button, 1993). Cultivating relationships with the news media by using an articulate, credible spokesperson, issuing press releases, and developing information kits is crucial to successful public education (Rienzo, in review). These efforts are particularly important in preparing for organized opposition, which may be small in number but very vocal. Opposition forces are often supported by organizations outside the community to be served, and are potentially persuasive enough to block establishment of or reduce services, particularly for reproductive care (McCormick, 1989; Lear et al., 1991; Elders, 1992; Rienzo, in review; Rienzo and Button, 1993).

Two major barriers with which organizers must contend are silence on the part of community supporters and emotionally laden resistance tactics of organized opponents, which usually focus on sexuality issues. Strategies used by successful planners include:

- use of surveys to provide objective evidence of community support
- public meetings or hearings that employ methods to identify parents and local residents versus those appearing from outside the community (e.g., speakers may be required to state their address and whether they have children in the school, or be community residents)
- testimony by articulate, credible supporters

- assurances of clinic policies related to service provision, particularly regarding parent permission

The latter is especially useful when school-based services have been labeled "sex" or "abortion" clinics, terms designed to incite fear (Rienzo and Button, 1993).

Coordination of Services and Confidentiality

Principals and other middle managers facilitate the structural and functional changes necessary to provide school-based services. They provide information to teachers, other staff and students; design policy; and make the practical arrangements for facilities or transportation. Teachers, whose support and involvement is critical for student referral, often have concerns related to whether services will disrupt instruction and interfere with their primary focus on teaching (Jehl and Kirst, 1992). Arrangements also must take into consideration the role of the school district nurses. Often nurses serve as clinic managers or function in a referral capacity for students who require primary care (Lear et al., 1991; Fox, Wickham and Lipson, 1992).

Also considered important is clinics' capacity to respond without delay to adolescents' requests for service. For this reason, most offer "drop-in" as well as scheduled appointments and aspire to remain open after school hours and summer (Hechinger, 1992; Levy and Shepardson, 1992; AMA Council on Scientific Affairs, 1989). Unfortunately, the latter attribute is rare due to financial constraints.

Confidentiality is key to overcoming major barriers to adolescent health care and is a vital characteristic of school-based services (Schlitt, 1991; U.S. Congress Office of Technology Assessment, 1991; AMA Council on Scientific Affairs, 1989;

Lear et al., 1991). However, protection of confidentiality some-times can interfere with coordination of community agencies' efforts to assist the youth and their families. Planners are advised to comply with state and school district legislation, due to differ-ing laws related to confidentiality, informed consent, and minors' access to selected health services (Gomby and Larson, 1992).

Sources of information on these issues include *School-Based Health Clinics: Legal Issues* (English and Tereszkiewicz, 1988), and *Tackling the Confidentiality Barrier: A Practical Guide for Integrated Family Services* (Hobbs, 1991). The National Center for Youth Law in San Francisco provides expertise in areas of the law that affect children and adolescents.

Evaluation

Evaluation is considered an essential component of school-based services. Because many agencies are involved and there are mul-tiple goals (for students, families and the system), assessing stu-dent services is complex and should be planned carefully to include both process and outcome evaluation within appropriate time periods. In addition to complying with research design and statis-tical requirements, evaluations must address concerns for too-narrowly defined outcomes, measuring less tangible changes, and not interfering with effectively offering services.

Outcome evaluation must be longitudinal (several years) to appropriately measure effects and should not be undertaken for at least a year after the program is initiated, although planning for this effort from program inception is advised. Program evaluators should work closely with clinic staff to accommodate their needs related to provision of quality service and to gather their ideas for process and outcome effectiveness measures (Gomby and Larson, 1992).

Conclusion

School-based and school-linked clinics are promising models for addressing the health needs of American youth. It is, however, difficult to predict whether significant changes in youth health status, especially problems related to premature or unsafe sexual behavior, will result from these initiatives. Significant barriers—such as funding, cooperation of health and education agencies, and organized opposition—continue to plague supporters.

School-based services should optimize their potential by integrating programs with the educational mission of the school. For example, offering physical examinations to all incoming students provides the opportunity for risk assessment and health promotion efforts. A visit to the clinic as part of comprehensive health education course could contribute to knowledge of preventive medicine as well as increase teachers' and students' familiarity with the clinic and its staff.

As other authors (Gomby and Larson, 1992; Kirby, 1992) have noted, it is unlikely that these efforts in themselves—no matter how well developed—will be able to effect changes without concurrent comprehensive efforts on the part of the larger community to reduce risk behavior. There is, nevertheless, reason for optimism: as school-based and school-linked services continue to engender support, grow in number, and document (with increasingly sophisticated evaluation) desired effects, they may act as catalysts for improvements in community health promotion efforts.

References

Advisory Council on Social Security. 1991. *Commitment to change: Foundations for reform.* Washington, DC.

Alexander, E. 1990. School-based clinics: Questions to be answered in the planning stages. *High School Journal* 73 (2): 133-138.

AMA Council on Scientific Affairs. 1989. Providing medical services through school-based health programs. *Journal of the American Medical Association* 261 (23): 1939-1942.

Bar-Cohen, A., B. Lia-Hoagberg and L. Edwards. 1990. First family planning visit in school-based clinics. *Journal of School Health* 60 (8): 418-422.

Brindis, C. 1990. Reducing adolescent pregnancy: The next steps for program, research and policy. *Family Life Educator* (Special Issue) 9 (1).

Center for the Future of Children staff. 1992. Analysis. *The Future of Children* 2 (1): 6-18.

Chaskin, R. J., and H. A. Richman. 1992. Concerns about school-linked services: Institution-based versus community-based models. *The Future of Children* 2 (1): 107-117.

Donovan, P., and C. Waszak. 1989. *School-based clinics enter the 90s: Update, evaluation and future challenges.* Washington, DC: Center for Population Options.

Dryfoos, J. 1985. School-based health clinics: A new approach to preventing adolescent pregnancy. *Family Planning Perspectives* 17 (2): 70-75.

Elders, M. J. 1992. School-based clinics to the rescue. *The School Administrator* 49 (8): 16-18, 20-21.

English, A., and L. Tereszkiewicz. 1988. *School-based health clinics: Legal issues.* San Francisco: National Center for Youth Law.

Fox, H. B., L. B. Wicks, and D. J. Lipson. 1992. *Improving access to comprehensive health care through school-based programs.* Washington, DC: Fox Health Policy Consultants, Inc.

Gardner, S. L. 1992. Key issues in developing school-linked, integrated services. *The Future of Children* 2 (1): 85-94.

Gomby, D. S., and C. S. Larson. 1992. Evaluation of school-linked services. *The Future of Children* 2 (1): 68-84.

Hadley, E. M., S. R. Lovick and D. Kirby. 1986. *School-based health clinics: A guide to implementing programs.* Washington, DC: The Center for Population Options.

Hechinger, F. M. 1992. *Fateful choices: Healthy youth for the 21st century.* New York: Carnegie Corporation of New York.

Hobbs, L. J. 1991. *Tackling the confidentiality barrier: A practical guide for integrated family services, a special new beginning report.* San Diego: County of San Diego Department of Social Services.

Jehl, J., and M. Kirst. 1992. Spinning a family support web. *The School Administrator* 49 (8): 8-13, 15.

Kirby, D., and S. Lovick. 1989. School-based health clinics: Improving adolescent health and reducing teenage pregnancy. In *Sexuality Education: A Resource Book,* ed. C. Cassell and P. Wilson, 169-178. New York: Garland Publishing.

Kirby, D. 1992. School-based programs to reduce sexual risk-taking behaviors. *Journal of School Health* 62 (7): 280-287.

Lear, J. G., H. B. Gleicher, A. S. Germaine and P. J. Porter. 1991. Reorganizing health care for adolescents: The experience of the school-based adolescent health care program. *Journal of Adolescent Health* 12 (6): 450-458.

Levy, J. E., and W. Shepardson. 1992. A look at current school-linked service efforts. *The Future of Children* 2 (1): 44-55.

McCormick, K. 1989. Bringing health care to the kids. *Governing* 2 (4): 56-61.

Millstein, S. G. 1988. *The potential of school-linked centers to promote adolescent health and development.* Washington, DC: The Carnegie Council on Adolescent Development.

Morrill, W. A. 1992. Overview of service delivery to children. *The Future of Children* 2 (1): 32-43.

Penning, N. 1992. School readiness goal begins with health care reform. *The School Administrator* 49 (8): 33.

Rienzo, B. A. Critical factors in the successful establishment of school-based clinics. Unpublished manuscript under review.

Rienzo, B. A., and J. W. Button. 1993. The politics of school-based clinics: A community-level analysis. *Journal of School Health* 63 (8): 266-272.

Saba, M. R. 1991. Expanding health care for the young: A school-based approach. *The Delta Kappa Gamma Bulletin:* 57 (4): 36-37.

Schlitt, J. J. 1991. *Bringing health to school: Policy implications for southern states.* Washington, DC: Southern Center on Adolescent Pregnancy Prevention.

Support Center for School-Based Clinics. 1988. *School-based clinics: A guide for advocates.* Houston, TX: The Center for Population Options.

U.S. Congress Office of Technology Assessment. 1991. *Adolescent health—volume I: Summary and policy options.* (OTA-H-468) Washington, DC.

Vincent, M., A. Cleary and M. Schluchter. 1987. Reducing adolescent pregnancy through school and community-based education. *Journal of the American Medical Association* 257 (24): 3382-3386.

Waszak, C., and S. Neidell. 1992. *School-based and school-linked clinics: Update 1991.* Washington, DC: The Center for Population Options.

Zabin, L. S., M. B. Hirsch, R. Streett, M. R. Emerson, M. Smith, J. B. Hardy and T. M. King. 1988. The Baltimore pregnancy prevention program for urban teenagers. *Family Planning Perspectives* 20 (4): 182-192.

Chapter 28

Adolescent Pregnancy and Parenting Programs

Karen Cancino, LCSW, and Jodie B. Rieger Fischer, MS, LCSW

Pregnancy and parenting programs can be considered both prevention and intervention. They are prevention programs in that they are attempts to prevent school drop out, infant mortality, child abuse and neglect, Aid to Families with Dependent Children (AFDC) dependency, and to delay additional pregnancies. They are intervention programs in the sense that they become necessary when primary prevention programs such as family life education or family planning services were not available or could not overcome significant factors in young women's lives to prevent pregnancy.

A continuous and comprehensive program that would serve the adolescent mother and father and their child, their families, and their new partners is the ideal model. Services would include education, medical care, social services and childcare, all located within the same facility or at least in close proximity. In reality, most programs start very small, attending only to the basic educational needs of the pregnant students. Most programs add on components as gaps in services and/or the dismal school return and graduation rates for parenting students become known.

Classrooms for pregnant and parenting students are located in various settings: comprehensive or continuation high schools, specialized or adult schools, hospitals or health centers, social service agencies or organizations (e.g., YWCA, family service agencies) and, frequently, wherever space is donated. The location is often determined by the degree of willingness of the community to admit that pregnant and parenting students exist and that they are entitled to an education.

There is no one "perfect" adolescent pregnancy and parenting program that will fit every community; each community is unique. There are, however, general guidelines that, when followed, can help planners establish a basic program that fits the needs of their community. Once support for the program has been demonstrated, social services, health and other components that enhance the basic educational program can be added.

Although the needs of the currently pregnant and parenting adolescents may seem overwhelming and in need of immediate attention, time taken in developing a community foundation for the development of a program will pay off, if and when there is opposition, if and when budget cuts are considered, and/or if and when there is a need to expand services in the future.

Documenting the Need

A first step in determining a need for services is to establish connections with others who have contact with these young people in other settings. A school social worker, nurse or counselor might talk with staff in other schools. A family planning clinic counselor might contact a public health nurse or meet with youth-serving agencies and organizations. Such contacts can be the beginning of a community group that comes together to determine the needs of the adolescent who is pregnant or already a parent.

This informal exploration is a means to begin assessing the community's readiness to respond to the need for a pregnancy program. Others working with youth and families may have recognized the same need. Or there may be a great degree of denial on the part of community leaders or service providers—"Our students don't get pregnant," or "That is the family's problem." Such information is vital to understanding what will be needed to build community support.

Once the concern has been established, a needs assessment must be done to measure the extent of the situation. Statistics can encourage many people, agencies and organizations to become involved. A state department of vital statistics or the local health department can provide information on the number of pregnancies or births to minors, mothers' ages, location in the community, socioeconomic status, ethnicity, prematurity, low birthweight and infant mortality. This information will be important for planning the program and eliciting community support. Information from hospitals and clinics on month of entry into prenatal care and the number of infants in the intensive care unit born to adolescent mothers will also be useful, as adolescents in school programs have been shown to have better medical outcomes for themselves and their infants (Loomis and Simpson-Brown, 1990).

An assessment of services available in the community for pregnant and parenting adolescents should also be made to identify gaps and duplications in services. This assessment can provide valuable information about potential service provider collaborations in whatever program or service is ultimately developed. This same information can also be useful in establishing baseline data for evaluating the program or service once it is established.

Building Support

Once demographic information is gathered and needs are identified, a planning or task force composed of community representatives who have expressed interest in working on the issue can be brought together. These representatives could come from public health, public and private social service agencies, the PTA, neighborhood organizations, clinics and hospitals, and local government, businesses and foundations. Pregnant and parenting adolescents, as well as their partners, should be participants in program development. The charge of the task force should be the development of a realistic mission statement and short- and long-range goals and objectives.

Building a broad base of support can decrease the impact of any opposition to the development or expansion of needed programs and services. The success of any program will depend on the ability of all participating agencies and organizations to put aside their "turf" issues and focus on the needs of the adolescents and their children. Many successful campaigns have effectively used influential community leaders to raise the awareness of policy-makers in education, public health and social services (Lindsay and Rodine, 1989a; Lindsay and Rodine, 1989b). In addition, the support of the general public will be paramount in times of budget cuts to the saving of any program, as well as to program expansion. Some of the planning task force participants might become members of an advisory group that would monitor and evaluate the finished program. If parents and students have not been involved before, they definitely should be involved in any ongoing group.

Opposition

Just as programs will vary, opposition may be very different from one community to the next. Some individuals and groups may oppose programs or services because they fear the programs or services will encourage additional pregnancies. Some may feel this population is not a priority and should not take valuable resources away from educational services for nonpregnant and parenting students.

The key is to identify potential sources of opposition, the basis of their concerns, and common values that may exist between them and the program or service goal. Explaining the long-range social and economic benefits can generate support. Education may lessen fears. Concerns can often be minimized by addressing objections and including them in the planning. If a common ground cannot be found, steps must be taken to minimize the impact of the opposition.

The most effective way to do that is to educate and keep informed those individuals (e.g., school board members, agency executive directors) who will ultimately have the power to approve or disapprove a program and/or its expansion. At the same time, ongoing dialogue with the opposition must be maintained. Above all, it is essential to always be prepared to address the issues raised by potential opponents and remain focused on the long-range goals of the program.

An additional step in the planning of a successful program is to review other community campaigns that succeeded in raising awareness and establishing needed programs. Information on how the organizers went about their task as well as similarities and differences between their programs and one for pregnant and parenting students can provide valuable lessons in building community support. Additional advocates for the pregnant and parenting program might even be found during this process.

Collaboration

Most individual school districts and community agencies do not have the resources to provide comprehensive services to pregnant and parenting students singlehandedly. Federal, state and local governments have become increasingly pressed to provide services when funds and staff become scarce. Private agencies, corporations and foundations and public agencies have formed partnerships to allow for allocation of efficient and effective services. Examples include the following partnerships: Family Service Agency of San Francisco and San Francisco Unified School District, the Mott Foundation and Oakland Unified School District, and New Futures School and the University of New Mexico Hospital. Historically, programs for pregnant and parenting students have recognized and utilized such collaborations often since the educational, health and social service needs of pregnant and parenting students are interdependent. Some examples include:

- a hospital donating classroom space
- public health nurses teaching nutrition
- childbirth and infant care classes in a pregnant and parenting program
- Girl Scouts providing camping experiences
- businesses providing mentors or work opportunities

Funding and Evaluation

The planning task force should look at all community agencies and organizations for possible support and involvement. State and local departments of education, health and social services are sources of funding. Other support might come from such diverse sources as the March of Dimes Birth Defects Foundation, the Private Industry Council, The Girl Scouts, Junior League, Lions

Club, private foundations and individuals interested in the issue of adolescent pregnancy and parenting.

Evaluation should be a primary consideration before the doors open to a program or service. A management information system which includes monitoring, evaluation and follow-up should be an integral part of the program or service from the beginning. Funding sources, whether public or private, will frequently request initial data on the population to be served (Lindsay and Rodine, 1989a). This data can provide a baseline from which specific objectives of the program can be established (e.g., decrease in number of low birthweight infants, or increase in the number of students remaining in school or graduating). An annual evaluation of data will determine whether the objectives were realistic or if the program needs to be changed.

In addition to statistical data, anecdotal material should be kept. Human interest information that highlights how the program or service has helped individual students, their partners or families is a very effective way to document how the program or service is assisting students. Written or oral presentations by the students themselves are very powerful. Photographs or video pictures, used with permission, add depth to presentations to raise awareness, solicit involvement, and/or secure funding.

Components of a Successful Program

If the goal of a pregnant minor program is to assist the pregnant student with educational attainment and a stable, self-sufficient future for both parents and child, a wide range of support services along with academics must be provided. A comprehensive pregnant minor program that addresses the educational, health and social service challenges of the pregnant adolescent is the ideal formula for enabling pregnant and parenting students to succeed in their various life roles of adolescent, daughter, parent and employee.

Staffing

Compassionate, creative, culturally competent and positive staff are the cornerstone of a successful program. Staff must be able to motivate students and mobilize resources. In addition, a sufficient number of staff is essential.

Staff might include an administrator/head teacher, teachers, aides, a clerk/secretary, social workers, case managers, guidance counselors, a nutritionist, public health nurses, childcare workers, a vocational educator, an employment/job developer, a child development specialist, a parenting educator, volunteers from families and the community, foster grandparents, peer helpers/ educators, an exercise specialist, and liaisons from public or private social service and health agencies.

Assessment

Outreach efforts should be an integral component of any program; many adolescent females drop out prior to pregnancy or upon learning of their pregnancy. Programs should also be targeted at parenting adolescents, many of whom drop out for lack of childcare (Brindis and Jeremy, 1988).

Choices regarding the pregnancy itself should be explored with each student—namely, a discussion regarding carrying the pregnancy to term, adoption and pregnancy termination. Planners in each state need to be abreast of the laws specifically related to adolescent sexuality, rights of minors, parental rights, partner rights and rights associated with pregnancy outcomes. Referrals and service linkages need to be in place and provided before a pregnant student is actually enrolled in a school program. Counseling is sometimes provided by other service providers and a referral to the pregnant adolescent program is made when the student has decided to continue her pregnancy. But the assumption that the student will carry the pregnancy to term should not be made, and an intake worker who is able to discuss every option with the pregnant student should do the initial interview.

A comprehensive intake interview should take place with the objective of developing an appropriate school plan that addresses not only the student's educational needs but also her social and emotional ones. In instances where the pregnancy is early enough and she is considering abortion, or when the young woman is thinking of adoption, a decision might be made not to bring her into a pregnant adolescent program because of potential peer pressure to conform to continuing the pregnancy and becoming a parent.

The Curriculum

Educational components of a program should include required courses for a high school diploma or GED preparation. Special education, remediation, ESL and advanced coursework should also be offered. Besides required academic subjects, other subjects need to be addressed: family life education (including sexuality education and family planning), HIV/AIDS education, health education (nutrition and exercise), childbirth education, child development, parenting and vocational education.

Pregnancy is the leading reason why females drop out of school (U.S. Department of Education, Office of Civil Rights, 1991; Scholl and Johnson, 1988). Therefore, the curriculum needs to be geared towards stimulating and maintaining student interest and involvement in her own learning. Lesson plans of special relevance and interest to the parenting student can be integrated into required knowledge bases. Reading culturally relevant literature on parenting, writing a paper on balancing adolescent and parenting roles, or utilizing math concepts in developing a budget are examples. As many different grade and ability levels are likely to be represented in a single classroom, individualized instruction is a necessity.

Skills

An important task during adolescence is searching for one's identity (Barr, Monserrat and Berg, 1992). Skill building is one way a school program can help with this developmental task. Skills such as problem solving, decision making, assertiveness, goal setting, communication and stress management increase a sense of competence and build self-esteem. The goal of developing these skills in pregnant and parenting adolescents is to enable them to make healthier decisions with regard to their lives and the lives of their children (Loomis and Simpson-Brown, 1990).

School programs for pregnant and parenting adolescents can tailor curriculum and services to foster student skills. Students who understand how to make decisions, set goals, etc., will be better equipped to succeed in school, parent their children, live independently and have fulfilling lives. Skill building can be taught when discussing subjects such as parenting, substance or alcohol use, relationships, and child abuse and neglect.

Flexible Scheduling

Educational expectations need to remain high; however, scheduling must be flexible for the pregnant and parenting student. Arrangements to accommodate students who are late or absent due to morning sickness, prenatal/postnatal and other appointments, and maternity leave need to be built in. Collaboration with medical and social service agencies to schedule appointments early in the morning or after school can minimize absences.

Social Work Services and Case Management

A social worker or case manager is the professional who works with students to assess their situation; coordinate needed services, for example, assistance with housing (maternity and group home placement, public housing, relatives or friends); and counsel and follow them until they graduate. The case manager may be the one consistent person involved over time with any and all aspects of the student's life.

Support Services

Individual counseling should be available because different issues will arise during this transitional period in the student's life and the lives of those significant to her. Having individual counseling services available on site will decrease barriers to counseling. Barriers to outside agency referrals could include long waiting lists, fees, location and an agency's lack of experience with the special needs of pregnant and parenting adolescents and their families. Barriers on the part of the adolescent and the family may include transportation, lack of familiarity with the agency and time commitments.

Support groups provide a safe place for students to express feelings. During adolescence, one's peer group plays an important part in developing one's sense of self. A trained group facilitator can help students support each other by encouraging discussions about feelings, concerns, problems and goals. Efforts should be made to include and/or develop support groups for others in the pregnant or parenting adolescents' lives as well: fathers of babies, and/or current partners and family members.

Peer Resources

Pregnant and parenting students can act as peer resources in two ways. They can be peer educators who make presentations to nonpregnant students about delaying pregnancy and parenthood. They can be peer helpers who provide support to newly pregnant or parenting students. Successful women in the communities who were teen parents themselves can speak in the classroom, lead group counseling sessions and be positive role models to students who are to become teen parents. One program that incorporates peer education is Chicanos por la Casa, a social services agency in Phoenix, Arizona, that provides employment training services, life skills and parenting classes, and prenatal care to women in transition.

Childcare

On-site or near-site childcare services are paramount to a comprehensive program serving pregnant and parenting students. Feeling good about the childcare situation is key to students staying in school (Cagampang et al., 1989). Childcare on-site serves two very significant purposes: (1) while pregnant, students can get practical, hands-on experience and parenting skills, and child abuse prevention education can be taught in the nursery, and (2) after a student delivers her baby, on-site childcare increases the chances that she will complete school (Cagampang et al., 1989). Many students do not have childcare resources, and many are not comfortable having their newborns away from them for any length of time. Having a nursery on-site allows new parents to be close to their infants and continue breastfeeding if they choose.

A comprehensive program needs to provide childcare services for toddlers also, as often the adolescents will have many years of schooling to complete. Childcare services should be considered for college-level and vocational school students as well to provide consistency in care for the child and opportunities for the parents to continue their education.

Transportation

Access to transportation positively affects attendance and, ultimately, school completion (Cagampang et al., 1989). Transportation needs between home and school depend upon the community being served. In rural communities, transportation could be a more salient and cost-intensive issue than in an urban area where public transportation is convenient and more affordable. Suburban areas will have different considerations. For example, when school buses are used for neighborhood schools, the cost of busing students from different schools to a separate program, which might not be on regular routes, will need to be explored.

After a student has her baby, transportation needs change. Purchasing car seats and liability insurance for infants and toddlers can dramatically increase transportation costs. Some programs purchase buses with grant monies. They use classroom aides and childcare workers as drivers, thereby reducing the number of staff required.

Forms of transportation can enhance a pregnant and parenting program. A driver with a car could accompany school staff with outreach efforts—with the goal of identifying students not in school or at risk of dropping out of school due to pregnancy or parenthood. A driver with a car could also accompany school social workers on home visits.

Nutrition Services

Nutritionally adequate meals for pregnancy as well as nutrition counseling services need to be provided for pregnant and parenting students. School meals should include breakfast, lunch and snacks. A nutritionist on staff would ensure that students receive all needed food services, such as WIC (Women, Infants and Children program), and make certain that students receive prenatal vitamins or nutrition supplements. Weight gain can be monitored weekly.

Nutrition education should take place in a classroom or group setting as well as individually. A nutritionist can help new parents with their own postpartum nutrition needs as well as provide appropriate nutrition education related to their infants and toddlers. Breastfeeding and bottle feeding information and assistance can be provided on-site. These services support the efforts of the medical care providers working with pregnant and parenting students.

Career/Vocational Education

Career counseling services can facilitate further education or vocational training. Job preparation/job readiness can be an integral part of a comprehensive program for the older student. With career exploration, exposure to colleges and vocational programs, and job preparation, students can begin to become more "future oriented" by being encouraged to develop their own goals and aspirations regarding their education, training and employment. Some job skills such as word processing, data entry and office skills can be developed while in the program. School sites can be job sites, allowing students to work in the administrative office and as teacher or staff aides. Showing these students that decisions they make today can positively affect their future needs to be woven throughout the curriculum. To prepare pregnant students for future challenges for themselves and their children, discussion of life options such as college and career choices must be included in the program.

Conclusion

Ideal programs for pregnant and parenting students would meet all their educational, health and social service needs. In addition, programs would help delay repeat pregnancies. Few communities will be able to initially provide all the components of an ideal program. However, it is important to begin where each community can, based on commitment and available resources. The components of a comprehensive program discussed here can serve as future goals as needs are identified through the planning and evaluation processes.

Resources

The following agencies and organizations can provide valuable information on the national level for anyone interested in beginning an adolescent pregnancy and/or parenting program, expanding already existing programs or services, or initiating policy changes at the school district level that affect programs and services to pregnant and parenting adolescents.

For more specific information related to individual state laws, policies, and programs and services, contact your state's department of education or the health and welfare departments.

Alan Guttmacher Institute
111 Fifth Avenue
New York, NY 10003
212-254-5656

American School Health
Association
7263 State Route 43
P.O. Box 708
Kent, OH 44240
216-678-1601

Center for Population Options
1025 Vermont Avenue NW,
    Suite 210
Washington, DC 20005
202-347-5700

Child Welfare League of America
440 First Street NW
Washington, DC 20001
202-638-2952

Children's Defense Fund
25 E Street NW
Washington, DC 20001
202-628-8787

Cities in Schools, Inc.
1023 15th Street NW, Suite 600
Washington, DC 2005
202-861-0230

National Center for Education in
    Maternal and Child Health
R and 38th Streets NE
Washington, DC 20057
202-625-8400

National Organization on
    Adolescent Pregnancy and
    Parenting
4421-A East-West Highway
Bethesda, MD 20814
301-913-0378

Office of Adolescent Pregnancy
United States Department of
    Health and Human Services
200 Independence Avenue
Hubert Humphrey Building, 736 E
Washington, DC 20201
202-245-7473

School and Community Services
Academy for Educational
    Development
1255 Twenty Third Street NW
Washington, DC 20037
202-862-1900

United States Department of
    Education
Office of Civil Rights
400 Maryland Avenue SW
Washington, DC 20202-1100
202-205-5413

References

The AAUW report: How schools shortchange girls: A study of major findings on girls and education. 1992. Washington, DC: American Association of University Women Educational Foundation and National Education Association.

Barr, L., and C. Monserrat with T. Berg. 1992. *Working with pregnant and parenting teens. A guide for use with teenage pregnancy: A new beginning.* Revised ed. Albuquerque, NM: New Futures, Inc.

Blue, J. 1987. Teen pregnancy: It's time for the schools to tackle the problem. *Phi Delta Kappan* 68 (10): 737-739.

Brindis, C., and R. J. Jeremy. 1988. *Adolescent pregnancy and parenting in California. A strategic plan for action.* San Francisco: Center for Population and Reproductive Health Policy. Institute for Health Policy Studies, UCSF.

Cagampang, H. H. et al. 1989. *Pregnant and parenting minors and California schools.* Berkeley, CA: Analysis for California Education.

Daria, R. J. 1988. Counseling and caring keep teen mothers in school. *The Executive Educator* 10 (6): 25, 29.

Department of Education, Office of Civil Rights. 1991. *Teenage pregnancy and parenthood issues under Title IX of the education amendments of 1972.* Washington, DC.

Feldman, L. L. *Partnerships for youth 2000: A program models manual.* Tulsa, OK: National Resource Center for Youth Services, University of Oklahoma.

Henkel, G., ed. 1991. *Teen parents, their children and play: Teaching alternatives to violence.* Los Angeles: The Center for Childhood.

Hobza, M., and S. Young. 1988. Pregnant and parenting teens: The middle school model. Concrete to abstract. Presentation, 4 November, Sacramento, CA.

Kenney, A. M. 1987. Teen pregnancy: An issue for schools. *Phi Delta Kappan* 68 (10): 728-36.

Kimmich, M. 1985. *Addressing the problems of adolescent pregnancy: The state of the art and art in the state.* Washington, DC: National Governor's Association Center for Policy Research.

Lindsay, J., and S. Rodine. 1989a. *Teen pregnancy challenge, book 1: Strategies for change.* Buena Park, CA: Morning Glory Press, Inc.

Lindsay, J., and S. Rodine. 1989b. *Teen pregnancy challenge, book 2: Programs for kids.* Buena Park, CA: Morning Glory Press, Inc.

Loomis, A., and R. Simpson-Brown. 1990. *Teen pregnancy: A blueprint for comprehensive California school-based pregnancy prevention programs and programs for pregnant and parenting students.* Sacramento, CA: Department of Education.

McGee, E. A., and E. Archer. 1988. *Improving educational opportunities for pregnant and parenting students: A report on a survey of policies, program and plans for pregnant and parenting students in nine urban school districts.* New York: Academy for Educational Development.

McGee, E. A., and S. Blank. 1989. *A stitch in time: Helping young mothers complete high school.* New York: Academy for Educational Development.

Scholl, M. F., and J. R. Johnson. 1988. Keeping pregnant teens in school. *Vocational Education Journal* 63 (6): 42-43.

Seeking success: Educating pregnant and parenting teenagers. 1990. Albany, NY: Conference of Large City Boards of Education.

Simpson-Brown, R. 1991. *Legislative history of major policy changes for educational programs serving pregnant and parenting teens.* Sacramento, CA: California Department of Education.

Simpson-Brown, R. 1992. *School-based programs serving pregnant/parenting teens: Guidelines for implementing a quality program: Checklist.* Sacramento, CA: California State Department of Education.

Toward a state of esteem: The final report of the California task force to promote self-esteem and personal and social responsibility. 1990. Sacramento, CA: California State Department of Education.

Weiner, R., ed. 1987. *Teen pregnancy: Impact on the schools.* Alexandria, VA: Capitol Publications, Inc.

Chapter 29

Student Assistance Programs

Kenneth M. Newbury, PhD

For most of my life as a student, I was all alone. I carried secrets with me like other students carry books in a backpack. But unlike books, my secrets could never come out. They were too scary and deep. I would rather die than tell anyone about what happened. I thought I could handle it, by pushing my secret into some deep dark place. But it changed me. My grades fell, my friends changed, and I stopped caring. Until this one teacher saw what was happening to me. She dared to talk to others about me. She was part of the student assistance team....

—Amy, age 15.

Amy had been sexually abused. For students like Amy, student assistance appears more like an invisible helping hand or guardian angel than a program. With 12 other students at an urban high school, Amy attends weekly support group meetings where she confidentially shares her story of abuse and suicide attempts. With other students, Amy builds the courage and skill to deal with her problems. Amy openly credits her support group with saving both her life and school career.

For thousands of students like Amy, and others challenged by problems ranging from chemical dependency to violence, student assistance programs help remove barriers to learning. For a large number of these students, student assistance programs are also helping to prevent future problems through proactive planning and training. For schools that are reluctantly foisted into a primary socialization and health care provider role, student assistance offers an integrated approach to meeting changing needs. Unlike other programs with a singular focus, such as a pregnancy prevention or suicide prevention program, the student assistance approach is integrated to help schools realize their own mandate: for students to achieve their fullest potential.

Student Assistance: The Evolution

Student assistance programs are rapidly evolving from a single problem focus to a systems approach to enhance student welfare. A systems approach is comprehensive in nature. Unlike school-based programs that target one type of student problem, a systems approach is concerned with the many relationships that affect a student's life. These relationships include those of family, school and community. A successful student assistance program provides a network of prevention, intervention and support services to overcome conditions that interfere with a student's ability to achieve his or her full potential.

A decade ago, student assistance emerged as a way to battle the drug epidemic in our schools and communities. The primary role of these programs was the identification and referral of substance-using students to treatment. These programs also provided after-care support groups for students returning from treatment. The mechanism for change was the school "core team"—building staff at all levels who were trained in the mechanics of identifying and linking students to needed community services. Some core team members also facilitated school support groups.

Core teams, or student assistance teams as they are sometimes called, have many responsibilities. When these teams meet, they review confidential reports from other staff and students detailing specific student behaviors. A core team might receive a report from a teacher that her student sleeps in class and is prone to violent verbal outbursts. By comparing the behavior of this student in all his classes with his home behavior, the core team can determine the need for further action or evaluation. This team approach provides a more comprehensive view of a student's behavior. It also prevents students from "slipping through the cracks."

Once a problem is identified, core teams often refer the student and family to one or more community and school resources. However, core teams do not provide diagnosis or treatment for these student concerns. These chores are managed by professionals in the community.

Expanding Student Assistance

Most student assistance programs maintain their major focus on substance use-related problems. This focus is reinforced through state and federal grants that target alcohol and other drug use by our nation's youth. Educational goals developed during the 1980s also enhance the substance use focus. National education goal number six places a priority on drug-free and violence-free schools by the year 2000 (U. S. Department of Education, 1991).

The structure of student assistance and the recognition of substance use-related problems has focused attention on other issues. As a result, many student assistance programs have extended program goals to include students at risk for other problems. Included among these problem areas are students who have been sexually abused and children of alcoholics. The argument for including students victimized by their family context or abuse is that these students are at a perceived higher risk for substance use.

As a matter of practice, student assistance programs do engage students in nearly every area of dysfunction. A guiding principle of student assistance in the 1990s is involvement with students for any condition that interferes with optimal performance in the school setting. Successful student assistance programs conform to the needs of their local district and the problems of students. Thus, pregnancy, parenthood, sexual abuse, HIV infection, sexual orientation and other issues of sexuality are increasingly a focus of student assistance programs. Each of these concerns presents unique challenges and opportunities for schools and professionals. But a comprehensive student assistance program is fully capable of responding to the needs of most sexuality issues.

Changes in School and Community Services

In many schools and communities, there appears to be a reshaping of the traditional boundaries between school and community services. The school setting is still viewed as an appropriate environment for prevention of problems through education. Community groups continue to provide needed treatment and intervention. However, partnerships between the community and schools has increased the range of prevention and intervention programs in both the school and the community. Examples of these programs include community recreation programs that also provide training in life skills and conflict management. Community agencies also operate within the school building to provide medical and mental health services to students during the school day. These newly forged relationships between schools and community groups show every indication of further blurring the traditional roles that each has played in the past.

Many of the conditions that interfere with healthy functioning are well-known targets in both the community and schools. Changes in our understanding of effective approaches to reduce risks and resolve problems have focused on cooperation between schools and community resources. The logical outcome of cooperative school and community programming is to better target the known risk factors which interfere with healthy student functioning. Certainly prevention and intervention will be more successful when students are equally supported in different settings. Cooperative programming can also extend the continuum of care. For example, some agencies are willing to continue student support groups during summer months when schools are not in session.

Connecting Drug and Sexuality Education

A tremendous opportunity exists for cooperation between traditional drug education, a component of many student assistance programs, and sexuality education. The cooperation stems from a commonality in teaching methodology, and, to some extent, content area. Both subject matters share a common interest in self-esteem, relationship skills, refusal skills and decision making. Integrating these overlapping areas reduces the burden on teachers trying to "make room" for a curriculum.

One way to facilitate prevention education is to appoint selected teachers to the role of health resource teacher. Each health resource teacher receives comprehensive training in both human growth and development (i.e., sexuality education) and drug education. Health resource teachers then help facilitate instruction in both areas.

Health resource teachers can be important advocates for their respective areas. These teachers help other faculty when they have concerns. They communicate problems and concerns to key administrators who can quickly meet teacher needs. Health resource teachers also serve as an invaluable means of disseminating new information. When new resources become available or special programs are offered, health resource teachers share with their teaching peers. Information about new videos, books, medical news, and special events and contests are examples of the information health resource teachers are likely to share.

Structure and Function of Programs

There are several key components in successfully designed student assistance programs. The first is commitment to a student assistance approach by both the school administration and the community. Too often, a staff member is saddled with additional responsibilities to handle alone. A well-meaning administrator might ask a school counselor to run the "drug program" or "have a support group." Of course, these new duties are in addition to a mounting burden of testing, scheduling, student advising and monitoring the lunch room. At best, such programs assist a small number of students. They are not systemic or comprehensive. When the counselor is transferred or suffers from burn-out, the program may disappear.

Commitment can be demonstrated several ways. These include staffing positions from general funds, establishing supportive policy, and creating a school climate which is genuinely concerned with the welfare of all students. Without funding, student assistance programs can still do well. However, a fail-safe commitment of the administration to addressing student needs is required.

Programs must actively promote a team approach to student assistance. In a team approach, staff members work together to help students identify and overcome problems. Every staff member matters. Often school secretaries, bus drivers, custodians and nurses are among the first to spot problems. Working with other staff they can comprise a type of "early warning system" for students. The involvement of all staff, and, to a degree, students and the community in the design of student assistance programming increases program ownership, viability and outcomes. A core team and student assistance advisory board can include school officials and key members of the community. The board can serve as an invaluable resource in program promotion, a sounding board for new and existing programs and a buffer against critics of any particular program. Another important way to demonstrate commitment is to provide release time or staff meetings for inservice education programs. A fully educated staff is vital to making appropriate referrals and understanding the role of student assistance.

Another key ingredient to success is found in programs that are comprehensive. A comprehensive student assistance program integrates three important approaches: prevention, intervention and support.

Prevention

Early student assistance programs did not include a prevention focus. These programs were most concerned with identification of and intervention for students suspected of substance use or chemical dependency. It is now widely recognized that prevention programs increase the effectiveness of intervention and support programs. Prevention generates increased referrals of student problems and increased acceptability for seeking assistance. For example, following an HIV-awareness program, a student who is concerned about his or her own risk of exposure may self-refer to a student assistance counselor or community resource.

Today, prevention programs occupy up to 50 percent of all student assistance activities. Prevention programs might include peer listening programs, peer youth group meetings, leadership training, and a variety of alternative-based youth activities. Peer listening programs train a small group of students identified by their peers as good listeners in a variety of skills, including active listening skills and understanding youth problems and appropriate community resources. Programs such as peer listening demonstrate the role of prevention in assisting in problem referral and intervention. A trained peer listener may learn of a friend's suicide intent or substance use and make an appropriate referral to trained staff. Peer youth group meetings are social in nature and focus on providing activities which are fun, healthy and an alternative to destructive activities associated with boredom and unsupervised time.

Intervention

Successful intervention programs must include at least three basic components: identification, assessment and referral to appropriate community resources. A typical student assistance problem may be identified by staff referral on a "concerned person's report." Confidential reports are collected from all staff and key individuals who know an identified student. Once collected, a core team of individuals or a trained student assistance professional assesses the data for a disposition. If a decision is reached that further evaluation or treatment may be needed, the student is linked with appropriate community resources.

Support

Support is an integral part of student assistance. The ability to receive support in a safe environment is central to personal development and growth. The availability of support groups, groups of students with common needs and interests facilitated by a trained leader, is one way that support is provided to students. Students who are identified by counselors, self-referrals and other means attend a group meeting. Support group meetings are used to discuss common student concerns and learn problem-solving skills. Support is most commonly provided through support group sessions. Support groups typically meet once a week on a changing class period. Time changes ensure that students will not miss the same class frequently. Support can also be provided by community groups, self-help groups such as Alcoholics Anonymous, or aftercare groups run by treatment centers.

All support groups are built on a foundation of trust. A central element in this foundation is confidentiality. Students and support group leaders are expected to follow specific rules that maintain the confidentiality of group members. The rule is often stated as: "What's said in group, stays in group." Group leaders also make certain to explain that life-threatening incidents, such as intention to commit suicide or reported abuse are not confidential. As required by state laws and ethical standards of behavior, group leaders are required to take appropriate action on these matters.

Integrating Resources and Managing the Program

Successful student assistance programs are equally concerned with issues of school climate, staff training and intervention with single students. A systemic approach integrates all resources in a school and community to best assist students. This requires student assistance planners to balance the amount of time spent working with students directly with time spent maintaining the skill and resources of all care providers. A trained staff is necessary for there to be referrals to support groups, evaluation or intervention of student problems.

Investment in staff training also pays other dividends. For instance, consider the differences between spending one hour training a large group of teachers and one hour working with a student. The hour with the student will surely benefit the student. However, the hour with the teachers will result in benefits to all students for many years. Trained teachers can increase results from "informal interventions"—caring approaches that lead to student change.

A provider of student assistance works to develop a network that combines the resources of the school building and the community. In many communities, local treatment agencies will provide free in-school assessment and management of support groups. Some agencies are now providing medical care in school buildings as an auxiliary to student assistance programs.

Student assistance programs are generally managed using existing school resources, such as counselors, core team members and other staff members. However, there are successful student assistance models which rely on agency or other outside assistance for management and service to students and the school building. These "externally" managed programs provide services, such as support groups, and identification and referral of problems on a contractual basis with the school system or school itself. Often times, agencies provide staff who work with students and faculty to design programs and procedures that meet school needs.

A more common arrangement is internal management of student assistance programs. In this arrangement, one or more professionals are hired or assigned by the school to manage the student assistance program. This program coordinates the activities of school staff and develops a helping network with the larger community.

Single-Focus Support Groups

A common response to student needs is the provision of single-focus support groups. For example, support groups to address the special needs of pregnant students and student parents are common in many schools. These weekly support groups offer a variety of educational opportunities for participants. At a minimum, students receive information regarding key community resources and parenting skills. The groups also provide social support and a shared identity. Although all support groups for student parents address the physical and emotional challenges of parenting, other topics are also likely to be discussed, including meeting financial needs, parent skill building, working through family conflict and meeting the dual demands of school and family life. Another common topic is working through problems with the baby's biological parent and the student's present boyfriend or girlfriend.

These students, and students in many single-focus support groups are more concerned and troubled by relationship problems of all descriptions. In some instances, the relationships have a direct bearing on a student's child's welfare. Concerns about childcare and relationships with her family of origin are frequently a topic of discussion. But students are also concerned with day-to-day needs including getting along with current partners and relating to teachers, caseworkers and employers.

The goal of the support groups in dealing with relationship problems is to build relationship skills through roleplaying, discussion and example. Skills are modeled in the group and might include listening, problem solving and conflict mediation. A larger goal is to help students stay in school while remediating difficulties that interfere with school performance. Regardless of the type of support group, this latter goal is the real raison d´être of student assistance and support groups.

Another support group focus is students who have been sexually abused. These students may be self-identified, but it is more usual that a concerned counselor or student assistance staff member recognizes the need from other referrals. In one school with a successful support group called Kids Against Rape (KAR) in the Toledo Public Schools, students meet weekly to address the impact of sexual abuse. Similar to other groups, students describe the ongoing relationship problems that interfere with school functioning, but these students also help each other deal with the pain and stigma of victimization. When a student must confront a parent or other adult in court on charges of sexual abuse, other students who have been through this experience provide support and counseling. The group also discusses the health consequences of sexuality and promiscuity.

No support group or student assistance service will be successful unless it meets the conditions previously outlined. Without commitment and a comprehensive approach that integrates resources, some needs may get overlooked or ignored. Ignored groups may include students who suffer from a recent death in the family or in a close personal relationship and students who are new to the school. These students may need support and be dealing with feelings that affect their academic and personal success. But perhaps the most overlooked group is gay, lesbian and bisexual students. These students experience the additional burden of stigmatization, which may even include physical threats. Many school districts and student assistance programs have not successfully provided services to these students.

Without an understanding staff and administration, resistance to programming such as support groups for gay students can develop. To counteract this resistance, inservice education programs about the needs of this population can be provided. A range of services to gay and lesbian students can be provided through the usual student assistance channels. These students can be incorporated into generic support groups that address a variety of concerns that can impede academic and personal success. Of course, students with concerns related to sexuality can also visit with a student assistance or academic counselor. A leading cause of self-referral are issues related to sexuality. Although most referrals are about pregnancy, students are also referred for HIV testing and AIDS information.

Summary

The future vitality of student assistance depends on meeting the changing needs of our student population. An effective student assistance program cannot be labeled comprehensive until it is prepared to address each threat to a student's academic success and well-being. A partnership between sexuality educators and student assistance is being formed in many schools. It is important that this partnership be nurtured and continued for the sake of all students.

Present school resources in many communities are shrinking. While the community resource-base may also be getting smaller, the advantages of partnerships are growing. Schools provide a captive base from which to address student concerns. A coordinated, planned student assistance approach, enhanced with the expertise and resources of the community, is an ideal milieu for prevention or intervention. In addition, schools and community agencies bring different perspective on the nature of youth problems.

An old African proverb says, "It takes a whole village to raise a child." Neither schools nor communities can afford the presumption that they have all the answers, skill or manpower. Successful programs have learned that schools and communities must work together to raise healthy children.

References

U. S. Department of Education. 1991. *America 2000: An Education Strategy.* Washington, DC.

Chapter 30

The Role of Media in Sexuality Education

Susan Giarratano, EdD, CHES

In 1984, the American Academy of Pediatrics (AAP) Task Force on Children and Television issued a statement cautioning parents and pediatricians about the influence of television on early sexual activities, among other risky behaviors (AAP, 1990). According to the AAP, by the time today's child reaches 70 years of age, he or she will have spent seven years watching television, which may displace active experience in the real world.

Approximately 14,000 sexual references and innuendos per year occur on television; only 150 of these references deal with sexual responsibility, abstinence or contraception. Hayes (1987) notes that "the media provides young people with lots of clues about how to be sexy, but...little information about how to be sexually responsible."

Such messages are not confined to TV, but are found in all types of media, including music, magazines, movies and advertising (Peterson, Moore and Furstenberg, 1991). Mass communication is the use of the media to reach a large audience. Its purpose varies, but most media provide information and they entertain. Standards of practice and ethics are inherent obligations of the media to the public they serve. The public *assumes* that the media performs its journalistic duties with integrity, intelligence, objectivity, accuracy and fairness. But the content of a program, advertisement, song, music video or story, may be intended to "grab" the audience's attention without regard for the appropriateness of the message to the age, developmental level or culture of the audience. The potential viewing or reading audience may or may not be the target audience intended for the messages presented (Talbott, 1992). This is particularly true in regard to sexuality-related depictions.

How important is the media as a source of sexuality education for young people? According to Haffner and Kelly (1987), teenagers rank the media as a major source of information about sexuality issues and an important influence on their values and behaviors. They think television is an accurate source of information about sex and birth control, and many of them feel that television gives them a realistic picture about sexually transmitted disease, pregnancy and the consequences of sexual activity.

In fact, the media plays an enormous role in our sexuality education, including information about sex roles, family life, physical attractiveness, body image, friendship, parent/child communication, pregnancy and childbearing, and working relationships, as well as suggestive behaviors, sexual innuendo, sexual situations, sexist images and sexual violence.

At the same time, the media is carefully using sexuality to sell products and programming. Sexuality is effectively used to get audience attention and to gain credibility for the product (Flay, DiTecco and Schlegel, 1980). Ads at network prime time use sex appeal, youth and physical attractiveness as a selling point (Brown,

Childers and Waszak, 1990). In fact, the less sexually related the product (e.g., cars, alcohol and food), the more likely sexual depictions will be used to promote it (Brown, Childers and Waszak, 1990).

Issues concerning the media portrayals of sexuality, their impact on adolescent sexual behavior and attitudes, and the contradictory messages given to teenagers must be explored. Communication between the media industry and those in health care, along with parents/guardians, educators and community coalitions is essential to communicate and understand the impact of these messages and develop strategies for balancing them (Bearinger, 1990).

In this chapter we will explore how young people are influenced by sexual images in the various media and how adults can counter negative messages by giving youth more appropriate information, values, role models and support so that they can recognize media messages for what they are (National Commission on the Role of the School and the Community in Improving Adolescent Health, 1990).

Television

Television includes any image which one can access by turning on the television set—cable stations, advertising, independent stations, network programming, music videos, and, with the aid of VCRs, movies (Bearinger, 1990). Entertainment that uses sexual innuendo and messages to encourage viewership may not always provide an accurate and informative depiction of sexual values, attitudes and beliefs. These depictions may conflict with the messages that parents/guardians, schools and the religious groups want to give children.

Television viewing may act indirectly by teaching certain values, using language and scripts that are consistent with and perhaps encourage sexual activity. One of television's strongest influences may be in what children learn about sex roles and the ways in which men and women relate to each other in all spheres of behavior, not just erotic behavior. Sex role attitudes ultimately do affect sexual activity, pregnancy and childrearing (Peterson, Moore and Furstenberg, 1991).

Research has tallied physical, verbal and implied acts or references to sex (Workman, 1989):

* touching behaviors (kissing, hugging and other activities)— 24.5 acts per hour
* suggestions and innuendo (flirtatious behavior or allusions to sexual behavior)—16.5 times per hour
* sexual intercourse—2.5 times per hour
* discouragement of sexual practices—6.2 times per hour
* educational information about sex—1.6 times per hour.

Commercial television is becoming more sexually explicit, and cable channels, films, movies, videos and music videos may feature explicit adult sexual content. Content analyses have shown that unmarried heterosexual couples on television engage in sexual intercourse from four to eight times more frequently than married men and women. Contraceptives are rarely referred to or used, but women seldom get pregnant; and men and women rarely contract sexually transmitted diseases unless they are prostitutes or homosexuals (Brown and Newcomer, 1991).

Commercial television is more likely to affect beliefs than knowledge levels (Buerkel-Rothfulls, 1981). Thus, regular viewing of sexual references on television would relate to the beliefs that sexual relations among unmarried persons are prevalent; that deviant sex (i.e., prostitution, rape) is prevalent; that sex as an activity is important; that it is less taboo to talk and think about sex; and that sexual affairs are common (Greenberg, Perry and Cover, 1983).

Recent studies show that references to and depictions of sexual activity have increased dramatically in the last ten years. In soap operas, popular with adolescents, sexual content has increased by 21 percent since 1982 and 103 percent since 1980. In 1987, the average program on the major networks contained two references to intercourse and none to birth control. Sexually transmitted disease was mentioned one time in every ten program hours. Nighttime soap operas made ten references to sex per hour.

Not only has the frequency of sexual references increased, but those references have become more explicit in TV programs and advertising. The few studies that exist (Brown, Childers and Waszak, 1990) suggest that adolescents who rely heavily on television for information about sexuality will believe that premarital and extramarital intercourse with multiple partners is acceptable. They are unlikely to learn about the need for contraceptives as a form of protection against pregnancy or disease.

Television programs and advertising also present extreme ideals of physical attractiveness and thinness, which are often reinforced by families and friends. Those ideals may exacerbate the difficulties and conflicts adolescents may have in accepting their own appearance, and may contribute to development of depression, excessive use of cosmetics, abuse of cosmetic surgery, preoccupation with weight loss, and even more severe eating disorders, such as anorexia nervosa. The "standard" of attractiveness portrayed in the media is slimmer for women than men, and is slimmest since the last epidemic of eating disorders occurred in the mid-1920s (Brown, Childers and Waszak, 1990).

Although there has been a great deal of research about the effects of TV on social behavior, little has focused on the consequences of viewing portrayals of sexuality (i.e., how this content is interpreted or how it affects the individual viewer). Just counting the incidence of particular activities does not convey the full message of these portrayals. For example, although two characters in a program may engage in extramarital intercourse, it may be regretted by the participants or criticized by other characters. What may be particularly relevant to viewers is the portrayal of social reaction, including reaction to pregnancy or sexually transmitted disease.

The viewer's perception and understanding of what is viewed is also an important consideration in interpreting sexuality messages in the media. For example, verbal humorous sexual innuendo is less likely to be understood by 12 year old than the visual implications of such a scene (Brown, Childers and Waszak, 1990).

According to Eisenstock (1984) it appears that television may be a more potentially effective vehicle for expanding sex-role consciousness among young people than previously assumed. TV has been found to facilitate young people's awareness of recent and ongoing changes in division of labor between sexes and the sex-role ideologies consistent with these changes. Young viewers associate primarily with same-sex characters, and, as a result of current portrayals, youth tend to stereotype males as aggressive and females as attractive (Remafedi, 1990). Gender-role development profoundly influences career planning, intimate relationships, sexual behavior, decision making, attitudes toward parenthood, substance use and other areas.

Television has the opportunity, the time and the economic position to inform and educate children and youth about sexuality. In 1981, a special science series, afternoon specials on CBS network, *The Body Human*, provided straightforward, accurate information about sexual facts and feelings for 10- to 14-year-old boys and girls. However, such programming is rare. The mass media is not organized to provide a comprehensive sexuality education program; it is set up to inform and entertain (Greenberg, Perry and Cover, 1983).

Music

Since the advent of music television, MTV, critics have argued its pros and cons, but certainly not its influence on youth. Between the seventh and twelfth grades, the average teenager listens to 10,500 hours of rock music—uncensored, unsupervised and unguided by parents. This is just slightly less than the entire number of hours spent in the classroom from kindergarten through high school; often television viewing decreases and music becomes an increasingly powerful medium in an adolescent's life (Brown and Hendee, 1989). Music plays an important role in adolescent socialization, informing about sexuality, alternative lifestyles and political topics. Music is also an important symbol in adolescents' search for independence and autonomy. Preteens and teenagers are impressionable and may be particularly sensitive to the messages of rock music. According to Bloom (1987), the pervasiveness of rock music undermines parental control over a child's moral education.

MTV has come under scrutiny from parents, educators and coalitions. While some people find value in MTV's ability to promote female and minority artists and to open discussion about social issues, others say the station promotes consumerism and sexism (Aufderheide, 1991). The National Coalition on Television Violence (NCTV) would like to have MTV offer specific viewing times that are "safe" for children. Their claim is that the violence and sexually explicit material permeates MTV programming, so that a viewer cannot pick out a certain "safe" period for a child to view, although an NCTV study in progress shows that

MTV programs contain less violence and sexually degrading material in 1991 than they did in the 1980s (MTV turns 10 years old, 1992).

Certainly music, a prominent medium in the lives of adolescents, sends conflicting messages. Rock songs symbolize the adolescent themes of rebellion and autonomy; some with disturbing lyrics that connote violence and pornographic sexual imagery. In contrast to these media messages are the themes of abstinence and reasoned, responsible behavior promoted by authority figures such as parents, teachers, government officials and health care professionals. Commitment to a rock subculture, such as heavy metal, is symptomatic of adolescent alienation from these authority figures (Brown and Hendee, 1989).

Music videos add a visual dimension to music. The multisensory input reinforces any message by enhancing learning and recall. Music videos are three- to six-minute commercials for a performer or performance, and some create unhealthy perceptions of human sexuality. A sampling of the content of 200 rock videos indicated that they contained sexual intimacy, violence and sexual references, and that women were dressed provocatively and portrayed in a condescending manner (Brown and Hendee, 1989). A video called *Dreamworlds* analyzes the use of women and sex in music videos to sell not only music but also attitudes about male and female relations.[1]

Magazines

Teen magazines are primarily targeted to teenage girls, to entertain, inform and give them the information they need to make "sound" choices in their lives. Traditional messages in the maga-

---

[1]For more information, contact the Foundation for Media Education, P. O. Box 2008, Amherst, MA 01004-2008; (413) 586-8398, (413) 586-4170.

zines focus on appearance, male/female relations and the home. They tend to give clear messages about the role of females in society. Feminist messages emphasize self-development, being independent, taking care of oneself, self-reliance, education, vocations and physical and mental health. These magazines also include movie and music reviews, and personality profiles of music, television and movie stars. Magazines provide both a traditional orientation and a more feminist approach to their content. Although magazines are only a small part of the media, and a small part of the socialization of teens, in conjunction with other media, they can be a powerful reinforcer of media messages about sexuality.

Several teen magazines are discussed here. Most of the magazines directed to the teenage population are for females.

Seventeen purports to focus on traditional orientation and ideology of womanhood. It suggests that the concerns of a teenage girl are primarily her appearance, household activities, romance and dating (Pierce, 1990). *Seventeen's* purported purpose is "to inform, entertain and give teenage girls all the information they need to make sound choices in their lives...the fashion and beauty sections are to make girls feel good about themselves." *Seventeen's* motto is, "It's where the girl ends and the woman begins." The magazine imitates the covers of women's glamour magazines, and features women in advertisements more than girls, with provocative content and layout.

Sassy, the controversial teen magazine for the 18 and younger female, converses on subjects such as homosexuality, sexual arousal and loss of virginity (White, 1989). It carried an ad for condoms in its first issue. It is unique with a fresh, direct voice.

'Teen is less sophisticated and sensual than *Sassy* or *Seventeen,* and its models look like real teenagers, not pouting or wearing revealing clothing. Neither its ads nor its articles deal with birth control or sex; romance is portrayed as puppy love. Innocence and abstinence are the messages conveyed.

Advertisements in teen magazines tend to promote what advertisers call "identification." If the consumer uses a certain perfume, wears a certain pair of jeans, or uses a certain type of makeup, she or he will be as glamorous and attractive as the model and will have the kind of excitement and romance implied in the advertisement. These messages are used in most media to sell products.

Recognizing the limitations of television advertising, reaching teens in other ways may be appropriate. For example, ads for contraceptives may be carried in *Seventeen* and *Sassy, Cosmopolitan, Glamor, Ebony,* and *Jet* magazines, to name a few popular with female teens. *Junior Sports Illustrated, Sports Illustrated,* and other sports-related magazines (e.g., *Baseball Weekly* and others) appear to be the magazines for or read by male teens. Although those magazines, with the exception of *Junior Sports Illustrated,* are not published for teens, ads for contraceptives would probably be appropriate and wise to include.

Advertising

It is the business of the media industry to sell audiences to advertisers (Centerwell, 1992). A basic advertising technique is to insert a message which is novel, shocking and/or entertaining (to ensure attention) into a specific program or magazine which is already determined to have a large audience, to ensure exposure (Flay, DiTecco and Schlegel, 1980).

In a study by Baran and Blasko (1984), the college students who viewed the advertisements perceived that young men who drove Camaros and brushed their teeth with Ultrabrite toothpaste were more sexually aggressive on a date than young men who drove Honda Accords and brushed their teeth with Crest. The sex appeal toothpaste versus the cavity fighter, respectively, and the type of car an individual drove, obviously influenced their expectations. Commercials for toys, food and clothing, carried with children's cartoon programming, show that the media differentiate between males and females, not in the emphasis of the product, but in the importance of appearance for the female (Ogletree et al., 1990).

Currently advertisers can promote condom use for protection from disease, but are not allowed to discuss protection in terms of birth control. Prescription products cannot be advertised on TV, which restricts ads for oral contraceptives. Yet over-the-counter douche products, creams for vaginal infections and female sanitary products are readily discussed in advertisements. Advertisements for these types of personal products tend to use a factual, caring, nonsexual approach, in contrast to the widespread use of sexual depictions in advertisements for cars, alcohol, clothing, perfume and colognes, and food. This paradoxical portrayal of sexuality sends mixed messages to young people.

In a Louis Harris poll in 1987, the majority of adults surveyed approved of condom advertisements on TV. Adolescents also approve of such ads (Buchta, 1989). It may be that the threat of HIV/AIDS has changed parents' and adolescents' perspective on aspects of adolescent sexuality. When the major concern was pregnancy, parents felt morally and ethically justified in maintaining status quo concerning public education and information about birth control and sexually transmitted disease; but now we are no longer dealing with a strictly cultural/social/moral issue, but a life and death situation. This information demonstrates a shift in public attitudes and suggests that advertisements could play a strong educational role in pregnancy and sexually transmitted disease prevention.

Opportunities for Sexuality Education in the Media

The media is everywhere. It is a powerful communicator that can influence the thinking and attitudes of viewers of all ages. Parents and other caregivers, teachers, school administrators and health care professionals need to understand the impact of the media and how it can be used to communicate more effectively with youth.

According to *Code Blue: Uniting for Healthier Youth,* "the entertainment industry should use positive role models and health messages in programming; emphasize the negative consequences of health-risking behaviors; and voluntarily establish and enforce codes of ethics and responsible standards for programming and products influencing children and adolescents. The advertising industry should voluntarily reject advertising aimed at adolescents...that endanger young people's health" (National Commission on the Role of the School and the Community in Improving Adolescent Health, 1990).

To some extent, the media industry has been responsive to the concerns of parents, educators and coalitions advocating for children with regard to the sexual content in programming and have included more sexual responsibility, consequences and decision-making activities in their processes.

Afterschool Special, Children's Television Workshop, Public Broadcasting, Fox Television, and network and cable prime time programming have produced programs exploring HIV/AIDS and other issues for children. These have been pioneering efforts to provide viewers with a sensitive, responsible, accurate and scientific-based approach to discussing sexuality-related issues. For example, in a CBS daytime *School-Break Special,* "Babies Having Babies," and another CBS program, *Choices,* actual methods of contraception were discussed.

Health-enhancing storylines, based on the realities of the social morbidities of adolescents, that have the potential of entertaining as well as educating, can and have been developed. Some daytime soap operas and network evening programs have integrated sexually responsible behavior, debate and decision-making skills into segments. Public broadcasting stations have effectively dealt with issues of sexuality, with PBS's *Kids, Sex and Choices,* and *The Body Human* among them. *Kids, Sex and Choices* discusses sex education from a variety of perspectives—from a Catholic girls' school to a public elementary and a high school in Los Angeles.

Viewership and the commercial value of educational and informative stories and docudramas that are health-promoting have been demonstrated. Network affiliates and independent stations run public service announcements that urge teenagers either to delay having sex or to use contraceptives.

Alternative media that presents responsible messages about sexuality can be developed; cable TV programs and local radio stations can make air time available. The Center for Population Option's *Rock Project* uses teen media idols to promote positive sexuality messages. MTV ran a rock video focusing on the plight of teenage parenthood. Local disc jockeys may be persuaded to balance certain songs with on-air messages about responsibility. Public service announcements can be broadcast by local television stations and in movie theaters; concert arenas can include ads for family planning services in their programs (Haffner and Kelly, 1987).

The three major television networks, who have maintained a board of internal "censors" (Department of Broadcast Standards and Practices) responsible for considering the taste and appropriateness of all programming and advertising, agree that their standards have been more conservative than those of other media. Faced with increasing competition from independent and cable stations, and videocassette recorders, network television may loosen those standards, particularly for programs aimed at adults and for advertising (Mandese, 1987).

Bergman (1980) suggested that "it is possible that appearance of one or two condom ads on Monday Night Football programs could do more to lower teen pregnancy rates than five years' worth of federally funded adolescent health programs." What he doesn't understand is that youth also need to know how to properly use them, and to understand their effectiveness, combined with spermicides, to prevent pregnancy or transmission of sexually transmitted disease. Federally funded programs, as well as state and local ones, in combination with parents/guardians, school health education, health care professionals and coalitions, are needed to effectively educate youth about sexuality issues.

Opportunities for collaboration between parents/guardians, health care professionals and the media industry exist and they need to be used. Parents and teachers need to develop and become involved in helping children acquire critical viewing and reading skills. Adults need to participate in the selection of what children watch, and preview the kinds of magazines, music and videos they see. Coalitions of parents/guardians and representatives from community agencies, schools, health care professions, broadcast and print media, can work together to support legislation to make the broadcast of high quality programming a condition of license renewal and urge that sexuality be portrayed responsibly by the media.

Parents and health care professionals can use the forum of the broadcast and print media to make their views known. Radio and television talk show programs that allow home audience participation by interactive telephone calls offer opportunities for concerned citizens to voice opinions about the need for responsible sexuality education by the media. Individuals and groups or coalitions can prepare letters to the editors or articles for print in newspapers about these issues.

The American Psychological Association and the American Academy of Pediatrics have specific task forces for the study, policy and development of television standards. Annual conferences to bring together those in health care, psychology, sociology, communications, the television industry, advertising, government and concerned parents and guardians need to continue. These kinds of conferences could be conducted at the local level to help educate the community and develop its clear and concerted voice to promote media policy changes.

The Center for Population Options (CPO) gives a Nancy Susan Reynolds Award for responsible portrayal of sexuality on television. Community coalitions of parents/guardians, school boards and school administrators can review and critique sex education programming on television and in other media. They can share this information and recognize positive efforts as well as identify programs or magazines to be avoided. Local community groups may want to give local awards for positive programming efforts. Letters to the editors or program directors may be in order for media which do not promote programming, stories, ads or music which match the critical viewing, reading and/or listening guidelines of the group or coalition. Media officials need to know that parents encourage positive programming, appreciate certain shows, dislike negative messages about women, families and sex, and want to see contraceptives advertised on television.

Media Literacy

Parents and guardians need to be taught how to identify the blatant and subtle ways sex is dealt with in the media and how to use the media as a point of discussion with their children. C. Everett Koop, the former surgeon general, recommended that media literacy programs be developed to teach children the skills of selecting and interpreting television experiences. A companion curriculum for parents to enhance their critical viewing skills should also be used.

CPO publishes *Talking with TV,* a guide to assist parents and other caregivers to use television to communicate about sensitive subjects. This guide includes how to use TV in discussions, interactive activities, a program review guide for current TV programs, and a list of production companies and advocacy organizations to contact regarding programming. Many citizen groups are organizing across the country to promote media literacy, citizen participation and access to the media. They are creatively planning media awareness projects. For example, media workshop kits that explore how advertising and the media teach us about sex roles, body image and beauty, and how to analyze and evaluate film, video, TV and music are available.[2]

The American Academy of Pediatrics, Committee on Communications, has addressed the issue of the influence of television on early sexual activity, among other health issues (American Academy of Pediatrics, 1990). They concur with Koop that critical viewing skills are needed by children, and that parents should be aware of the influence of television. They recommend that parents limit their young children's viewing to one to two hours per day, participate in the selection of the programs their children watch, and encourage television substitutes, such as reading, athletics and hobbies.

The Committee advocates the active participation of health care professionals, especially pediatricians, in supporting legislation to make broadcasting of high quality children's programming a condition of license renewal. They also support research on the effects of television on children, and the building of coalitions to monitor and improve television for children.

---

[2]For more information, contact the Center for Media and Values, 1962 S. Shenandoah, Los Angeles, CA 90034; (310) 559-2944.

Opportunities in the Classroom

Since television is an integral part of the American family life, like it or not, it needs to be recognized. Educators must include it in sexuality education, because it pays a significant role in the development of sex values, attitudes and possibly behavior. Sexuality educators can use the media to supplement lessons (Haffner and Kelly, 1987; American School Health Association, 1991). A variety of teaching strategies involving the media messages may be integrated into interdisciplinary instruction. For example:

- Students can be asked to clip advertisements as a springboard for a discussion of standards of physical attractiveness and sex role stereotypes.
- Movies such as *Still Killing Us Softly* and *Stale Buns* can help sensitize students about the role that sex plays in advertising.
- Students can learn to critique the use of sex in the media to sell products.
- Students can analyze the lyrics of popular songs to explore sexual messages.
- Parents/guardians and children can be asked to discuss what their favorite shows tell them about sex roles, family life, intimacy and communications.
- Parent seminars can focus on how to use the media to stimulate discussions about sexual topics with their children.

Sexuality and family life educators can influence media programming. Coalitions of agencies have organized to encourage producers of programs to include adolescent issues. But network executives, MTV, cable stations, and radio stations need to know that we encourage sexual responsibility and appreciate and/or dislike certain shows. As educators, administrators and parents, we should listen to teen music, watch their television shows and go to the movies they frequent, so we may better understand the influence that the media has upon adolescents and children's values, attitudes and behaviors (Haffner and Kelly, 1987).

Summary

The responsibility for helping today's youth understand their sexuality must be shared among parents and guardians, churches, schools, citizen groups, health care practitioners and the media. Parents can help to offset some of the impact of the media by setting examples of selective and critical media use and by talking with their children about media content. They can criticize television and print media producers and advertisers when they don't like the messages conveyed and can urge and work with producers and advertisers to present more appropriate images of sex and sexuality. Health care practitioners can help parents in this process and can work both locally and nationally to improve the media picture of sexuality. Community organizations can work effectively with local media to develop innovative public service campaigns that heighten awareness about sexual responsibility.

The media is an especially compelling and accessible source of information to youth. It can portray human sexuality in a socially responsible manner and be a positive force in healthy adolescent development. The media could do much to help adolescents learn that sex and sexuality can be a healthy part of their lives as men and women.

References

American Academy of Pediatrics. 1990. Children, adolescents and television. *Pediatrics* 85 (6): 1119-1120.

American School Health Association. 1991. *Sexuality education within comprehensive school health education.* Kent, OH.

Aufderheide, P. 1991. Quoted in E. Brown. Music Television turns ten. *The Christian Science Monitor* (August 6): 10.

Baran, S. J., and V. J. Blasko. 1984. Social perceptions and the by-products of advertising. *Journal of Communication* 34:12-20.

Bearinger, L. H. 1990. Study group report on the impact of television on adolescent views of sexuality. *Journal of Adolescent Health Care* 11 (1): 71-75.

Bergman, A. 1980. Condoms for sexually active adolescents. *American Journal of Disease and Children* 134 (2): 247-249.

Bloom, A. 1987. *The closing of the American mind.* New York: Simon and Schuster.

Brown, E. F., and W. R. Hendee. 1989. Adolescents and their music: Insights into the health of adolescents. *Journal of the American Medical Association* 262 (12): 1659-1663.

Brown, J. D., K. W. Childers and C. S. Waszak. 1990. Television and Adolescent Sexuality. *Journal of Adolescent Health Care* 11 (1): 62-70.

Brown, J. D., and S. F. Newcomer. 1991. Television viewing and adolescents' sexual behavior. *Journal of Homosexuality* 21 (1/2): 77-91.

Buchta, R. M. 1989. Attitudes of adolescents and parents of adolescents concerning condom advertisements on television. *Journal of Adolescent Health Care* 10 (3): 220-223.

Buerkel-Rothfulls, N. 1981. Soap opera viewing: The cultivation of effect. *Journal of Communication* 31 (3): 108-115.

Centerwell, B. S. 1992. Television and violence: The scale of the problem and where to go from here. *Journal of the American Medical Association* 267 (22): 3059-3063.

Drabman, R. S., S. J. Robertson, J. N. Patterson, G. J. Jarvie, D. Hammer and G. Cordua. 1981. Children's perception of media-portrayed sex roles. *Sex Roles* 7 (4): 379-389.

Dreamworlds. 1990. Amherst, MA: Foundation for Media Education. (Video)

Eisenstock, B. 1984. Sex-role differences in children's identification with counterstereotypical televised portrayals. *Sex Roles* 10 (5/6): 417-430.

Flay, B. R., D. DiTecco and R. P. Schlegel. 1980. Mass media in health promotion: An analysis using an extended information-processing model. *Health Education Quarterly* 7 (2): 127-147.

Garrity, J. 1989. Teachable moments: Using media to teach responsibility and caring. *Media & Values* 46: 21-22.

Graham, L., and L. Hamdan. 1987. *Youth trends: Capturing the $200 Billion youth market.* New York: St. Martin's Press.

Green, D. L. 1982. *Sex on TV: A guide for parents.* Santa Cruz, CA: ETR Associates.

Greenberg, B. S., K. L. Perry and A. M. Cover. 1983. The body human: Sex education, politics and television. *Family Relations* 32 (3): 419-425.

Haffner, D. W., and M. Kelly. 1987. Adolescent sexuality in the media. *SIECUS Report* 15 (4): 9-12.

Hayes, C. D., ed. 1987. *Risking the future: Adolescent sexuality, pregnancy, and childbearing.* Vol.1. Washington, DC: National Academy Press.

Mandese, J. 1987. The network's revenge: How high will it go? *Channels* 7: 39-40.

MTV turns 10 years old. 1992. *Connect: Newsletter for Members of the Center for Media and Values* 4 (1): 5.

National Commission on the Role of the School and the Community in Improving Adolescent Health. 1990. *Code Blue: Uniting for Healthier Youth.* Alexandria, VA: National Association of State Boards of Education.

Ogletree, S. M., S. W. Williams, P. Raffeld, B. Mason and K. Fricke. 1990. Female attractiveness and eating disorders: Do children's television commercials play a role? *Sex Roles* 22 (11/12): 791-797.

Peterson, J., K. Moore, and F. Furstenberg. 1991. Television viewing and early initiation of sexual intercourse: Is there a link? *Journal of Homosexuality* 21 (1/2): 93-118.

Pierce, K. 1990. A feminist theoretical perspective on the socialization of teenage girls through *Seventeen* magazine. *Sex Roles* 23 (9/10): 491-500.

Remafedi, G. 1990. Study group report on the impact of television portrayals of gender roles on youth. *Journal of Adolescent Health Care* 11:59-61.

Resources. 1992. *Connect: Newsletter for Members of the Center for Media and Values* 4 (1): 7.

Talbott, F. 1992. Working with the media for desired outcomes. Paper presented to managing controversy in health care. Association for the Advancement in Health Education. Summer Institute, 8 August, Reston, Virginia.

White, B. 1989. *Sassy* and *Seventeen*: Do teen magazines reflect or influence sexual attitudes? *Media & Values* 46: 11.

Workman, D. 1989. What you see is what you think. *Media and Values* 46: 2-5.

Evaluation and Research

Chapter 31

Evaluating Sexuality Education Programs

Joyce V. Fetro, PhD, CHES

"The purpose of evaluation is to improve, not to prove." (Stufflebeam et al., 1971)

A cross the United States, there is a growing awareness that healthy sexuality is integrated with all aspects of human life and that education about human sexuality is a lifelong process that should be addressed within the broader context of comprehensive school health education (Bruess and Greenberg, 1988; Cassell and Wilson, 1989; Steed, 1989; National Guidelines Task Force, 1991). This growing awareness, combined with the increases in early sexual activity, sexually transmitted disease and unplanned pregnancies among adolescents (Alan Guttmacher Institute, 1989) has led to increased efforts toward developing and/or updating school-based sexuality education programs.

To meet a wide range of community and individual needs, these programs have been developed with a variety of goals:

providing accurate information, reducing fears and anxieties, developing more tolerant attitudes, promoting responsible decision making, and reducing STD, HIV infection and pregnancy rates, to name a few (Bruess and Greenberg, 1988; Kirby, 1984; Scales, 1984; National Guidelines Task Force, 1991). Yet, efforts to evaluate sexuality education programs have not paralleled development and implementation. In fact, when evaluations are conducted, they often are included as an afterthought, are based on the assumption that the program actually has been implemented the way it was planned, and measure indicators that are not addressed as part of the program.

Evaluation can be a valuable means of measuring the effectiveness of sexuality education programs and determining if newly developed or existing programs are accomplishing their objectives. This chapter will discuss the importance of program evaluation and will outline steps for conducting comprehensive evaluations of a school-based sexuality education program.

Why Evaluate Sexuality Education Programs?

Implicit in program development is the belief that certain educational strategies will bring about certain changes in those individuals receiving the program (Windsor et al., 1984). Program evaluation can be the primary channel through which teachers and other school personnel learn whether their programs are working. Simple, carefully designed evaluations, based on program goals and objectives, serve many purposes, including:
* discovering problem areas
* setting priorities for program development
* guiding allocation of resources

- improving developing or ongoing programs and services
- assessing short-term program effects
- determining whether the program is serving the intended audience
- identifying program strengths and weaknesses
- determining the extent to which the program or service was successful
- drawing conclusions about program impact or outcome
- making decisions about future program directions
- determining cost effectiveness of program activities

Although evaluation studies require careful planning and effort, they can be completed by classroom teachers and school personnel with limited background in measurement theory and statistics. Evaluation activities include collecting, analyzing and interpreting information about the need for, implementation of and impact of sexuality education (Rossi and Freeman, 1982).

Three major types of evaluations are used in educational settings: evaluations of educational needs, formative evaluations and summative evaluations. Decisions about the scope and focus of the evaluation should be based on program goals and objectives, the purpose of the evaluation, the availability of resources, and the character and setting of the community (Herman, Morris and Fitz-Gibbon, 1987; Stecher and Davis, 1987; Windsor et al., 1984). Although it is not always possible in educational settings, the evaluation process should be built into all developmental stages and continue through implementation and beyond (see Figure 1).

Figure 1
Making Decisions About School-Based Program Evaluation

Purpose	Evaluation of Educational Needs	Formative Evaluation	Summative Evaluation
	To discover problem areas	To improve developing or ongoing programs and services	To determine extent to which the program or service was successful
	To set priorities for program development	To assess short-term program effects	To draw conclusions about program impact or outcome
	To guide allocation of resources	To determine if program is serving the intended audience	To make decisions about future program directions
		To identify program strengths/weaknesses	To determine cost effectiveness of program activities

Figure 1 (continued)
Making Decisions About School-Based Program Evaluation

	Evaluation of Educational Needs	Formative Evaluation	Summative Evaluation
Evaluation Activities	Assess existing programs and services. Collect baseline data about students' knowledge, attitudes, skills and behaviors. Identify students' concerns and interests. Identify and prioritize "gaps" in programs and services.	Field test classroom activities. Pilot test program with small group. Monitor implementation process. Assess how well program or service is being received by students, teachers and administrators. Assess if staff were adequately trained. Determine if students are learning what was intended.	Administer pre/posttest to determine changes in students' knowledge, attitudes, skills and behaviors. Assess changes in health status indicators by examining existing records.

Figure 1 (continued)

Making Decisions About School-Based Program Evaluation

	Evaluation of Educational Needs	Formative Evaluation	Summative Evaluation
Questions Answered	What are the priority program needs? Where should program resources be allocated? What are the program goals and measurable objectives?	Is the program or service being implemented as planned? Does implementation of the program vary from site to site or classroom to classroom? Should the program or service be revised related to activities, staffing, curriculum, training and instruments?	Is the program or service meeting its objectives? How effective is the program or service? Should the program or service be continued? What conclusions can be made about the short- and long-term effects of the program or service?

Figure 1 (continued)
Making Decisions About School-Based Program Evaluation

	Evaluation of Educational Needs	Formative Evaluation	Summative Evaluation
Data Collection Methods	Self-report surveys of students' knowledge, attitudes, skills and behaviors	Daily logs from teachers	Pre/posttest measures of students' knowledge, attitudes, skills and behaviors
	Focus group interviews with students, teachers, parents and administrators to determine concerns	Written surveys of administrators, teachers and students about program	Classroom observations
	Nominal group process with school community leaders	Tracking forms for program implementation	Videotapes of student skill-building activities
	Delphi technique with key experts	Classroom observations	Focus group interviews with students and teachers
	Indepth interviews with school staff	Focus group interviews with students and teachers	Indepth interviews with school staff
			School/community records
			Morbidity, mortality and natality data

Adapted from J. V. Fetro. 1990. *Step by step to substance use prevention: A planner's guide to school-based programs.* Santa Cruz, CA: ETR Associates.

Evaluation of Educational Needs

Evaluation of educational needs is a prerequisite to effective program planning. Before designing sexuality education programs, a needs assessment should be conducted to determine school district needs from the perspective of administrators, teachers, students, parents/guardians and community members. In addition, a needs assessment will identify available staff, programs and resources to meet those needs. The needs assessment will help identify and prioritize gaps between "what is" and "what should be" (Cassell and Wilson, 1989; Kaufman and English, 1979; Stufflebeam et al., 1985).

Collecting Baseline Information About Students

Baseline information about students—what they know about sexuality, their perceptions and beliefs about sexuality-related behaviors, and the specific behaviors in which they are engaging—is critical to program planning. This information can be used to determine what, when and how information about sexuality is presented to students.

Numerous survey instruments have been developed to assess students' knowledge, attitudes, beliefs and practices related to sexuality (Davis, Yarber and Davis, 1987; Kirby, 1984; Solleder, 1986). Other national surveys, such as the *Youth Risk Behavior Survey* (Division of Adolescent and School Health, n.d.) and the *National Adolescent Student Health Survey* (ASHA, AAHE and SOPHE, 1989) contain sections about sexuality-related attitudes and behaviors. These and other surveys can be adapted by school districts to determine ongoing student needs.

Determining Student Interests and Concerns

Program planners and educators sometimes make assumptions about sexuality education content without considering those who actually will be receiving the program. The student needs assessment should not be limited to what students know and what they are doing. More important, as shown in *Teach Us What We Want to Know* (Byler, Lewis and Totman, 1969) and *Students Speak* (Trucano, 1984), students should be asked about their interests, concerns, worries and needs. What students would like to know and what they feel is important to know should be carefully considered when planning programs for each grade level.

Determining School and Community Needs

School- and community-based programs should be examined to determine "what exists." That is, what sexuality-related information and activities are currently being presented to students at each grade level. Specifically, what content is being taught? What is the method of presentation? How many lessons are presented at each grade level? Who is teaching sexuality education? Is sexuality education included as part of a comprehensive health education program or as part of another discipline, such as science, home economics, social studies or physical education?

Administrators, teachers, parents/guardians and community members should be surveyed as to what "should be" included in the sexuality education curriculum or program. The importance of involving representatives from each of these groups *before* development, implementation and evaluation should not be underestimated. Community values and timing of the program are critical for success. Ongoing school/community interaction will increase the probability of support for future decisions.

In some school districts, community health advisory groups may serve this purpose. In others, selected community members should work with school administrators, teachers and parents/ guardians to identify key program components. Identified needs and how they will be achieved then are translated into program goals and specific, measurable objectives (Isaac and Michael, 1984).

Using Needs Assessment Results

Information gleaned from needs assessment activities can be used to determine what "should be" included in sexuality education programs and can be used as a baseline for comparison during and after program implementation. Program goals and objectives should be tailored to meet identified student and community needs, and needs assessment data should be reviewed on an ongoing basis to determine if the adopted program is actually meeting those identified needs.

Formative Evaluations

Formative evaluations provide information which can be used to refine existing or newly developed programs and to assess immediate or short-term program effects (Green and Lewis, 1986). Before looking at program impact or outcome, teachers and school district personnel must answer a number of questions, including: Is the program appropriate for the specified age group? Are the curriculum materials culturally sensitive? Can the lessons and activities be implemented with ease in the classroom? Is the sexuality education program well received by teachers, students, parents/guardians, administrators and community members?

Although formative evaluations do not demand the same degree of precision as summative evaluations, they are equally important. Decisions about the amount of time and effort devoted to formative evaluations should be based on program goals/objectives and available funding. Ultimately, conducting a strong formative evaluation will increase the validity of measured impact in the summative evaluation.

Conducting Preprogram Studies

Initial stages of formative evaluations include preprogram activities, such as selecting appropriate sexuality education curricula or programs; field testing classroom activities; conducting focus group interviews with students, teachers and others; pilot testing newly developed or selected programs; and pilot testing student questionnaires. Results of preprogram activities can be used to make revisions and refinements in the program before its full implementation in the school district.

Selecting or developing a sexuality education curriculum or program. In response to increases in sexual risk-taking behavior, numerous sexuality education curricula and programs have been developed, implemented and evaluated. Evaluation of prevention programs based on psychosocial theories have identified several key elements necessary for program success (Howard and McCabe, 1990; Kirby et al., 1991; Schinke, Blythe and Gilchrist, 1981).

These key elements include accurate information about the short- and long-term physical, psychological, social and legal consequences or risks of sexuality related decisions; the internal and external influences on personal health practices and the normative behavior of the peer group; activities to enhance self-esteem; opportunities to build personal and social skills; a peer helper component; and parent/guardian involvement. Newly developed or adopted curricula should be carefully examined to determine if they include these key elements of effective programs.

Field testing lessons and activities. Specific lessons or classroom activities can be field tested by experienced teachers to see if they actually work and to determine how much variation in student response and time spent, if any, occurs from class to class. Classes should be selected to represent a broad range of student learning styles, levels of achievement and cultural backgrounds.

Field testing will identify problem areas to be reviewed and revised. Teacher input and suggestions, as well as student comments, can be utilized to make lessons more developmentally and culturally appropriate.

Conducting focus group interviews. Students often are an underutilized resource in curriculum and program development. Focus group interviews with students at all grade levels can provide important information about student response to proposed activities (Fetro, 1990; Folch-Lyon and Trost, 1981; National Cancer Institute, 1984; Patton, 1987).

Focus group interviews are structured discussions conducted with six to twelve students to obtain insights about their perceptions and beliefs as well as their reactions to classroom activities (e.g., Did they like the activities? How could activities be changed to make them better? Were roleplay situations or scenarios realistic? Are there more effective ways of getting sexuality-related information across to young people?). Student comments and suggestions should be incorporated in program revisions.

Pilot testing the curriculum or program. Pilot testing the entire curriculum in two or more classes at each grade level can provide valuable information about how well the sequence of lessons and student activities fit together. Other important assessments include whether enough time was allotted for each activity, whether directions were clearly written and adequate, and whether enough background information was provided.

When sexuality education programs are designed to be incorporated within a comprehensive school health education program, pilot testing can identify potential problem areas, such as curriculum gaps and overlaps. Since teacher experience and competency may vary, pilot testing also will identify areas where additional inservice training is needed.

Pilot testing student questionnaires. If changes in students' knowledge, attitudes, perceptions, beliefs, intentions and/or practices will be measured to determine program impact, existing or newly developed questionnaires should be pilot tested with the curriculum. Questionnaires should be examined for comprehensibility, readability, reliability and validity. (For more information about reliability and validity, see Babbie, 1986; Berdie and Anderson, 1974; Borg and Gall, 1983; Green and Lewis, 1986). If possible, groups of students should review questionnaires item by item to identify questions that are unclear or difficult to understand.

Conducting Process Evaluations

Process evaluations are conducted during the initial implementation phases of newly developed programs and on an ongoing basis in existing programs. They monitor the implementation process; determine the response of administrators, parents, students and teachers, and assess the ability of teachers to deliver the program (Green and Lewis, 1986).

Monitoring the implementation process. Even the best of programs are not always implemented as planned. A variety of factors can interfere with successful implementation, including but not limited to the complexity of program activities, available staff time, available resources, and perceived benefits of the sexuality education program.

Knowing what is "actually going on" is essential for evaluating whether a sexuality education program is effective. Evaluations conducted after program completion may show significant changes in student knowledge, attitudes, beliefs and skills, but will not provide information about why those differences occurred and how effective various sections of the program were (Basch et al., 1985). Similarly, a summative evaluation may indicate no significant changes, but closer examination of the implementation process may discover that important activities were omitted and others were changed during delivery of the sexuality education program.

Evaluation of the implementation process can focus on specific components or on the program as a whole. Information can be gathered through classroom observations, teacher interviews, tracking forms and/or teacher logs. Although these activities are time consuming, they will help program planners understand the best ways to begin and maintain implementation as well as indicate areas where program modifications could improve program effectiveness (Basch, 1984).

Determining the site response. Site response evaluates how well the sexuality education program is being accepted in the school community. This evaluation gathers information from all concerned groups about whether key needs are being met. In addition, it identifies obstacles to implementation and provides possible solutions.

Formal and informal surveys of administrators and other staff should identify concerns related to scheduling, facilities and program cost; compatibility with community values, school district policies and existing programs; and perceived responses of community members, other staff and parents and guardians.

Determining parent/guardian response. If feasible, written surveys or telephone interviews with a sample of parents and guardians could be conducted to determine if they are aware of the program, if they have discussed sexuality-related issues with their children, if the sexuality education program has helped them talk with their children about sensitive issues, and if they support continuation of the sexuality education program.

Determining student response. In the process evaluation, three levels of student response can be assessed. First, information about the actual number of students reached and the number of hours of sexuality education received by students at each grade level can be obtained by having teachers document which lessons were taught and how many students were present.

Second, quality of participation can be assessed through written or oral measures of student comprehension of information, sexuality-related attitudes, and personal and social skills. Classroom teachers can determine whether students are learning what was intended by observing student interactions, examining student worksheets, evaluating classroom discussions and giving short quizzes about key information.

Third, but equally important, is student satisfaction with the program. Students should be given an opportunity to evaluate their own experiences. Written evaluation forms or focus group interviews could gather information such as whether students liked the content of the sexuality education program; if they thought the activities were worthwhile; if they felt comfortable during classroom discussions; whether discussion in class made it easier for students to talk about sexuality with their parents or guardians; if students would have liked to have received the information and skills at an earlier age; and whether they would recommend the program to other students their age.

Determining teacher response. Teachers implementing sexuality education programs can make considerable contributions to program refinement. Most important, teachers can identify strengths and weaknesses of the program and make suggestions for improvement. For example: Was the curriculum easy to implement? Could students complete the program activities? Were the activities, roleplays and scenarios relevant to today's adolescents? Which activities should be changed to elicit better student response?

Teacher logs or surveys and/or individual interviews can assess developmental appropriateness and cultural sensitivity of student activities, determine whether stated program goals and objectives are met by student activities, and determine whether identified student needs can be met by the program. This information can be used to make critical revisions that may lead to more successful implementation and ultimately increase program effectiveness.

Assessing teacher competency. Oftentimes, new sexuality education programs are implemented with little or no inservice training. Teacher training is especially important due to the controversy often associated with implementation of sexuality education and personal sensitivity to sexuality issues. If formal inservice training is provided, teachers should evaluate whether it adequately prepared them to implement the sexuality education program. A follow-up survey will elicit suggestions for improvement and identify additional needs for inservice training.

Teacher competency is critical to successful implementation of sexuality education. Ideally, all elementary teachers should receive preservice training, and secondary teachers responsible for implementing sexuality education programs should receive professional preparation before teaching sexuality-related topics. Teachers must be knowledgeable about the physical, psychological, emotional, social and spiritual dimensions of a healthy sexuality *and* they must have strong communication skills, be culturally competent, and be respectful of individual differences in values, beliefs and practices (Wagman, 1989). Self-assessment of knowledge, skills and performance can provide information about teacher competency. That is, do teachers feel they have the information and skills necessary to implement the curriculum?

Even when inservice training is provided, often minimal support is given once teachers return to the classroom with the new curriculum materials. As part of the process evaluation, teachers in the same school or district can serve as "peer coaches." In this role, they can work together, observe each other and provide feedback about curriculum activities and teacher skills. This information will guide future continuing education efforts.

Using Formative Evaluation Results

Formative evaluations are considered the "quality control" of programs in practice. Information gained from preprogram studies provides feedback about the initial program planning. For example, results of student focus groups and pilot testing may indicate that a proposed curriculum may not be appropriate because it is not sensitive to the ethnic and cultural diversity of students in the district. In this case, program planners should reevaluate the adoption decision or make appropriate curriculum changes before implementation.

Information gained from process evaluations provides feedback to improve the implementation process. For example, a sexuality education program with multiple components may not be implemented as planned because of limited administrative support and/or inadequate staff and resources. Before attempting to determine program impact, planners must meet with administrators to increase program support and suggest possible changes in staff assignments or resource allocations.

Ultimately, these two feedback loops from preprogram studies and process evaluations will improve overall program quality.

Summative Evaluations

Summative evaluations provide a summary about effectiveness of a program over a period of time (Green and Lewis, 1986; Windsor et al., 1984). Summative evaluations allow program planners to draw conclusions about the impact and outcome of sexuality education programs. In other words, was the sexuality education program successful in meeting the program goals and objectives? Is it reaching the intended target audience? Is it providing the services and benefits envisioned by the program planners? Is the program causing any unanticipated negative side-effects?

Ideally, summative evaluation results stem from carefully designed quasi-experimental studies that include a control group (which does not receive the program). Realistically, these controlled studies often do not occur due to budget constraints and/or an unwillingness to withhold sexuality education programs from some students. Program planners need to understand that nonexperimental summative evaluations *are* a valuable means for improving the planning process and determining school district policies about sexuality education.

Determining Program Impact
Program impact evaluations assess the overall effectiveness of sexuality education in bringing about changes in student knowl-

edge, perceptions/beliefs, attitudes, skills and practices. Program goals and objectives determine not only which changes should be measured, but also how much emphasis should be placed on different indicators of success. Impact evaluation efforts are dependent upon the amount of time, resources and personnel available.

To determine program impact, questionnaires should be administered before and after the sexuality education program. Students' responses then are compared to determine changes as a result of the program. (School districts wishing to conduct more scientific educational research should consult Babbie, 1986; Borg and Gall, 1983; Campbell and Stanley, 1963; Isaac and Michael, 1984; Posavac and Carey, 1980; Windsor et al., 1984).

There are several categories of measure that could be included in an impact evaluation: knowledge, perceptions, beliefs, attitudes, skills, intentions and practices. Although categories are interrelated, program planners may choose to measure some effects and not others.

Knowledge. A primary goal of sexuality education programs is to provide accurate information about human sexuality, including growth and development, human reproduction, anatomy and physiology, masturbation, family life, pregnancy, childbirth, parenthood, sexual response, sexual orientation, contraception, abortion, sexual abuse, HIV/AIDS and other sexually transmitted disease (National Guidelines Task Force, 1991).

Knowledge items in student pre/posttests should be age-appropriate and reflect the actual content of the sexuality education curriculum. For example, classroom discussions about various methods of contraception are not developmentally appropriate for early elementary school students; thus, knowledge items about these issues should not be included in pre/posttests of these students. If a pregnancy prevention curriculum does not specifically address male and female anatomy, students should not be expected to label the parts of the male and female reproductive systems.

Based on developmental appropriateness and curriculum objectives, knowledge items could include, but not be limited to, questions about physiological and psychological changes that occur during puberty; physical changes during pregnancy; stages of development of the fetus; effects of substance use on fetal development; methods of transmission of sexually transmitted disease, including HIV; methods of protection from pregnancy; and methods of protection from STD and HIV infection.

Perceptions, beliefs and/or attitudes. Students' perceptions of potential risk or harm that may result from their personal health practices (e.g., having sex or having unprotected sex), their perceptions about peer approval and norms, and their beliefs about their sexuality and relationships directly affect their sexuality-related decisions.

Items about students' perceptions, beliefs and attitudes could include, but not be limited to, perceptions about their risk of pregnancy and/or STD/HIV infection; how many people their age are having sex or using protection and whether their friends would approve of their sexual practices (e.g., it's OK to have sex; it's OK to say no to sex; it's OK to use condoms); their beliefs about their personal attributes and relationships; and their beliefs about gender roles and/or sexual orientation.

Personal and social skills. Many sexuality education programs offer opportunities for young people to build personal and social skills (i.e., decision making, communication, stress management and goal setting) that are an essential part of normal psychosocial development and are critical for dealing with the myriad of situations, problems and pressures students face on a daily basis.

Knowledge of the steps to making a good decision, the types of communication, how to be an active listener, personal stressors, steps to setting achievable goals, and so on, can be evaluated through student worksheets and classroom discussions.

Students' ability to actually execute learned skills can be observed in classroom activities, such as roleplays, real-life scenarios and case studies. If feasible, video tapes of skills practice and rehearsal can indicate changes in students' level of competency.

Behavioral intentions and personal health practices. Young people engage in a variety of behaviors that put them at risk for sexually transmitted disease, HIV infection and unplanned pregnancy. Students' intentions or actual behaviors related to sexuality could include whether they have ever had sexual intercourse, whether they have had sex in the last three months, whether they drank alcohol or used other drugs before having sex, and whether they used any method of protection from transmission of STD/HIV or unplanned pregnancy.

Determining Program Outcome

Program outcome evaluations assess changes or improvements in health status indicators for specific target groups (e.g., pregnancy, sexually transmitted disease and HIV infection rates). When considering program outcomes of educational programs, planners, administrators and teachers should be cautious. Changes in health status occur only after long periods of time, and changes in pregnancy, STD and HIV infection rates may be affected by a variety of intervening variables that cannot be addressed or changed by educational programs alone (e.g., cultural norms).

In some cases, sexuality education could actually increase reported rates of particular indicators of health status. For example, STD rates reported at the local health clinic may increase after sexuality education because students are more aware of symptoms and will now seek treatment.

Using Summative Evaluation Results

Results of summative evaluation efforts can be used to determine if the program has succeeded or failed (based on previously established criteria). Although many school districts have neither the staff time nor the funding to conduct carefully designed quasi-experimental evaluation studies, the value of summative evaluations should not be minimized. Results of summative evaluations are critical to improving the program planning process, changing school district policy, making decisions about resource allocations and providing future program directions.

Evaluation as an Ongoing Process

Evaluation is an integral part of program planning and development. Comprehensive program evaluations contain evaluations of educational needs, formative evaluations and summative evaluations. They are ongoing processes of collecting, interpreting and using information in a series of feedback loops (see Figure 2).

Evaluations of educational needs identify what sexuality-related content and process should be addressed by program goals and objectives. These goals and objectives guide the planning process and the development of classroom strategies and activities.

Preprogram studies, such as field tests, focus group interviews and pilot studies, determine whether proposed activities are developmentally and culturally appropriate. Feedback from preprogram studies is used to make improvements before full program implementation in the school district.

A process evaluation during implementation identifies strengths and weaknesses by monitoring what is actually happening in the classroom and assessing the school community's response to the sexuality education program. Program design and procedures are refined based on feedback from the process evaluation.

After program completion, an impact evaluation determines changes in students' knowledge, perceptions, beliefs, attitudes, skills, intentions and practices related to sexuality. An outcome evaluation determines whether changes in health status indicators have occurred. Feedback from both the impact and outcome evaluations is used to reevaluate program goals and objectives and guide future program directions.

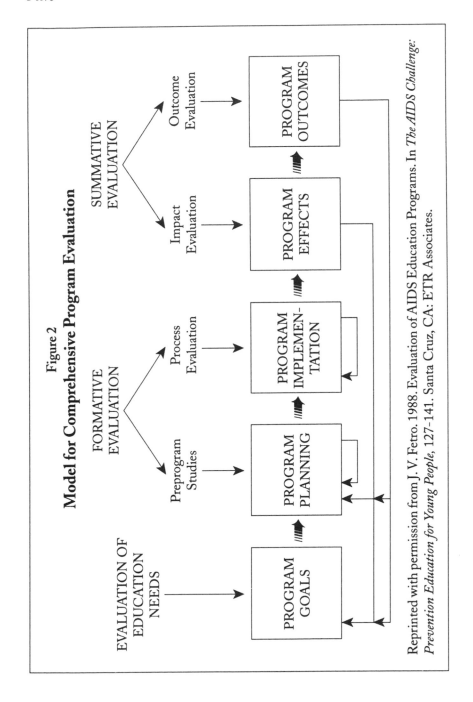

Figure 2
Model for Comprehensive Program Evaluation

Reprinted with permission from J. V. Fetro. 1988. Evaluation of AIDS Education Programs. In *The AIDS Challenge: Prevention Education for Young People*, 127–141. Santa Cruz, CA: ETR Associates.

References

Alan Guttmacher Institute. 1989. *Risk and responsibility: Teaching sex education in America's schools today.* New York.

Alreck, P. L., and R. B. Settle. 1985. *The survey research handbook.* Homewood, IL: Irwin.

American School Health Association, Association for the Advancement of Health Education, and Society of Public Health Educators. 1989. *The national adolescent student health survey.* Oakland, CA: Third Party Publishing.

Babbie, E. 1986. *The practice of social research.* Belmont, CA: Wadsworth.

Basch, C. E. 1984. Research on disseminating and implementing school health education. *Journal of School Health* 54 (6): 57-66.

Basch, C. E., E. M. Sliepcevich, R. S. Gold, D. F. Duncan and L. J. Kolbe. 1985. Avoiding type III errors in health education program evaluations: A case study. *Health Education Quarterly* 12 (3): 315-331.

Berdie, C. E., and J. F. Anderson. 1974. *Questionnaires: Design and use.* Metuchen, NJ: Scarecrow Press.

Byler, R. V., G. Lewis and R. Totman. 1969. *Teach us what we want to know.* New York: Mental Health Materials Center.

Borg, W. R., and M. D. Gall. 1983. *Educational research: An introduction.* New York: Longman.

Bruess, C. E., and J. S. Greenberg. 1988. *Sexuality education: Theory and practice.* 2d ed. New York: Macmillan.

Campbell, D. T., and J. C. Stanley. 1963. *Experimental and quasi-experimental designs for research.* Boston: Houghton Mifflin.

Cassell, C., and P. M. Wilson, eds. 1989. *Sexuality education: A resource book.* New York: Garland.

Centers for Disease Control and Prevention, U.S. Public Health Service, Department of Health and Human Services. 1992. *Chronic disease prevention and health promotion reprints from the MMWR: 1990 youth risk behavior surveillance system.* Atlanta, GA.

Davis, C. M., W. L. Yarber and S. L. Davis. 1987. *Sexuality-related measures: A compendium.* Lake Mills, IA: Graphic.

Division of Adolescent and School Health, Centers for Disease Control and Prevention. n.d. *Youth risk behavior survey.* Atlanta, GA.

Fetro, J. V. 1988. Evaluation of AIDS education programs. In *The AIDS challenge,* ed. M. Quackenbush and M. Nelson, 127-141. Santa Cruz, CA: ETR Associates.

Fetro, J. V. 1990. *Step by step to substance use prevention: A planner's guide to school-based programs.* Santa Cruz, CA: ETR Associates.

Fetro, J. V. 1990. Using focus group interviews to design materials. In *Getting the word out: A practical guide to AIDS materials development,* ed. A. C. Matiella, 37-48. Santa Cruz, CA: ETR Associates.

Fetro, J. V. 1991. Evaluation. In *Sexuality education within comprehensive school health education,* ed. J. Neutens, J. C. Drolet, M. L. Dushaw and W. Jubb, 13-25. Kent, OH: American School Health Association.

Fitz-Gibbon, C. T., and L. L. Morris. 1987. *How to design a program evaluation.* Beverly Hills, CA: Sage.

Folch-Lyon, E., and J. F. Trost. 1981. Conducting focus group sessions. *Studies in Family Planning* 12:443-449.

Fowler, F. J. 1987. *Survey research methods.* Beverly Hills, CA: Sage.

Green, L. W., and F. M. Lewis. 1986. *Measurement and evaluation in health education and health promotion.* Palo Alto, CA: Mayfield.

Henderson, M. E., L. L. Morris and C. T. Fitz-Gibbon. 1987. *How to measure attitudes.* Beverly Hills, CA: Sage.

Hermann, J. L., L. L. Morris and C. T. Fitz-Gibbon. 1987. *Evaluator's handbook.* Beverly Hills, CA: Sage.

Howard, M., and J. McCabe. 1990. Helping teenagers postpone sexual involvement. *Family Planning Perspectives* 22 (1): 21-26.

Isaac, S., and W. B. Michael. 1984. *Handbook in research and evaluation for education and the behavioral sciences.* San Diego, CA: Edits.

Kaufman, R., and F. English. 1979. *Needs assessment: Concept and applications.* Englewood Cliffs, NJ: Educational Technology.

King, A., L. L. Morris and C. T. Fitz-Gibbon. 1987. *How to assess program implementation.* Beverly Hills, CA: Sage.

Kirby, D. 1984. *Sexuality education: A handbook for the evaluation of programs.* Santa Cruz, CA: ETR Associates.

Kirby, D., R. Barth, N. Leland and J. Fetro. 1991. Reducing the risk: Impact of a new curriculum on sexual risk taking. *Family Planning Perspectives* 23 (6): 253-263.

Morris, L. L., C. T. Fitz-Gibbon and E. Lindheim. 1987. How to measure performance and use tests. Beverly Hills, CA: Sage.

National Cancer Institute. 1984. Focus group interviews. *Pretesting in health communications: Methods, examples and resources for improving health messages and materials.* NIH Publication No. 84-1493. Washington, DC.

National Guidelines Task Force. 1991. *Guidelines for Comprehensive sexuality education: Kindergarten-12th grade.* New York: Sex Information and Education Council of the United States.

Patton, M. Q. 1987. *How to use qualitative methods in evaluation.* Beverly Hills, CA: Sage.

Posavac, E. J., and R. G. Carey. 1980. *Program evaluation: Methods and case studies.* Englewood Cliffs, NJ: Prentice-Hall.

Rossi, P. H., and H. E. Freeman. 1982. *Evaluation: A systematic approach.* Beverly Hills, CA: Sage.

Scales, P. 1984. *The front lines of sexuality education.* Santa Cruz, CA: ETR Associates.

Schinke, S. P., B. J. Blythe and L. D. Gilchrist. 1981. Cognitive behavioral prevention of adolescent pregnancy. *Journal of Counseling Psychology* 28 (6): 451-454.

Solleder, M. K., ed. 1986. *Evaluation instruments in health education.* Reston, VA: Association for the Advancement of Health Education.

Stecher, B. M., and W. A. Davis. 1987. *How to focus an evaluation.* Beverly Hills, CA: Sage.

Steed, S. 1989. Sexuality education within health education curricula. In *Sexuality education: A resource book,* ed. C. Cassell and P. M. Wilson, 155-160. New York: Garland.

Stufflebeam, D. L., W. J. Foley, W. J. Gephart, E. G. Guba, R. L. Hammond, H. O. Merriman and M. M. Provus. 1971. *Educational evaluation and decision making.* Itasca, IL: F. E. Peacock.

Stufflebeam, D. L., C. H. McCormick, R. O. Brinckerhoff and C. O. Nelson. 1985. *Conducting educational needs assessments.* Boston: Kluwer-Nijhoff.

Wagman, E. 1989. Family life education teacher training. In *Sexuality education: A resource book,* ed. C. Cassell and P. M. Wilson, 161-168. New York: Garland.

Windsor, R. A., T. Baranowski, N. Clark and G. Cutter. 1984. *Evaluation of health promotion and education programs.* Palo Alto, CA: Mayfield.

Trucano, L. 1984. *Students speak.* Seattle, WA: Comprehensive School Health Foundation.

U.S. Department of Health and Human Services, Public Health Service. 1991. *Healthy people 2000: National health promotion and disease prevention objectives.* DHHS Publication No. (PHS) 91-50212 Washington, DC.

Zabin, L. S., and M. B. Hirsch. 1988. *Evaluation of pregnancy prevention programs in the school context.* Lexington, MA: Lexington Books.

Chapter 32

Sexuality-Related
Research in Schools

David K. Lohrmann, PhD, CHES

T he telephone buzzes. The local school administrator in charge of health education picks it up and greets a caller who identifies himself as the father of a 16-year-old female high school student. In very heated tones the father demands to know why his daughter has been asked questions about her personal sex life on a survey given in school that day.

"Why would you ask innocent young women questions like that?" the irate father demands. "Why wasn't I informed? I'd have put a stop to this nonsense if you hadn't sneaked it by me. Wait 'til other parents find out!"

The incident described above actually occurred in a suburban community known for its conservatism. It isn't an isolated incident, but happens in communities across the country when school districts elect to conduct research to improve the quality of the sexuality education program. This chapter discusses several important points to remember when conducting research in schools:

- It *is* possible to conduct sexuality-related action research in schools, even in conservative communities.
- Broadbased input and support need to be developed before conducting such research.
- Complaints can be minimized if students and parents are fully informed beforehand, have an opportunity to review procedures and instruments, and have the option to not participate.
- Some controversy can be expected, although many challenges will dissipate when parents realize that the school has nothing to hide.
- A "happy ending" is most likely to result if all steps in conducting the research are carefully planned and implemented.

What Is Research?

Research is the process of collecting data in order to discover new information, or, in many cases, to develop generalizations. It involves a number of steps including generating an hypothesis, developing a process for gathering data designed to test the hypothesis, gathering the data, and analyzing the data to determine whether the hypothesis proved correct.

A hypothesis is usually generated from previous research findings reported in the literature, the experience of the researcher and/or the need to answer a vital question. Research is designed and implemented in order for the researcher to determine whether what she or he predicted would occur in a specific situation actually occurred.

To test a hypothesis the researcher designs an experiment. This is the most crucial part. If the research design is done well, the results will withstand the criticisms of other scientists (peer review). If it is done poorly, the results of the experiment will be suspect.

Individuals sometimes think that the statistical procedures applied to collected data are the most important aspect of the research process. While it is important to apply the most appropriate statistical procedures and to follow the specifications for applying statistical procedures, the data analysis is only as good as the research design used to gather the data. If the design is faulty, the results may be less valid. Researchers design experiments to control for as many variables as possible.

Results are usually expressed as significant or not significant, based on the preset statistical level. The most commonly accepted level of significance is .05; that is, the probability of the results occurring by random chance is less than 5 in 100. If the results of the statistical procedure used to test the hypothesis are less than .05, they are said to be significant. The researcher is confident that the results of the test of the hypothesis were actually caused by whatever treatment was applied.

Basic Versus Educational Research

Research can be conducted under rigorously controlled laboratory conditions including the use of a control group. This, however, is seldom the case with educational research. Most educational research is conducted in the field where it is difficult to control for extraneous influences on the results (statistical procedures can be used to make up for this shortcoming to some extent). Using a control and a treatment group is often not possible for several reasons:

- Outside of a designated experimental school, it is often difficult for researchers to gain access to students to use as subjects. School administrators are wary of potential problems with parents and do not like to take the time necessary to conduct research away from time devoted to instruction.

- There are ethical problems involved in withholding a "treatment" from some students. If students in the experimental group benefit from the research study, the students in the control group do not. How can withholding the treatment from the control group be justified, and at what point does it become detrimental to them?

Another difference between basic research and educational research is that educational research is usually conducted in order to improve educational practice, whereas much scientific research is conducted solely to add to the body of knowledge without any real practical intent. Practical application is often a byproduct or is serendipitous. Best (1977) identifies the following characteristics of research. In general, research:

- is directed toward the solution of a problem
- emphasizes the development of generalizations, principles or theories that will be helpful in predicting future occurrences
- is based on observable experience or empirical evidence
- demands accurate observation and description
- involves gathering new data from primary or firsthand sources or using existing data for a new purpose
- is more often characterized by carefully designed procedures, although research activity may at times be somewhat random and unsystematic
- requires expertise
- strives to be objective and logical, applying every possible test to validate the procedures employed, the data collected and the conclusions reached
- is characterized by patient and unhurried activity
- is carefully recorded and reported
- sometimes requires courage

In *quantitative* research, numerical data are gathered and then treated statistically in some way in order to determine significance. In other words, the variables to be studied through the research are quantified. Much educational research has historically been quantitative in that it statistically compares such things as test scores of two or more groups or pre- and post-scores of the same students on tests or surveys.

Another type of research is *qualitative* research, in which the researcher gathers data by observing subjects or the interactions among subjects (e.g., teachers and students) and records them in script form. A script may be continuous for a specified period of time or may be drawn from samples derived from a specified amount of time (e.g., one minute) at predetermined intervals (e.g., every ten minutes). The script is then analyzed to determine frequencies and trends in the observations. Qualitative studies usually are very time intensive and involve a small number of cases (ten or fewer). While the results of a single qualitative study may not be conclusive, the results of a number of repeated or similar studies may be very revealing. Qualitative research provides an avenue for studying issues that may not be readily quantifiable.

Qualitative research has historically been considered "soft" research because data were not readily quantifiable. It has recently gained in acceptability because procedures have become more rigorous and effective computer software packages have become available for use in analysis of gathered data. Qualitative research is now frequently used to conduct research in education and the social sciences.

Reading Research

Most educators never conduct research; however, all educators should be capable of reading research studies in order to use new information to improve their professional practice. Research studies published in the professional literature provide new information about issues such as approaches to curriculum design, effectiveness of curricula, classroom management, student achievement and effectiveness of methodology.

To read research, educators need to know something about the proper use of statical procedures in order to judge for themselves whether research findings are valid and/or practically significant. Educators should also be able to recognize a concept called *external reliability* or *generalizability*. That is, was the sample of subjects used in the study representative enough of the national student population to warrant the generalization that the research results will hold true for students anywhere in the country. Unless subjects are chosen by a very deliberate sampling procedure, they seldom are representative enough to allow general application of research results. In most cases, the results are only true for the subjects involved in the study or for subjects very similar to them (e.g., similar in ethnicity, income, type of school, type of community, etc.). All too often in education, research findings are generalized to whole populations when this is not warranted.

With the advent of modern, powerful mainframe (and desktop) computers, statistical procedures have become so complex that it is difficult even for educators trained in research to keep up. One way of ensuring that the research is of value is the quality of the journal or book in which it is published. Just because something is in print does not mean that it is accurate or correct. Almost anything can get published, even if the author has to pay the publisher.

Studies published in professional, refereed journals are most likely to be of high quality. This means that the articles in which studies are reported are sent out for blind review by experts in that field. The reviewers receive the manuscript without knowing who wrote it, and, therefore, evaluate it on the basis of established criteria for research design and statistical data analysis.

At the very least, an educator reading research should:

- Determine whether it is reported in a reputable, refereed professional journal or in a book printed by a respected publisher.
- Read the original study (instead of relying on reports of studies published in summary documents or the popular press).
- Determine the level of statistical significance of findings and whether the results are applicable beyond the population that was the direct subject of the research.

Action Research and Needs Assessment

Action research is generally understood to be field and practitioner based. It is used to gather data about programs and issues at the local level that can be used in planning and decision making. Those conducting action research should attempt to apply recognized standards in study design and data treatment in order to generate valid and reliable results. Action research, however, usually has a basic limitation. The population is composed of available subjects in a restricted locale who may be very different from research populations found in studies in the professional literature, which are drawn from many locales and represent a variety of demographic variables. Therefore, research results will most likely not be generalizable (Best, 1977).

It is appropriate to include the gathering of information about sexual issues in a general needs assessment for a comprehensive health promotion program. Data can be gathered from student surveys, teacher surveys, interviews with school nurses and health providers, and existing school district policies and procedures.

Local statistics routinely gathered by the health department comprise an additional excellent data source regarding student sexual behaviors.

Program evaluation is often research based and usually involves the gathering of pretreatment data, the gathering of posttreatment data and a comparison of the two to determine whether change occurred as a result of program implementation. Gathering of pretreatment data can be the needs assessment process. Following program revision and implementation over time, data measuring the same variables as in the needs assessment are gathered for comparison to determine whether change occurred. The needs assessment, as research, "involves gathering new data from primary or firsthand sources or using existing data for a new purpose" (Best, 1977). Through the needs assessment process, existing data may be gathered for the purpose of determining the extent and quality of programming as compared to the "state of the art." New data may be gathered in order to make the case for implementation of proven curricula or programs and/or to compare with data gathered in the future to determine the impact of new programs— whether and to what extent programmatic changes affected the behaviors of students.

A needs assessment is usually associated with evaluation rather than research. While program evaluation is most concerned with recommendations and decisions, it can also be research in that results can lead "to new truths" (Best, 1977). The basic purposes of research and evaluation may differ, but the problems and procedures faced by educators in the field for conducting either are very similar. Therefore, the needs assessment process will be used to illustrate the process of conducting sexuality-related research in schools.

Using the Needs Assessment

A number of reasons exist for conducting a needs assessment in the curriculum renewal process as it applies to sexuality education. A needs assessment will determine the extent of implementation and quality of the existing program. It is not unusual to find that the written curriculum is not being implemented, or, if implemented, is not being implemented as designed. It is also not unusual to find that the existing curriculum is inconsistent with the prevailing standard as defined by research findings. With sexuality education curricula, this may mean that the program does not exist or is not being initiated early enough to provide true primary prevention, or that it is not consistent with known research on effective instruction.

Primary prevention of behavioral health problems means that prevention programs have been implemented before members of the target population have initiated health-compromising behaviors. It has to do with sustaining healthy behaviors as opposed to changing unhealthy ones. For example, while there are exceptions, most seventh graders have not engaged in intercourse (an unhealthy behavior for their age group). The best health guidance that can be given to young teens is that they should abstain from intercourse because of the physical, mental, social and emotional risks involved. However, students beyond the seventh grade are more likely to question or resist this guidance. Therefore, sexuality education intended to reduce risky behavior should be initiated at the seventh grade level or before.

An often overlooked purpose of a needs assessment is to inform key decision makers about the program. A data-gathering interview is an excellent avenue for providing important information, stimulating inquiry and changing attitudes. The interview is especially effective for raising important issues and questions, identifying gaps in knowledge, and stimulating the interviewee to seek additional information. A superintendent, for example, may have little knowledge of the importance of sexuality education or may view it as a headache she or he does not need.

Many state laws governing sexuality education are intricate. For example, Michigan law has distinct definitions for sex education and reproductive health, does not allow the teaching of abortion as a method of reproductive health or family planning, does not allow the distribution or dispensing of family planning devices in schools, allows parents to exclude children from instruction in sexuality education and reproductive health, and allows the teaching of family planning information only if a properly constituted advisory committee exists. A needs assessment should determine whether a local school district program is in compliance with these types of requirements.

The needs assessment will generate a database that can be used to (1) demonstrate the need for program development and resource allocation, (2) overcome community denial and institutional resistance, (3) secure support from community-based agencies, and (4) stimulate community-based organizations to provide additional services. Many communities continue under the delusion that teenage pregnancy, sexual assault, HIV and STD transmission, and other sexuality-related problems do not exist and that, therefore, no programs are needed.

Some sexuality educators attempt to use nationally generated data to overcome this denial, but locally gathered data about percentage of sexually active teens, use of contraceptives, numbers of sex partners, attitudes about engaging in intercourse, and pregnancy rates can be more effective for making this point. Broad dissemination of these data can generate demand for programming and identify gaps in community-based adolescent health services.

Needs assessment data can be presented to school district decision makers, curriculum committees and advisory committees in order to demonstrate the need for program changes and programmatic additions. They also can be used to garner resources such as instructional time in the curriculum, funds for materials purchases, and funds and time for the staff development necessary to upgrade and implement the health/sexuality education curriculum. When priorities change and resource allocations wane, needs assessment data can be reintroduced to remind decision makers of the reasons why resources were allocated in the first place.

Finally, needs assessment data can be used as a baseline to determine program effectiveness. Data gathered at a future date can be compared with the baseline data to determine whether program goals and objectives are being achieved. Several sexuality curricula that have been shown to be effective in changing adolescent sexual behavior exist, as do complex school/community prevention models. Comparison of needs assessment baseline data with data gathered following implementation of these types of programs can determine whether research results are replicable at the local level.

Barriers and Issues

While conducting a needs assessment is well recognized as the first step in program initiation and/or revision, several barriers exist that can prevent or hinder a needs assessment. The first of these is the lack of true appreciation of the importance of conducting a systematic assessment of the existing program as the initial step in curriculum or program development.

Conducting a needs assessment requires human, financial and time resources. (It is also important to involve knowledgeable people as well as to take the time to carefully plan and implement a needs assessment.) Some school districts have these kinds of resources. Many, especially smaller ones, do not. If resources are lacking, a school district may be able to ally with an outside agency such as a community coalition, health department, college or university, or local foundation to acquire needed resources. Many of these types of agencies will willingly participate because they are rarely given access to students for data-gathering purposes.

Another barrier is that both educators and the lay public are skeptical of educational research. When needs assessment data are published, one of the first questions asked is, "How do you know these data are valid and reliable?" Lack of valid and reliable survey instruments can be a problem. Issues to be addressed include establishing a uniform protocol adhered to by all those who administer surveys, selecting an instrument, and selecting a representative student sample to complete the surveys. Faculty surveys and validation of results through secondary sources can also be important aspects of the process.

Establishing Protocol

Employees of agencies external to schools may not appreciate the sensitivity of gathering data about school practices, and, in particular, school employees and students. Public schools are subject to many regulations, including the need to protect minors from unwarranted intrusions on their privacy. School personnel can be held liable for information in student files that could be detrimental to the child, although any school information not specifically protected by statute can be requested by the public under the U.S. Freedom of Information Act.

Anyone working with schools should be very sensitive to data about children and is advised to follow federal protocols for minor subjects when gathering and reporting such data. School authorities should also be sensitive to these issues and should establish written ground rules about how data will be used. All of these issues should be resolved before an outside agency is given permission to access school records and documents or given access to children for purposes of data collection.

Selecting an Instrument

Surveys for gathering data about adolescent sexual attitudes and behaviors exist. For example, the most recent edition of the Michigan Educational Assessment Test (MEAP) health test for eleventh grade includes a separate Responsible Sexuality Booklet which is a series of questions designed to assess students' knowledge about substance use and sexual risk taking, peer pressure and sexuality, teen pregnancy consequences, structure and function of the reproductive system, pregnancy risk factors and resources for sexual abuse (School Health Unit, 1992). Noted adolescent psychologist Robert Coles, along with Geoffrey Stokes (1985), developed and used a 96-item instrument to conduct a national survey of adolescent sexual attitudes and behavior.

Prior to selecting and administering such an instrument, however, all available information about it should be thoroughly reviewed by someone with appropriate expertise to determine whether the instrument has been validated and how it has been validated. It may be advisable to collect data about adolescent sexual attitudes and behaviors via a survey that assesses health attitudes and behaviors in a number of areas. A valid and reliable instrument for doing this is the *Youth Risk Behavior Survey* developed by the U.S. Public Health Service, which may be available through a state department of education or the Centers for Disease Control and Prevention. This survey contains fourteen questions related to sexual behavior and HIV infection.

Selecting a Sample

Researchers often gather data from only a portion of a population and then draw conclusions abut the entire population based on responses given by the sample. Political pollsters very carefully analyze the entire population for a number of variables to establish categories of respondents. They then survey a sample based on their analysis and predict an election. The survey results are reported with a sample error (+ or − X) since data from a sample are not absolutely accurate. Nevertheless, careful, scientific sampling of large populations is much less costly and much more practical than surveying an entire population and provides relatively accurate results.

Educational researchers may attempt to gather data based on a sample of students in a school or school district. However, given all the impediments in a school, and given the fact that most schools are not that large, it often is easiest and most advisable from a validity standpoint to survey all students in the school or grade. Call a homeroom or use an assembly hall and administer the survey to all students at the same time. If computer mark-sense (Scantron) sheets are used, data analysis is no more difficult with large numbers of subjects. Electronic measures also can be used to detect answer sheets of students who purposely sabotage the survey by making response patterns (e.g., answering all one number or outlining a Christmas tree).

It is important to administer the survey to all subjects in a school at the same time to avoid contamination of the data. If a survey is administered to different groups during different class periods, students may discuss questions and answers prior to completing the survey. Surveys should be given on the same day in all schools (but not necessarily at the same time) when being administered at more than one school in a district for the same reason.

If possible, specially trained professionals should be engaged to administer the surveys. If this is not possible, faculty members can administer the surveys, but only if they are provided with a strict protocol to follow, including a common script to read to students. Important points to include in the protocol are the following:

- Teachers should read the directions and script prior to administering the survey.
- Teachers should stick to the script and not ad lib.
- Teachers should stress the voluntary nature of the survey and the fact that it is anonymous.
- Teachers should minimize responses to student questions, especially any related to interpretation of survey questions.
- Teachers should stay apart from students while they are completing the survey to protect students' anonymity.
- A student in each group should collect all answer sheets, seal them in an envelope in full view of other students, and deliver the sealed envelope to a central collection point.

Faculty Surveys

It may be appropriate in a needs assessment to gather data from faculty members. Data may be related to acceptance of sexuality education and the relative importance a faculty ascribes to teaching sexuality education. Such data can be a powerful tool for making a case for sexuality education in the curriculum if faculty support is strong. It can also point out the need to do extensive preparation with a faculty before proposing sexuality education if support is weak.

Many issues come into play if faculty members are surveyed about program implementation and program priorities. Like all busy people, teachers are notorious for not completing surveys distributed via mail boxes. Care must be taken to keep the length of staff surveys to an absolute minimum. The best strategy is to

administer such instruments at a faculty meeting where all attendees complete and return the survey at one time. This ensures a
high response rate.

Secondary Sources

Prior to publishing needs assessment data, efforts should be made
to validate them through secondary sources, to determine whether
they are consistent with the "perceived" situation. Data can be
compared with existing records from other agencies such as pregnancy rates collected by local health departments.

Focus group interviews with various "expert" sources are another source of secondary data. Focus group interviews are carefully planned interactive discussions designed to obtain the attitudes
and opinions of a particular group about a particular topic in a
permissive, nonthreatening environment (Krueger, 1988). In materials development, they can provide indepth information about
the needs, interests, perceptions, beliefs, motivations and concerns
of the target audience. More important, they provide information
about why particular groups of people think and feel the way they
do. Focus groups may include faculty members who teach related
courses, counselors and school nurses, local health professionals
such as nurses and physicians who work in family planning clinics,
and students of various ages and backgrounds.

Validation by secondary sources can strengthen the "believabil-
ity" of the data, or, if data are inconsistent with perceptions, allow
generation of answers to explain the differences. For example,
professionals who work with high-risk adolescents may overesti-
mate the extent of "unhealthy" behavior within a teenage population. This can be pointed out as a possible explanation if incidence
rates are lower than some expected them to be.

Gaining Support for Needs Assessment

Legitimate apprehensions may be raised within schools by a needs assessment. School authorities may be concerned that results may reflect negatively on the school or the community. They may feel that the needs assessment process itself will raise expectations that cannot be met (i.e., if you ask about an issue, the expectation is that you intend to do something about it). They may be apprehensive of having to allocate scarce resources to health programs in competition with resource allocation for other areas of the curriculum. There may be a fear that some school personnel will develop a power base outside the school system which may challenge existing structures, procedures and resource allocations. There may also be a concern that the needs assessment will create premature expectations for program change.

Stakeholders may want to take action to "fix" something before results are published or before a well-thought-through program plan is developed. Ready answers for addressing apprehensions such as these may not be available; nevertheless, those considering a needs assessment should recognize the existence of these apprehensions and consider strategies for addressing them.

Convincing School Administrators

School administrators may be reluctant to allow access to students for data collection purposes, and for good reason. When data about sensitive issues are gathered, it is important to seek approval from authority and develop a broad support base prior to data collection. School authority is vested in boards of education, superintendents and other central office administrators. Approval, at least at the conceptual level, should be granted by these authorities.

Building administrators can be very sensitive because they are the ones who "catch the flak" when parents are dissatisfied (even in noncontroversial areas). Every effort should be taken to ensure that building administrators are afforded an opportunity to provide input and are kept fully informed of the process. The success of the data-gathering process may very well be dependent on the level of support these administrators provide.

Another "authoritative" strategy is to request that an advisory group that includes parents review survey instruments prior to data gathering. Sexuality education advisory groups can be comprised of teachers, administrators, health professionals, clergy, parents and students. When such a plan has been reviewed and recommended by a formally appointed group such as this, school board members and superintendents are more likely to approve the gathering of data about adolescent sexual attitudes and behaviors via a survey administered in school. In addition, an advisory committee can serve as an advocacy group in the community and can accurately represent needs assessment instruments and processes to parents and special interest groups.

Parental Consent

Schools legally do not have to inform parents when administering tests or surveys (e.g., parental permission is not needed for achievement tests or vocational interest surveys); however permission to gather data in this instance is more likely to be given if parents have been involved all along. Provisions for informing parents, allowing them to review survey instruments ahead of time, and allowing them to opt their children out should be included from the inception. Approval for inclusion of survey questions about controversial issues will more likely be given if sensitivity to parental concerns is perceived to be a high priority.

Steps for Completing a Needs Assessment

The list below outlines the steps involved in conducting a health/ sexuality education needs assessment. Many of these steps have been discussed in this chapter.

- Acquire needed resources for conducting the needs assessment, such as funding to cover costs, personnel to plan and implement the needs assessment and staff time to complete planning.
- Acquire assurance of administrative support at the highest levels.
- Develop a list of the questions the needs assessment should answer.
- Develop a list of potential sources of data, such as existing health department records, individuals with special knowledge to be interviewed, and populations to be surveyed.
- Create a master plan by matching questions to be answered with potential data sources.
- Select an instrument (e.g., survey instruments, interview schedules, questionnaires).
- Seek advice and generate support from members of the informal leadership, including building administrators. The formal decision-makers are central administrators and school board members; however, middle level and building administrators often command great influence since they ultimately have to implement decisions and take the heat from parents. It is essential to gain the support of these administrators before seeking central office or board permission to gather data. Informal decision-makers often have years of experiences at "getting things done" and may suggest procedures and processes that can save a researcher much time and effort. Finally, building administrators are more likely to be cooperative even

if reticent about the task if they feel that they have at least been consulted.

- Meet with individuals and leadership groups, as appropriate, to present the needs assessment plan.
- Include mechanisms for following protocols for use of human subjects who are minors (even though these may not be required for action research).
- Implement the needs assessment as planned.
- Analyze collected data and validate through secondary sources. Statistical procedures are usually accurate if data are collected via a good research design. Nevertheless, sometimes data are skewed. In order to assure that data are accurate (especially when related to controversial issues), they should be compared with data from secondary sources such as public health records or focus groups interviews of knowledgeable individuals to make sure they accurately reflect the actual situation before they are released.
- Develop a needs assessment report including (1) accepted standards of practice in the field, and (2) the status of the present program, including its positive qualities, as compared to standards of practice. Present a draft of the report to administrative leadership and revise as necessary.
- Present the final needs assessment report to the Superintendent and Board of Education.
- Broadly disseminate results to other audiences. Data are very expensive to collect and should be used to the greatest extent possible. Needs assessment data designed for use in schools can also be used by other agencies such as public health departments, voluntary and community health agencies and fellow researchers. Appropriate data dissemination can lead to program development or change in practice far beyond the original school or school system.

Conclusion

Can sexuality-related research be conducted in schools? The answer is yes, if adequate steps are taken to ensure that formal and informal leaders are sure that such research is needed and that the children in their care are adequately protected. In addition, leaders may be more receptive to the gathering of sexuality-related data if it is done as part of a broader health-related data-gathering process.

Parents, too, can be supportive of such research if they perceive that it can be of benefit to their children. There really is broadbased support for sexuality education in schools. Parents want their children informed about human sexuality and how best to protect themselves from harmful consequences. They naturally want programs that will best accomplish these aims. Parents also want to be kept informed about events and programs that involve their children.

Two strategies have proven most important to both data gathering and program implementation. The first is to keep parents informed and involved whenever possible. The second is to convene a committee representative of the key stakeholder groups in the community to review the human sexuality curriculum and/or any related data-gathering efforts. Both these strategies serve to generate community support and to convince the public that schools have nothing to hide. Use of action research findings as a basis for improving instruction also demonstrates that educators care about the students entrusted to them.

References

Best, J. W. 1977. *Research in education.* 3d. ed. Englewood Cliffs, NJ: Prentice-Hall.

Coles, R., and G. Stokes. 1985. *Sex and the American teenager.* New York: Harper Colophon Books.

Krueger, R. A. 1988. *Focus groups: A practical guide for applied research.* Newbury Park, CA: Sage Publications.

School Health Unit. 1992. *MEAP Health Test.* Lansing, MI: Michigan Department of Education.

Chapter 33

Changing Risk-Taking Behavior: Preliminary Conclusions from Research

Douglas Kirby, PhD, and Karin Coyle, PhD

O ver the years sexuality educators have developed a large and diverse set of goals for sexuality education. Given the high rates of unintended pregnancy and STD in this country and the increasing threat of HIV transmission, some sexuality educators have focused primarily upon the goal of reducing unprotected sexual intercourse that may lead to pregnancy, STD and HIV infection. In contrast, other sexuality educators have recognized the importance of reducing unprotected sex, but have maintained their beliefs that sexuality education should be far more comprehensive and should address the broader concerns of adolescent and adult sexuality (e.g., sexual development, interpersonal relationships, affection and intimacy, body image, gender roles). Despite the breadth of these goals, most research on sexuality education programs has focused upon the more limited goal of reducing unprotected sex.[1]

The primary purposes of this chapter are to review some of the research evidence regarding the effectiveness of sexuality education programs aimed at reducing unprotected sex and to identify key elements of the most promising sexuality education programs to date.

Research on Program Effectiveness

If one examines the history of research in the field of sexuality education and HIV/AIDS education, this is a particularly exciting and historical time for two reasons: (1) there are now about a dozen methodologically sound evaluations of specific sexuality education and HIV/AIDS education programs, and (2) several of these studies demonstrate reductions in sexual risk-taking behavior. Thus, for the first time, it is possible to reach preliminary conclusions about the important characteristics of effective programs.

Twelve evaluations of sexuality and/or HIV/AIDS prevention programs are reviewed here (see Figure 1 at the end of this chapter). All of these evaluations measured the programs' impact upon sexual behavior and all of them presented their results in professional journals, books, monographs and/or government reports.

---

[1] Studies define "unprotected intercourse" differently. Some of them, especially those concerned with pregnancy prevention, define unprotected intercourse as vaginal intercourse without any type of effective contraception. Other studies, especially those concerned with STD or HIV, define unprotected intercourse as either vaginal or anal intercourse without condoms. Still others consider anal intercourse too sensitive a topic either to discuss in class or to measure, and thus, implicitly, define unprotected intercourse as vaginal intercourse without condoms.

The programs include:
- *AIDS Prevention for Adolescents in School* (APAS) (Walter and Vaughan, 1993)
- The Jemmott curriculum (Jemmott, Jemmott and Fong, 1992)
- *Life Skills and Opportunities Curriculum* (LSO) (Baldwin-Grossman and Sipe, 1992)
- The Mathtech programs (Kirby, 1984)
- The *McMaster Teen Program* (Thomas et al., 1992)
- *Postponing Sexual Involvement* (PSI) (Howard and McCabe, 1990)
- *Reducing the Risk* (RTR) (Kirby, Barth, Leland and Fetro, 1991)
- The Schinke, Blythe and Gilchrest curriculum (hereafter referred to as the Schinke curriculum) (Schinke, Blythe and Gilchrest, 1981)
- *Sex Respect* (Weed, Olsen, DeGaston and Prigmore, 1992)
- *Teen Aid* (Weed, Olsen, DeGaston and Prigmore, 1992)
- *Teen Talk* (Eisen, Zellman and McAlister, 1990)
- *Values and Choices* (Weed, Olsen, DeGaston and Prigmore, 1992)

All but two of these studies evaluated a single program: Weed and colleagues (1992) evaluated the combined impact of *Sex Respect, Teen Aid,* and *Values and Choices* without fully examining the effects of each individual program. Kirby (1984) assessed the individual impact of 11 different sex education programs as part of the Mathtech study.

The programmatic goals of these curricula covered a broad spectrum. Several of the Mathtech programs, the *McMaster program* and the LSO program addressed sexuality broadly and included instruction on sexual development, relationships, problem solving/decision making, intimacy, pregnancy and parenting, gender roles and future goals. The Mathtech programs and LSO (but not the *McMaster program*) also discussed contraception. The remaining programs were very focused: *Sex Respect and Teen Aid* addressed abstinence only and excluded discussion of contraception. PSI, RTR, APAS, *Teen Talk,* the Schinke curriculum and the Jemmott program focused on reducing unprotected intercourse, either by delaying the onset of intercourse or increasing the use of protection against pregnancy, HIV or other STD.

Program length also varied across the curricula. The amount of instruction ranged from five hours to a quarter-long course; however, the majority of the curricula included between 10 and 15 sessions.

Of the 12 programs reviewed, five (APAS, Jemmott, PSI, RTR and Schinke) were found to be effective in reducing students' sexual risk-taking behavior by either delaying the onset of sexual intercourse (PSI and RTR) or increasing the use of contraception (APAS, PSI, Jemmott, RTR, Schinke). The evaluations of the remaining programs found either mixed results (*Sex Respect, Teen Aid, Teen Talk, Values and Choices*)[2] or no significant impact (LSO, Mathtech programs, the *McMaster program*).

---

[2]*Teen Talk, Sex Respect, Teen Aid* and *Values and Choices* were found to be somewhat effective for some subgroups and had either no impact or a negative impact on other groups. *Teen Talk* was found to be effective in delaying sexual onset among sexually inexperienced males, but not females. Moreover, one year following the program, females in the control group were *more* likely to use contraception consistently than were females in the program group.

Similarly, a recent evaluation of *Sex Respect, Teen Aid* and *Values and Choices* found no positive behavioral effects among sexually inexperienced middle or high school youth. There was, however, a significant positive effect for sexually inexperienced high school students whose pre-program values were not supportive of abstinence (Weed et al., 1992). It is difficult to understand the true effect of these four programs given these patterns of inconsistent results; thus, they are not discussed more fully in this chapter.

Among all 12 studies, half measured whether or not the programs hastened the onset of sexual intercourse; none of them—not even those that included instruction on contraception—increased the initiation of intercourse. Four of the evaluations measured the impact of the program on the frequency of sexual intercourse among youth who had already initiated intercourse; none of them increased the frequency of intercourse. Thus, these studies should reduce concerns that sex and/or HIV/AIDS education programs increase sexual activity.

Similarities Among Effective Programs

There are several common elements among the five effective programs that may be linked to their success. Each of these characteristics is discussed briefly below.

Used social learning theories as a foundation for program development. In general, the effective programs were based upon theoretical approaches that have been demonstrated to be effective in other health areas (e.g., social learning theory, cognitive behavioral theory, social influence theory).

When applied to sexual behavior, social learning theories posit that behavior such as delaying the initiation of intercourse or using protection will be affected by: (1) an understanding of what must be done to avoid sex or to use protection (knowledge), (2) a belief in the anticipated benefit of delaying sex or using protection (motivation), (3) the belief that particular skills or methods of protection will be effective (outcome expectancy) and (4) the belief that one can effectively use these skills or methods of protection (self-efficacy). Social learning theories give considerable recognition to the fact that youth gain these understandings and beliefs directly through education and indirectly through observation.

Cognitive behavioral theory is consistent with these elements of social learning theory and places considerable emphasis upon the importance of students personalizing the information through active learning methods of instruction and through curricular activities that are realistic for specific groups of students.

Finally, social influence theory addresses the societal and peer pressures upon youth and the importance of helping youth understand, recognize and resist those pressures.

Included a narrow focus on reducing sexual risk-taking behaviors. All five effective programs focused upon a small number of specific behavioral goals, such as delaying the initiation of intercourse, always using condoms, or consistently using some method of contraception. They devoted relatively little attention to other topics considered important in comprehensive sexuality education, e.g., relationships, dating, parenthood and gender roles.

Provided basic, accurate information. Although increasing knowledge was not the primary goal of these programs, all five provided basic information about the risks of unprotected intercourse and ways to avoid it. This information was rarely provided through textbooks, lectures or other didactic instruction; most commonly, students were involved in generating, obtaining and/or sharing the information. More specifically, the information was personalized through experiential activities (e.g., visiting or calling local family planning clinics) or active learning methods of instruction (e.g., games, videos, simulation activities).

Included activities that address the social and/or media influences on sexual behaviors. The effective programs discussed social pressures to have unprotected sex. This took several forms. Some programs addressed media influences; others discussed "pressure lines" that are typically used to get someone to have sex; others discussed social barriers to using protection. In all programs, strategies for responding to these pressures were identified, discussed and/or practiced.

Reinforced clear and appropriate values. The effective programs focused upon and continually reinforced specific values or norms such as postponing sex, avoiding unprotected intercourse, using condoms and avoiding high-risk partners.

These values and norms were tailored for the age and experience of the target population. For example, PSI was developed for middle school youth and focused upon delaying intercourse; given that the majority of middle school youth in the targeted areas had not yet initiated intercourse, the message was appropriate for most students. The Schinke curriculum and RTR, on the other hand, were designed for high school students and explicitly emphasized that students should avoid unprotected intercourse, either by not having sex or by using contraception if they did have sex. Finally, APAS and the Jemmott program targeted higher-risk youth, many of whom were already sexually active; both these curricula emphasized the importance of using condoms and avoiding high-risk situations.

The importance of promoting age- and experience-appropriate values and norms is demonstrated by the fact that PSI did not significantly decrease sexual intercourse or increase contraceptive use among those students who had initiated intercourse prior to the curriculum. Thus, PSI is a less effective curriculum for students who have already initiated intercourse. Similarly, there is no evidence presented that the Jemmott curriculum delayed the onset of intercourse. Thus, it may be less appropriate and less effective for those students who have not yet initiated intercourse.

Values or norms were reinforced throughout each curriculum in a variety of ways. For instance, a few programs provided accurate information on the rates of certain sexual behaviors (e.g., the proportion of students who have engaged in sexual intercourse in the past three months) and/or acceptability of engaging in sex or unprotected sex to emphasize that "not everyone is doing it," as is often assumed by teens. Additionally, in some programs, students were guided through decision-making processes to reach appropriate conclusions about sexual risk-taking behaviors. Students also identified "pressure lines" and then shared and modeled personal approaches for responding to these lines. Finally, norms were further reinforced by participation in roleplaying activities in which one person pressured another to engage in sex (or unprotected sex) and the latter person successfully resisted. Collectively, these types of activities helped establish or clarify standards of group behavior and may have given students the support or "permission" they needed to feel comfortable using the strategies outside the classroom.

Provided modeling and practice of communication or negotiation skills. All of the effective programs devoted some time to personal and social skills development (i.e., communication, negotiation and refusal skills). Typically, the programs provided information about the skills, modeled effective use of the skills and then provided some type of skill rehearsal and practice (e.g., verbal roleplaying and/or written practice). There were, however, variations in the quality of and amount of time devoted to skill practice.

Provided training for individuals implementing the program. All of the effective programs provided training for the teachers, peers, or outside staff who implemented the program. Trainings ranged from approximately six hours (Jemmott) to three days (RTR). In general, the training was designed to give teachers and staff background information on the programs as well as practice in using the teaching strategies included in the curricula (e.g., conducting roleplays, leading group discussions, etc.). This type of training has been found to enhance the quality of implementation and overall effectiveness of the programs (Connell, Turner and Mason, 1985).

In summary, the five effective programs share seven common characteristics:
1. theoretical grounding
2. narrow focus on reducing sexual risk-taking behaviors
3. information on the risks of unprotected sex and how to avoid those risks
4. instruction on social influences
5. reinforcement of individual values and group norms against unprotected sex
6. skill development activities
7. training for program implementors

Despite these commonalities, there is very little evidence regarding which of these factors contributes most to the overall success of the programs. We do know, for example, that knowledge is not sufficient to change behavior (Kirby, 1984). It would be premature, however, to assume that the positive behavioral effects resulted from the skill practice alone or from the instruction on social influences alone. To begin to understand which characteristics affect risk-taking behavior change, it is worthwhile to compare the characteristics of effective programs with those of programs that had no impact on student risk behaviors.

Differences Between Effective and Ineffective Programs

Because only three of the programs reviewed were found to have no behavioral impact (LSO, the Mathtech programs and the McMaster program), generalizations about the differences between the effective and ineffective programs must be made cautiously. However, there do appear to be several differences that distinguish the two groups. First, the ineffective curricula tend to be more comprehensive and less focused. That is, they cover a broader array of topics and discuss many values and skills, but fail to place particular emphasis on those specific facts, values, norms and skills necessary to avoid sex or unprotected sex (e.g., the risks of unprotected sex; reasons for avoiding unprotected sex; examining personal risks for HIV, other STD and pregnancy; how to avoid situations which might lead to unprotected sex; how to avoid unprotected sex if in a difficult situation; ways to reduce the embarrassment of obtaining condoms; how to use a condom).

Second, the less-effective curricula tend to use a general decision-making approach in which the decision-making steps are taught, the model is applied to important decisions, and students are implicitly instructed to make their own decisions. This approach is in contrast to the methods used in the effective curricula, which do not implicitly suggest that students make their own decisions. The effective curricula present a clear stand and emphasize clear behavioral values and norms.

For example, one of the ineffective curricula asks students to identify reasons for and against having sex, but does not process the discussion beyond the generation of ideas. In contrast, PSI (one of the effective programs) requires students to identify reasons why teens have sex, asks them to identify reasons students should wait to have sex, and then asks them to discuss possible consequences of each decision and to assess the validity of the reasons. Given this structure, the student groups invariably conclude that the reasons to wait are more valid.

The fact that all five of the effective programs focused upon specific behavioral values and norms (such as postpone sex or use a condom), in combination with the fact that none of the ineffective programs did so, strongly suggests that this focus may be an important characteristic of effective programs.

Components Found in Comprehensive Programs

In addition to the curricula discussed above, several programs have added other school and/or community components to the classroom curriculum and have found evidence that the programs reduce unprotected sex.

In a rural isolated South Carolina community, sexuality education was integrated into all grades in the schools; peer counselors were trained; the school nurse counseled students, provided male students with condoms and took female students to a nearby family planning clinic; and local media, churches and other community organizations highlighted special events. All of these school and community components reinforced the value of avoiding unintended pregnancy (Vincent, Clearie and Schluchter, 1987; Koo and Dunteman, 1990). After the program was implemented, the pregnancy rate for 14 to 17 year olds declined significantly for several years.

In Baltimore, the staff from an adolescent reproductive health clinic provided educational and counseling services, a peer education program and after-school group discussions in two nearby schools. In the clinic itself, the staff provided individual counseling, group counseling and contraceptive services (Zabin et al., 1986). Based on the evaluation data, there was a delay in the onset of sexual intercourse among those teens who had not yet initiated sex and an increase in the use of birth control among those who had. These increases were not evident in the comparison schools.

Finally, in Muskegon, Michigan, a high school implemented a strong sexuality education program, provided counseling on sexual issues, gave pregnancy prevention a high priority in the school-based clinic, and issued vouchers for free contraceptives at a nearby family planning clinic. Students in this school were more likely to use both condoms and oral contraceptives than were students in a comparison school (Kirby, Waszak and Ziegler, 1991).

It is encouraging that these three studies produced some positive evidence for reducing unprotected sex. Given their apparent success, their common elements are important. All three programs focused intensely upon preventing pregnancy or HIV and STD, included educational components in the schools, and reinforced those educational components with linkages to reproductive health services nearby in the community.

Although it appears both likely and logical that multiple components will be more effective than single components, these studies were not designed to determine which components were the most critical, nor even whether multiple components were more effective than a single effective educational component. Thus, the full impact of additional components is not yet known.

Cross-Sectional Studies

In addition to the evaluations of individual programs, seven additional studies have used national survey data to examine the impact of a cross-section of sexuality and HIV/AIDS education programs. The studies were based upon nationally representative surveys of adolescents and included questions both about participation in sexuality or HIV/AIDS education programs and about personal sexual experience. The primary purpose of the cross-sectional analyses was to examine the correlation between students' participation in sexuality and HIV/AIDS education programs and their sexual behaviors.

Five of the studies examined whether receipt of sexuality education was related to initiation of intercourse (Dawson, 1986; Furstenberg, Moore and Peterson, 1985; Ku, Sonenstein and Pleck, 1993; Marsiglio and Mott, 1986; Zelnik and Kim 1982). These studies produced some seemingly inconsistent results and suggest that the impact of instruction might vary with the topics covered and with the age of the students. A plausible interpretation of the findings is that instruction on abstinence and resistance skills may delay the initiation of intercourse, and instruction about contraception alone may hasten the onset of intercourse among younger teens, but not among older teens. Given that about 90 percent of all sexuality and HIV/AIDS education classes cover abstinence (Forrest and Silverman, 1989), these data indicate that sexuality and HIV/AIDS education, as they are taught today, do not hasten the onset of intercourse, even among younger teens.

Analyses of more recent HIV/AIDS education programs that included resistance skills training indicate that the programs may reduce the frequency of intercourse and the number of sexual partners (Anderson et al., 1990; Ku, Sonenstein and Pleck, 1992).

Several of the cross-sectional studies also examined the relationship between participation in a sexuality or HIV/AIDS education program and either contraceptive use or condom use specifically (Anderson et al., 1990; Dawson, 1986; Ku, Sonenstein and Pleck, 1992; Marsiglio and Mott, 1986; Zelnik and Kim, 1982). Four of the studies found a positive relationship between participation in a sexuality or HIV/AIDS education program and some, but not all, measures of contraceptive use. A fifth study (Anderson et al., 1990) failed to find a significant direct relationship between HIV/AIDS instruction and condom use.

Discussion

All of these studies, in combination, are most encouraging. Several specific programs have now been found to have significant behavioral impact in the desired direction. These programs tend to (1) be based upon social learning theory or its variations; (2) provide a good knowledge foundation and activities to help students personalize that knowledge; (3) emphasize explicit behavioral values, such as postponing sexual involvement or avoiding unprotected sex; (4) address social pressures; and (5) provide students with some opportunity for observing or practicing new skills. Additionally, several more comprehensive programs, which included sexuality education as a major component along with the provision of reproductive health services, provide further evidence for success in reducing unprotected sex among youth. This is a very different picture from that painted by research evidence available a decade ago.

As impressive as some of these results are, we should not allow ourselves to become complacent; none of these programs reduced unprotected sex to a tolerable level. Given the increasing threat of HIV/AIDS and the consequences of other STD and unintended pregnancy, we must continue to build upon what we have learned thus far and test new programs for reducing risk-taking behaviors using rigorous evaluations.

The results of these studies also pose a dilemma for sexuality educators. Traditionally, sexuality educators have been concerned with far more than reducing unprotected intercourse; rather, they have been concerned with sexuality broadly defined. The SIECUS guidelines well illustrate this breadth. And yet, those programs which were most effective at reducing unprotected intercourse were more narrowly focused and gave a clear message against unprotected sex. One possible solution to this dilemma is to prioritize all the important goals of sexuality education and target those goals of highest priority first, before addressing the others. Another approach is to embed effective components in larger, more comprehensive programs; further research is needed to determine whether this approach enhances or diminishes program effectiveness.

Similarly, the variation in the number of hours of instruction provided in the most effective curricula is somewhat perplexing. Three of the effective curricula were relatively short (five to six hours), which may lead one to conclude that five hours are sufficient for behavioral change. However, according to the research on instructional time needed to realize certain educational gains, it is surprising that a five- to six-hour program was able to effect change. For example, data from the School Health Education Evaluation indicated that approximately 12 hours are needed to achieve a small effect in health practices, and a greater number of hours are necessary to achieve a medium impact (Connell, Turner and Mason, 1985). Research conducted among African-American and Latino runaway youth in New York City showed that the strongest effects occurred after 22.5 to 30 hours of instruction (Rotheram-Borus et al., 1991). In addition, there is also evidence to suggest that sequential programming or periodic booster sessions in later years helps sustain and/or enhance positive outcomes (Botvin, Renick and Baker, 1983).

While definitive conclusions cannot yet be made regarding the specific number of hours that should be allotted to sexuality education programs, the evidence does suggest that stronger effects can be achieved with additional hours of instruction, and the effects can be sustained for longer periods of time with occasional booster or follow-up sessions in subsequent years.

Finally, with the demonstrated effectiveness of these programs to reduce unprotected sex, we should now devote more effort to their broad-scale replication. Given the limits on instructional time and the importance of these social issues, it seems more prudent to "go with a sure thing," and to modify effective curricula only as necessary to meet the special needs of particular populations, rather than starting from the ground up to develop new programs that may or may not be effective.

The percentage of adolescents throughout the country who receive effective programs to reduce high-risk behavior is unknown, but is probably small. Consequently, an enormous effort is needed among educators across the country to encourage the widespread adoption and implementation of effective programs.

Conclusions

There are many limitations in the research on programs to reduce unprotected intercourse and little is known with much certainty. Nevertheless, we have learned a great deal from past and current research:

- Changing adolescent sexual behavior is a daunting challenge and there are no "magic solutions" that dramatically reduce unprotected intercourse among all youth to acceptable levels.
- Sexuality and HIV/AIDS education programs throughout the country do not hasten the onset of sexual intercourse and may increase the use of contraception in general and/or condoms in particular.
- There are now several specific programs that delay the onset of intercourse, increase the use of protection against pregnancy or STD and HIV and/or reduce the number of sexual partners.
- Curricula based on appropriate behavior change theories (e.g., social learning theories) enhance the potential for altering students' risk-taking behaviors.

- To reduce unprotected sex, curricula must include more than just factual information and general decision-making and communication skills. Effective curricula should repeatedly emphasize and reinforce clear and acceptable values against unprotected sex, facilitate the development of group norms against unprotected sex, discuss social pressures to engage in unprotected sex, model very practical skills and behaviors to resist those pressures, and provide practice in those skills and behaviors.
- Individuals responsible for implementing sexuality education should receive adequate training directly related to the curricula they teach.
- Communities wishing to reduce unprotected sex should consider reinforcing effective educational components with other program components. Effective classroom curricula can be reinforced with schoolwide efforts designed to permeate the nonclassroom environment, such as peer programs, group discussion sessions, individual counseling, theatrical presentations, small media activities (posters, buttons, contests, school newspaper stories) and parent-education activities. Comprehensive programs to reduce unprotected sex can also improve students' access to health services through linkages with community-based health organizations.

Figure 1
Summary of Curricula Reviewed[1]

Program	Primary Focus	Effectiveness
AIDS Prevention for Adolescents in Schools (1993)	HIV/AIDS prevention; reduction of unprotected intercourse through abstinence or consistent use of condoms.	Increased consistent condom use; decreased intercourse with high-risk partners; increased involvement in monogamous relationships.
Jemmott, Jemmott, Fong (1992)	HIV/AIDS prevention; reduction of unprotected intercourse through abstinence or consistent use of condoms.	Decreased frequency of intercourse; decreased number of partners; increased condom use.
Life Skills and Opportunities (1992)	Delaying parenthood through abstinence or consistent use of contraception; preparing for future employment/goals.	No consistent and significant impact upon sexual and contraceptive behavior.
Mathtech Programs (1984)[2]	Reduction of unprotected intercourse through abstinence or use of contraception.	No consistent and significant impact upon sexual and contraceptive behavior.

[1] The curricula are listed in alphabetical order by title.
[2] This was a study of 15 different sexuality programs in the U.S. in early 1980s. Behavioral data were collected for 11 of the 15 programs.

Figure 1 (continued)
Summary of Curricula Reviewed

Program	Primary Focus	Effectiveness
McMaster Teen Program (1992)	Abstinence, sexual development, relationships, problem solving/decision making.	No significant impact upon sexual and contraceptive behavior.
Postponing Sexual Involvement (1990)	Abstinence only and human sexuality.[3]	Delayed initiation of intercourse; reduced frequency of intercourse; increased use of contraceptives among sexually inexperienced youth.
Reducing the Risk (1991)	Reduction of unprotected intercourse through abstinence or consistent use of contraception.	Reduced unprotected sex by delaying intercourse and increasing use of protection among sexually inexperienced youth.
Schinke, Blythe, Gilchrest (1981)	Reduction of unprotected intercourse through abstinence or consistent use of contraception.	Increased consistent use of contraception; decreased use of less effective birth control methods.

[3]The evaluation assessed the combined impact of PSI and a five-session human sexuality curriculum that included information on basic facts, decision making and family planning.

Figure 1 (continued)
Summary of Curricula Reviewed

Program	Primary Focus	Effectiveness
Sex Respect (1992)	Abstinence only.	Mixed results; no significant effects when evaluated alone; some positive effects among selected high school (but not middle school) students when data combined with two other programs (*Teen Aid* and *Values and Choices*).
Teen Aid (1992)	Abstinence only.	Mixed results; no significant effects when evaluated alone; some positive effects among selected high school (but not middle school) students when data combined with two other programs (*Sex Respect* and *Values and Choices*).
Teen Talk (1990)	Reduction of unprotected intercourse through abstinence or use of contraception.	Mixed results; no effect for total group; more effective among males than females.
Values and Choices (1992)	Abstinence only.[4]	Mixed results; no significant effects when evaluated alone; some positive effects among selected high school (but not middle school) students when combined with two other programs (*Sex Respect* and *Teen Aid*).

[4]The version of *Values and Choices* included in this evaluation did not include information on contraception.

References

Anderson, J. E., L. Kann, D. Holtzman, S. Arday, B. Truman and L. Kolbe. 1990. HIV/AIDS knowledge and sexual behavior among high school students. *Family Planning Perspectives* 22 (6): 252-255.

Baldwin-Grossman, J., and C. Sipe 1992. *Life skills and opportunities curriculum—summer training and education program: Report on long term impacts.* Philadelphia: Public/Private Ventures.

Botvin G., N. Renick and E. Baker. 1983. The effects of scheduling format and booster sessions on a broad-spectrum psychosocial approach to smoking prevention. *Journal of Behavioral Medicine* 6 (4): 359-379.

Connell D., R. Turner and E. Mason. 1985. Summary of findings of the school health education evaluation: Health promotion effectiveness, implementation and costs. *Journal of School Health* 55 (8): 316-321.

Dawson, D. A. 1986. The effects of sex education on adolescent behavior. *Family Planning Perspectives* 18 (4): 162-170.

Eisen, M., G. L. Zellman and A. L. McAlister. 1990. Evaluating the impact of a theory-based sexuality and contraceptive education program. *Family Planning Perspectives* 22 (6): 262.

Forrest, J. and J. Silverman. 1989. What public school teachers teach about preventing pregnancy, AIDS and sexually transmitted diseases. *Family Planning Perspectives.* 21 (2): 65-72.

Furstenberg, F., K. Moore and J. Peterson. 1985. Sex education and sexual experience among adolescents. *American Journal of Public Health* 75 (11): 1331-1332.

Howard, M., and J. McCabe. 1990. Helping teenagers postpone sexual involvement. *Family Planning Perspectives* 22 (1): 21-26.

Jemmott, J. B., L. S. Jemmott and G. T. Fong. 1992. Reductions in HIV risk-associated sexual behaviors among black male adolescents: Effects of an AIDS prevention intervention. *American Journal of Public Health* 82 (3): 372-377.

Kirby, D. 1984. *Sexuality education: An evaluation of programs and their effects.* Santa Cruz, CA: ETR Associates.

Kirby, D., R. Barth, N. Leland and J. Fetro. 1991. Reducing the risk: A new curriculum to prevent sexual risk-taking. *Family Planning Perspectives* 23 (6): 253-263.

Kirby, D., C. Waszak and J. Ziegler. 1991. Six school-based clinics: Their reproductive health services and impact on sexual behavior. *Family Planning Perspectives* 23 (1): 6-16.

Koo, H. P., and G. H. Dunteman. 1990. Research Triangle Institute. Reanalysis of changes in teenage pregnancy rates in Denmark area and comparison counties. Prepared for the Center for Chronic Disease Prevention and Health Promotion and the Centers for Disease Control and Prevention, Public Health Service, U.S. Department of Health and Human Services, Atlanta, Georgia.

Ku, L. C., F. L. Sonenstein and J. H. Pleck. 1992. The association of AIDS education and sex education with sexual behavior and condom use among teenage men. *Family Planning Perspectives* 24 (3): 100-106.

Ku, L. C., F. L. Sonenstein and J. H. Pleck. 1993. Factors influencing first intercourse for teenage men. *Public Health Reprints* 108 (6): 680-694.

Marsiglio, W., and F. Mott. 1986. The impact of sex education on sexual activity, contraceptive use and premarital pregnancy among American teenagers. *Family Planning Perspectives* 18 (4): 151-162.

Rotheram-Borus M., C. Koopman, C. Haignere and M. Davies. 1991. Reducing HIV sexual risk behaviors among runaway adolescents. *Journal of American Medical Association* 266 (10): 1237-1241.

Schinke, S., B. Blythe and L. Gilchrest. 1981. Cognitive-behavioral prevention of adolescent pregnancy. *Journal of Counseling Psychology* 28 (6): 451-454.

Thomas, B., A. Mitchell, M. Devlin, C. Goldsmith, J. Singer and D. Watters. 1992. *Small group sex education at school: The McMaster teen program.* In *Preventing Adolescent Pregnancy,* ed. B. Miller J. Card, R. Paikoff and J. Peterson, 28-52. Newbury Park, CA: Sage Publications.

Vincent, M., A. Clearie and M. Schluchter. 1987. Reducing adolescent pregnancy through school and community-based education. *Journal of the American Medical Association* 257(24): 3382-3386.

Walter, H., and R. Vaughan. 1993. AIDS risk reduction among urban minority high school students. Manuscript.

Weed, S., J. Olsen, J. DeGaston and J. Prigmore. 1992. *Predicting and changing teen sexual activity rates: A comparison of three title XX programs.* Salt Lake City, UT: The Institute for Research and Evaluation.

Zabin, L. S., M. B. Hirsh, E. A. Smith, R. Street and J. B. Hardy. 1986. Evaluation of a pregnancy prevention program for urban teenagers. *Family Planning Perspectives* 18 (3): 119-126.

Zelnik, M., and Y. Kim. 1982. Sex education and its association with teenage sexual activity, pregnancy, and contraceptive use. *Family Planning Perspectives* 16 (3): 117-126.

Appendixes

Position Statements on Sexuality Education

Many national associations develop and publish position statements on sensitive and/or controversial issues. These can be used as models for designing your own position statements, or as guides or background information when developing a sexuality education program in your community or district. As this publication goes to press, only two such associations—SIECUS and the National PTA Association—have updated position statements available for distribution.

The following associations are revising their position statements on sexuality education. They can be obtained by contacting the associations directly:

- Association for the Advancement of Health Education (AAHE), Reston, Virginia
- American Public Health Association (APHA), Washington, D.C.
- American School Health Association (ASHA), Kent, Ohio

National PTA

Position Statement on Adolescent Sexual Behavior and Pregnancy
(Adopted by the 1988 Board of Directors)

Studies show that parenthood during adolescence usually results in interrupted education, inadequate job skills, high unemployment, inadequate parenting skills and increased health risks to both mothers and babies. The National PTA urges PTAs to work for family life education curriculum that includes components on sexual restraint and responsibility and the risks associated with sexual activities and adolescent pregnancy.

While the rights and benefits of postponing sexual intercourse should be emphasized among the options available to adolescents, communities should be prepared to help with comprehensive prenatal care, education, job training and parenting skills. PTAs should encourage parents to discuss all aspects of human sexuality with their children and youth including family values and informed decision making related to responsible sexual behavior.

Reprinted with permission from the National PTA.

SIECUS Position Statements, 1991

Definition of Sexuality

Human sexuality encompasses the sexual knowledge, beliefs, attitudes, values and behaviors of individuals. It deals with the anatomy, physiology and biochemistry of the sexual response system; with roles, identity and personality; with individual thoughts, feelings, behaviors and relationships. It addresses ethical, spiritual, and moral concerns, and group and cultural variations.

Sexuality Education

Learning about sexuality goes on from birth until death. Parents, peers, schools, religion, the media, friends, and partners all influence learning about sexuality for people at all stages of life. All too often, conflicting, incomplete, or inaccurate messages are received, and this frequently causes confusion.

SIECUS endorses the right of all people to comprehensive sexuality education. Comprehensive sexuality education addresses the biological, sociocultural, psychological, and spiritual dimensions of sexuality from (1) the cognitive domain (facts, data and information); (2) the affective domain (feelings, values and attitudes); and (3) the behavioral domain (the skills to communicate effectively and to make responsible decisions).

SIECUS affirms that parents are—and ought to be—the primary sexuality educators of their children. SIECUS supports efforts to help parents fulfill this important role. In addition, SIECUS encourages religious leaders, youth and community group leaders, and health and education professionals to play an important role in complementing and augmenting the sexuality education received at home.

The Role of Schools

SIECUS endorses comprehensive sexuality education as an important part of the educational program in every grade of every school. SIECUS believes that classes conducted by specially trained educators complements the sexuality education given children by their families and by religious and community groups.

SIECUS recommends that school-based education programs be carefully developed to respect the diversity of values and beliefs represented in the community. Curricula and resources should be appropriate to the age and

---

Reprinted with permission from the Sex Information and Education Council of the United States, SIECUS Position Statement, updated version, 1991. Originally published in 1990. *SIECUS Report* 18 (2).

developmental level of the students. Professionals responsible for sexuality education must receive specialized training in human sexuality, including the philosophy and methodology of sexuality education. In addition, because sexuality issues touch on so many developmental issues of children and youth, SIECUS urges that all teachers from prekindergarten through twelfth grade receive a course in human sexuality.

Sexuality and Religion

SIECUS believes that organized religion can play a significant role in promoting an understanding of human sexuality as one of the most affirming expressions of equality, mutual respect, caring and love among human beings.

SIECUS therefore urges religious groups, and spiritual leaders, to involve themselves, not only in sexuality education, but also in discussion of the sexual concerns of all their constituents, including the young, the elderly, the ill and the physically or emotionally disabled.

SIECUS believes that it is important for religious institutions to minister and accord full religious participation to homosexual and bisexual women and men and to others living in nontraditional relationships.

Sexuality and the Media

SIECUS urges the media to present sexuality as a positive aspect of the total human experience, at all stages of the life cycle. Because of the media's powerful influence on all aspects of society, and particularly upon children. SIECUS believes the media has a responsibility to present matters relating to sexuality and accuracy without exploitation, and with sensitivity to diversity. SIECUS particularly condemns gratuitous sexual violence and all dehumanizing sexual portrayals.

Sexually Explicit Materials

SIECUS supports the use of a variety of explicit visual materials as valuable educational aids, to reduce ignorance and confusion, and to contribute to a wholesome concept of sexuality. Such visual materials need to be sensitively presented and appropriate to the age and developmental maturity of the viewer.

SIECUS supports the informed use of sexually explicit materials for educational and therapeutic purposes and also affirms adults' right of access to sexually explicit materials for personal use. SIECUS opposes legislative and judicial efforts to prevent the production and/or distribution of sexually explicit materials, insofar as such efforts endanger constitutionally guaranteed freedoms of speech and press. Furthermore, such actions could be used to restrict the appropriate professional use of such materials by sexuality educators, therapists and researchers. SIECUS supports the legal protection of minors from exploitation in the production of sexual materials.

SIECUS deplores violence, exploitation, and human degradation in our society and objects to the use of sexually explicit materials that condone or promote these negative values.

Sexual Health Care

SIECUS believes that all individuals have a right to information, education, and health care services that promote, maintain and restore sexual health. Providers of health services should (1) recognize the importance of sexual health for people of all ages and lifestyles; (2) understand how variations in health—such as those resulting from pregnancy, illness, disease, surgery, diet and medication—may affect an individual's sexuality; and (3) assess an individual's sexual functioning and sexual concerns as integral parts of his/her health care and make appropriate interventions and/or resources available.

SIECUS advocates that education about sexual health concerns, needs, and therapies be integrated into professional training in all health care fields, at both entry and continuing education levels.

Masturbation

Masturbation, or sexual self-pleasuring, is a natural and nonharmful behavior for individuals of all ages and both genders. It can be a way of becoming more comfortable with and/or enjoying one's sexuality by getting to know and like one's body. It can be a form of sexual pleasure and/or release, whether or not one is engaged in a sexual relationship.

SIECUS believes that because masturbation is a private behavior, no one should be made to feel guilty for choosing or not choosing sexual self-pleasuring. Parents and other adults should try to avoid making children feel guilty or ashamed about masturbating, but should teach them that this is appropriately done in private.

The Right to Choose Abortion

SIECUS deplores any attempts to undermine women's reproductive health rights. SIECUS believes that every woman, regardless of age or income, has the right to obtain an abortion under safe, legal, confidential, and dignified conditions, and at a reasonable cost. SIECUS support the 1973 Supreme Court decision (*Roe vs. Wade*) which affirmed the constitutional rights of a woman to seek and obtain an abortion. SIECUS advocates that no one be denied abortion services because of age, inability to pay, or other economic or social circumstances.

When making a decision to continue or terminate a pregnancy, SIECUS believes a woman is entitled to have full knowledge of the alternatives available to her and to have complete and unbiased information and counseling concerning the nature, the consequences, and the risks, both of the abortion procedure and of pregnancy and childbirth.

HIV/AIDS

HIV infection and AIDS are major public health concerns that affect all segments of the population. SIECUS calls upon society to accord the crisis the highest priority and to provide funds and strategies to combat this epidemic. Therefore, SIECUS strongly urges the following: (1) continued governmental and private support for research on prevention and treatment; (2) provision of adequate and confidential medical, financial, and social service resources for HIV-infected persons and their loved ones; (3) educational programs to enlighten the public about the scientific facts, as they become available, in order to allay unwarranted fears; (4) education at all age levels about the transmission of HIV and how to prevent such transmission; (5) opposition to discrimination against HIV-infected persons, including people with AIDS; and (6) opposition to mandatory testing and quarantine.

Contraceptive Care for Minors

SIECUS advocates that comprehensive information, education, and services in regard to contraception be readily accessible to all, regardless of gender, income or age. SIECUS believes that health care providers have a particular obligation to help adolescents understand the issues surrounding conception, contraception, parenthood and disease prevention.

SIECUS also believes that while it is generally desirable for parents to be involved in their children's contraceptive decisions, the right of every individual to confidentiality and privacy in receiving such information, counseling, and services is and should be paramount. SIECUS, accordingly, opposes any legislative or governmental attempts to infringe on this basic right and urges that all young people have ready access to low-cost prescription and nonprescription contraceptive methods.

Sexuality and Aging

Sexual feelings, desires and activities are present throughout the life cycle. SIECUS supports the right of older adults to receive sexuality education, sexual health care, and opportunities for socializing and sexual expression. SIECUS advocates the continued education of professionals, support staff, and family members concerning the sexual feelings, attitudes and behaviors of older individuals.

Sexual Orientation

SIECUS believes that an individual's sexual orientation—whether bisexual, heterosexual or homosexual—is an essential quality of humanness and strongly supports the right of each individual to accept, acknowledge and live in accordance with his/her orientation.

SIECUS advocates laws guaranteeing civil rights and protection to all people regardless of their sexual orientation and deplores all forms of prejudice and discrimination against people based on their sexual orientation.

Sexuality and Persons with Disability

SIECUS advocates that persons with a physical and/or mental disability receive sexuality education, sexual health care and opportunities for socializing and sexual expression.

SIECUS urges social agencies and health care delivery systems to develop policies and procedures that will insure that their services and benefits are provided on an equal basis to all persons without discrimination because of disability. SIECUS advocates educational and training programs for health care workers and family members to enable them to understand and support the normal sexual development and behavior of persons with disabilities. SIECUS advocates that both those who are disabled and those who care for them should receive information and education to deter sexual abuse or exploitation.

Sexual Exploitation

SIECUS believes that sexual relationships should be consensual, with participants developmentally, physically, and emotionally capable of understanding the significance of the interaction. SIECUS condemns all exploitative and coerced sexual acts and behaviors including rape, incest, sexual harassment and sexual abuse. SIECUS believes that forcing or coercing anyone to participate without consent in a sexual act is by definition exploitative and unethical.

SIECUS supports intensified efforts to prevent sexual exploitation through information and education programs, as well as through laws to deter and punish such acts. SIECUS also supports treatment programs to help victims of sexual exploitation. SIECUS advocates research to increase the understanding of the causes and effects of various forms of sexual exploitation and the development of appropriate treatment programs for offenders.

Criteria for Assessing Sexuality Education Curricula

The following criteria have been developed by the Association for Sexuality Education and Training (ASSET) in Oak Harbor, Washington. These criteria were designed to be used by sexuality educators in assessing existing curricula, or as a guide in developing new curricula. The guidelines can also be used to assess sexuality or HIV/AIDS curricula.

High-quality curricula:
1. *Are sequential, kindergarten through grade 12.* They provide knowledge and skills that build logically on earlier learning.
2. *Are educationally sound in form.* They reflect what is known about intellectual/academic development (including reading level and reasoning ability), visual appearance (print size, illustrations, layout), and learning style (with interactive, varied teaching methods that will be effective for kinesthetic, visual, and aural learners, right and left-brain thinkers).

3. *Are age-appropriate in content.* They reflect what is known about child and adolescent psychosocial and sexual development, behavior and experience. They should be anticipatory (e.g., learning about puberty should begin at least a year before young people begin puberty...by age eight at the latest).
4. *Are medically/scientifically/legally accurate.* They contain demonstrable facts. Hypotheses and theories are identified as such, and emphasized only if shared by most experts in a field.
5. *Are comprehensive.* Taking number 3 (above) into account, they cover, in the course of 13 years' schooling:
- Sexual anatomy and physiology:
  — male and female endocrine and reproductive systems including the physiology of menstruation
  — physical changes of puberty
  — sexual development from conception to death
  — physiology of pregnancy and fetal development
  — sexual response system including the physiology of erection and ejaculation

- Sexual health and safety:
  — acne
  — hygiene
  — fibrocystic breasts
  — dysmenorrhea
  — ovarian cysts
  — sexual exploitation
  — teen and unplanned pregnancy ·
  — gynecomastia
  — sexually transmissible diseases including HIV/AIDS
  — sexual dysfunction
  — cancers of the breast and reproductive system
  — infertility
  — birth defects/miscarriage/prematurity/low birthweight
  — testicular torsion
  — the meaning and consequences of each of the above, and the prevention, detection, treatment, coping/survival/recovery, and accessing resources for each

- Sexual aspects of social and emotional health:
  — family
  — friendship

- infatuation
- marriage
- gender identify
- body image
- love
- dating
- intimacy
- gender roles
- self-esteem
- affection
- commitment
- fantasy
- pornography
- touch
- attraction
- monogamy
- abstinence
- prostitution
- sexual and dating values
- peer and media pressure
- gender orientation
- law and policy re: sexual issues
- sexual decision making
- sexual stereotyping and prejudice
- communication, including how to say no and how to take no for an answer

6. *Teach relatively universal values.* Specifically, they:
- Encourage/enhance family communication.
- Are tasteful/tactful.
- Are respectful of learners (not condescending or patronizing).
- Promote intimacy, tenderness, caring, and honesty within all relationships (parent-child, friends, boyfriend-girlfriend, spouses).
- Foster thoughtful, sober decisions about sex, taking care not to foster fear about sex, nor to foster casual, flippant sexual decision making.
- Encourage students to abstain from sexual intercourse, taking care not to express a laissez-faire, casual attitude toward teen sexual activity, nor to express a punitive or degrading attitude toward nonvirgin teens.
- Encourage risk-reduction for teens who do have sex (or who will in the next ten years), without condoning their choice, and taking care not to convey a

punitive, they-deserve-what-they-get attitude toward these students, nor to suggest that condoms (for HIV/STD protection) or any contraceptives (for pregnancy protection) are 100 percent safe, easy "excuses" for casual sex.

- Foster healthy, positive body image, taking care not to promote the attitude that bodies are unclean or embarrassing, nor to infer that modesty or a desire for privacy are unimportant or juvenile.
- Express respect for diverse family constellations, teaching that healthy families are those which support their members' physical and emotional well-being, taking care not to assume homogeneity of family constellation or to characterize any one family pattern as the only model of "normalcy," nor to disparage the nuclear family as outmoded.

7. *Address controversial issues* (as opposed to avoiding them). When they do, they take care to:
- Clearly distinguish facts from beliefs/values.
- Evenhandedly, sensitively describe a full range of community values.
- Encourage students to find out the beliefs of their families and faiths (if they have one).
- Teach respect for all families and individuals, taking care not to promote any one value position. (Any position would offend or hurt some students' families on these issues.) Thus, for example, they:
  — Dispel sex role stereotyping (substituting accurate information), promoting respect for both males and females and their abilities, taking care not to express judgment of those who do not choose traditional roles, nor to denigrate those who do choose traditional roles.
  — Dispel sexual orientation stereotyping (substituting accurate information) and support the self-esteem of gay and lesbian students, without sanctioning their becoming sexually active, and taking care not to assume that all students/families are heterosexual, nor to encourage homosexual experimentation.
  — Discourage teen parenting, and convey the medical, legal and sociological facts, taking care not to express a laissez-faire, casual attitude toward teen parenting, nor to convey a punitive or degrading attitude toward teen parents.
  — Respect differing beliefs about premarital sex (for adults), taking care to convey the risks involved in casual or brief sexual relationships, without implying that premarital sex is wrong or sinful, nor suggesting that it is good or acceptable.

— Respect differing beliefs about contraception and abortion, conveying the medical, legal and sociological facts, without suggesting that everyone should use either or that they are risk-free, always easy or right, nor suggesting that nobody should use them, or that they are dangerous, always difficult or wrong.

— Respect differing beliefs about masturbation, artificial insemination, in-vitro fertilization, conveying the medical, legal and sociological facts about each, without expressing judgment of people who engage in or partake of each, nor expressing judgment of those who choose not to.

8. *Are "teacher-friendly."* They are well-organized with clear, thorough instructions. They are as self-contained as possible (minimal assembly time). Ideally, they are inexpensive enough that each building, if not each teacher, can have a copy/set.

Sexual Behavior Among High School Students— United States, 1990

Since the 1970s, sexually transmitted diseases (STDs) (including human immunodeficiency virus infection and Acquired Immune Deficiency Syndrome), unintended pregnancies, and other problems that result from sexual activity have increased among adolescents in the United States (Hayes, 1987; PHS, 1991). For example, approximately 1 million adolescent girls become pregnant each year (Hayes) and 86 percent of all STDs occur among persons ages 15 to 29 (CDC, 1991). This article presents self-reported data from 1990 about the prevalence of sexual intercourse, contraceptive use, condom use, and STDs among U.S. high school students.

The national school-based *Youth Risk Behavior Survey* is a component of CDC's Youth Risk Behavior Surveillance System that periodically measures the prevalence of priority health-risk behaviors among youth through comparable national, state and local surveys (Kolbe, 1990). A three-stage sample design was used to obtain a representative sample of 11,631 students in grades 9 through 12 in the fifty states, the District of Columbia, Puerto Rico and Virgin Islands. Students were asked if they had ever had sexual intercourse and if they had had sexual intercourse during the three months preceding the survey

Reprinted from *Morbidity and Mortality Weekly Report* 40 (51/52): 885-888. Atlanta, GA: Centers for Disease Control and Prevention.

(i.e., were currently sexually active). Students also were asked to identify the method, if any, they or their partner used to prevent pregnancy the last time they had sexual intercourse; if they had ever been told by a doctor or nurse that they had an STD; and if they or their partner used a condom to prevent STDs the last time they had sexual intercourse.

Of all students in grades 9 through 12, 54.2 percent reported ever having had sexual intercourse; 39.4 percent reported having had sexual intercourse during the three months preceding the survey. Male students were significantly more likely than female students to ever have had sexual intercourse (60.8 percent and 48.0 percent, respectively) and to have had sexual intercourse during the three months preceding the survey (42.5 percent and 36.4 percent, respectively). Black students were significantly more likely than White or Hispanic students to ever have had sexual intercourse (72.3 percent, 51.6 percent, and 53.4 percent, respectively) and to have had sexual intercourse during the three months preceding the survey (53.9 percent, 38.0 percent, and 37.5 percent, respectively). The percentage of students ever having had sexual intercourse and having had sexual intercourse during the three months preceding the survey increased significantly by grade of student from ninth through twelfth grade.

Among currently sexually active students, 77.7 percent of female and 77.8 percent of male students used contraception (birth control pills, condoms, withdrawal, or another method) during last sexual intercourse. White female students (81.1 percent) were significantly more likely than Black (71.4 percent) and Hispanic (62.6 percent) female students to have used contraception.

Four percent of all students reported having had an STD. Black students (8.4 percent) were significantly more likely to report having had an STD than White (3.1 percent) or Hispanic (3.5 percent) students. Among currently sexually active students, 49.4 percent of male students and 40.0 percent of female students reported that they or their partner used a condom during last sexual intercourse.

Editorial Note: National health objectives for the year 2000 include efforts to reduce the proportion of adolescents who have engaged in sexual intercourse to less than 15 percent by age 15 and less than 40 percent by age 17 (objectives 5.4, 18.3, and 19.9) and among sexually active, unmarried persons less than 19 years of age, increase to at least 90 percent the proportion who use contraception (objective 5.6) (PHS, 1991). To reach these objectives, the percentage of students who report ever having had sexual intercourse will have to be reduced substantially, and the percentage of sexually active students who use contraception will have to increase by 16 percent.

Two of the national health objectives are to increase the use of condoms to 60 to 75 percent among sexually active, unmarried persons age 15 to 19 during last sexual intercourse (objectives 18.4a,b and 19.10a,b) (PHS). To reach these objectives, sexually active students must increase their use of condoms by 50 percent.

These changes in behavior will require interventions that integrate the efforts of parents, families, schools, religious organizations, health departments, community agencies and the media. Education programs should provide adolescents with the knowledge, attitudes and skills they need to refrain from sexual intercourse (CDC, 1990). For adolescents who are unwilling to refrain from sexual intercourse, programs should help to increase the use of contraceptives and condoms.

References

Centers for Disease Control and Prevention. 1990. Premarital sexual experience among adolescent women—United States, 1970-1980. *Morbidity and Mortality Weekly Report* 39:929-932.

Centers for Disease Control and Prevention. 1991. *Division of STD/HIV prevention annual report.* Atlanta, GA: U.S. Department of Health and Human Services, Public Health Service.

Hayes, C. D., ed. 1987. *Risking the future: Adolescent sexuality, pregnancy, and childbearing.* Vol. 1. Washington, DC: National Academy Press.

Kolbe, L. J. 1990. An epidemiological surveillance system to monitor the prevalence of youth behaviors that most affect health. *Health Education* 21:44-48.

Public Health Service. 1991. *Healthy people 2000: National health promotion and disease prevention objectives—full report, with commentary.* DHHS Publication No. (PHS) 91-50212. Washington, DC: U.S. Department of Health and Human Services.

National Coalition to Support Sexuality Education

The National Coalition to Support Sexuality Education (NCSSE) was founded by SIECUS in the spring of 1990 and consists of over seventy national nonprofit organizations, many of which are noted role models and initiators in promoting the health, education and social concerns for our nation's youth. NCSSE is committed to the mission of assuring that comprehensive sexuality education is provided for all children and youth in the United States by the year 2000. These organizations represent a broad constituency of social workers, teachers, church leaders, advocates, physicians and other health care professionals and child development specialists. Combined, the agencies that make up the coalition reach the needs of more than 20 million young people.

The Alan Guttmacher Institute
New York, New York
(212) 254-5656
Washington, D.C.
(202) 296-4012
fax: (202) 223-5756

American Association on Mental
   Retardation
Washington, D.C.
(202) 387-1968
(800) 424-3688
fax: (202) 387-2193

American Association for Marriage
and Family Therapy
Washington, D.C.
(202) 452-0109
fax: (202) 223-2329

American Association of School
Administrators
Arlington, Virginia
(703) 875-0720
fax: (703) 841-1543

American Association of Sex
Educators, Counselors and
Therapists
Chicago, Illinois
(312) 644-0828
fax: (312) 644-8557

American College of Obstetricians
and Gynecologists
Washington, D.C.
(202) 863-2579
fax: (202) 488-0787

American Counseling Association
Alexandria, Virginia
(703) 823-9800
fax: (703) 823-0252

American Home Economics
Association
Alexandria, Virginia
(703) 706-4600
fax: (703) 706-4663

American Library Association
Chicago, Illinois
(800) 545-2433
fax: (312) 280-3255

American Medical Association—
Department of Adolescent
Health
Chicago, Illinois
(312) 464-5575
fax: (312) 464-5842

American Nurses Association
Washington, D.C.
(202) 554-4444
fax: (202) 554-2262

American Orthopsychiatric
Association
New York, New York
(212) 354-5770
fax: (212) 354-5770

American Psychological Association
Washington, D.C.
(202) 336-5500
fax: (202) 336-6063

American Public Health
Association
.Washington, D.C.
(202) 789-5600
fax: (202) 789-5681

American School Health
Association
Kent, Ohio
(216) 678-1601
fax: (216) 678-4526

American Social Health Association
Research Triangle Park, North
Carolina
(919) 361-8400
fax: (919) 361-8425

Association for the Advancement of
Health Education
Reston, Virginia
(703) 476-3437
fax: (703) 476-9527

Association for Sexuality Education
and Training
Olympia, Washington
(206) 754-1556

Association for Voluntary Surgical
Contraception
New York, New York
(212) 561-8054
fax: (212) 779-9439

Association of Reproductive Health
Professionals
Washington, D.C.
(202) 466-3825
fax: (202) 466-3826

Association of State and Territorial
Directors of Public Health
Education
Phoenix, Arizona
(602) 640-2198
fax: (602) 640-2557

ASTRAEA National Lesbian
Action Foundation
New York, New York
(212) 529-8021
fax: (212) 982-3321

Blacks Educating Blacks About
Sexual Health Issues
Philadelphia, Pennsylvania
(215) 546-4140
fax: (215) 546-6107

B'nai B'rith Women
Washington, D.C.
(202) 857-1370
fax: (202) 857-1380

Catholics for a Free Choice
Washington, D.C.
(202) 986-6093
fax: (202) 332-7995

The Center for Population Options
Washington, D.C.
(202) 347-5700
fax: (202) 347-5700

Child Welfare League of America
Washington, D.C.
(202) 638-2952
fax: (202) 638-4004

Children's Defense Fund
Washington, D.C.
(202) 628-8787
fax: (202) 622-3550

Coalition on Sexuality and
Disability, Inc.
New York, New York
(212) 242-3900

Commission on Family Ministries
and Human Sexuality
National Council of the
Churches of Christ
New York, New York
(212) 870-2074

ETR Associates
Santa Cruz, California
(408) 438-4060
fax: (408) 438-4284

Girls Incorporated
New York, New York
(212) 689-3700
fax: (212) 683-1253

The Hetrick-Martin Institute, Inc.
New York, New York
(212) 633-8920
fax: (212) 989-6845

The Institute for Advanced Study of
Human Sexuality Alumni
Association, Inc.
San Diego, California
(619) 276-3616

The Latina Roundtable on Health
and Reproductive Rights
New York, New York
(212) 206-1090
fax: (212) 206-8093

Midwest School Social Work
Council
Morton, Illinois
(309) 266-5859

National Abortion Rights Action
League
Washington, D.C.
(202) 973-3000
fax: (202) 973-3098

National Association of Counties
Washington, D.C.
(202) 393-6226
fax: (202) 393-2630

National Association of County
Health Officials
Washington, D.C.
(202) 783-5550
fax: (202) 783-1583

The National Association for Equal
Opportunity in Higher
Education
Washington, D.C.
(202) 543-9111
fax: (202) 543-9113

National Association of School
Psychologists
Silver Springs, Maryland
(301) 608-0500
fax: (301) 608-2514

National Coalition of Advocates for
Students
Boston, Massachusetts
(617) 357-8507
fax: (617) 357-9549

National Council on Family
Relations
Minneapolis, Minnesota
(612) 781-9331
fax: (612) 781-9348

National Council of State
Consultants for School Social
Work Services
Des Moines, Iowa
(515) 281-3782

National Education Association
Health Information Network
Washington, D.C.
(202) 822-7570
fax: (202) 822-7775

National Family Planning and
Reproductive Health
Association
Washington, D.C.
(202) 628-3535
fax: (202) 737-2690

National Gay and Lesbian Task
Force
Washington, D.C.
(202) 332-6483
fax: (202) 332-0207

National Information Center for
children and Youth with
Disabilities
Washington, D.C.
(800) 999-5599
fax: (703) 893-1741

National League for Nursing
New York, New York
(212) 989-9393
fax: (212) 989-3710

National Lesbian and Gay Health
Foundation
New York, New York
(212) 740-7320
fax: (212) 740-7329

National Medical Association
Washington, D.C.
(202) 347-1895
fax: (202) 842-3293

National Mental Health Association
Alexandria, Virginia
(703) 684-7722
fax: (703) 684-5968

National Native American AIDS
Prevention Center
Oakland, California
(510) 444-2051
fax: (510) 444-1593

National Network of Runaway and
Youth Services
Washington, D.C.
(202) 783-7949
fax: (202) 783-7955

National Organization on
Adolescent Pregnancy,
Parenting and Prevention
Bethesda, Maryland
(301) 913-0378
fax: (301) 913-0380

National Resource Center for Youth
Services
Tulsa, Oklahoma
(918) 585-2986
fax: (918) 592-1841

National School Boards Association
Alexandria, Virginia
(703) 838-6756
fax: (703) 683-7590

National Urban League
New York, New York
(212) 310-9000
fax: (212) 593-8250

National Women's Law Center
Washington, D.C.
(202) 328-5160
fax: (202) 328-5137

Planned Parenthood Federation of
America
New York, New York
(212) 261-4633
fax: (212) 247-6269

Religious Coalition for Abortion
Rights
Washington, D.C.
(202) 543-7032
fax: (202) 543-7820

Sex Information and Education
Council of the United States
New York, New York
(212) 819-9770
fax: (212) 819-9776

Society for Adolescent Medicine
New York, New York
(212) 920-6783
fax: (212) 920-5289

Society for Behavioral Pediatrics
New York, New York
(212) 920-6783
fax: (212) 920-5289

Society for Public Health
Education, Inc.
Berkeley, California
(510) 644-9242
fax: 644-9319

The Society for the Scientific Study
of Sex
Mount Vernon, Iowa
(319) 895-8407
fax: (319) 895-6203

Religious Education Department—
Unitarian Universalist
Association
Boston, Massachusetts
(617) 742-2100

United Church Board for
Homeland Ministries
Cleveland, Ohio
(216) 736-3800
fax: (216) 736-3263

U.S. Conference of Mayors/
U.S. Conference of Local
Health Officers
Washington, D.C.
(202) 293-7330
fax: (202) 293-2352

University of Pennsylvania
Philadelphia, Pennsylvania
(215) 898-5195
fax: (215) 898-4399

YWCA of USA
New York, New York
(212) 614-2700
fax: (212) 677-9716

Values Statement on Sexuality Education

W hen supporters can clearly articulate the values that underlie their programs, the great majority of the community can more readily recognize their own views embodied in the goals of contemporary sexuality education.

Statements can be distributed to parents and others at community meetings, used in mailings to parents, and provided to the media to ensure that local media have a full understanding of supporters' position.

A statement of values should not be embedded in dense paragraphs. The following sample statement may not be appropriate for every situation, but the values outlined in it do appear to be common values that many people share. The statement offers a good starting place for community planning groups to begin generating their own program values.

Sample Values Statement on Sexuality Education

The goal of (your group's) sexuality education program is to ensure that individuals have access to the knowledge, attitudes and skills to make and act

From *The Front Lines of Sexuality Education: A Guide to Building and Maintaining Community Support*. Peter Scales. Santa Cruz, CA: ETR Associates, 1984.

upon effective personal decisions that promote their sexual, reproductive and mental health within their own value systems. In so doing, (your group) helps people avoid unplanned and ill-timed sexual and reproductive consequences.

In order to meet that goal, (your group) is committed to offering educational programs, professional training and technical assistance to others consistent with the above. The following principles guide our sexuality education programs:

1. Sexuality is an integral part of personality and human relationships.
2. Sexuality education is a lifelong process that begins in the home and family.
3. Sexuality education includes formal education programs as well as the informal learning which comes from the influence of peer groups, cultural heritage, messages of the media, advertising, religious teachings and daily exposure to social custom and changing technologies.
4. Sexuality is more than sexual activity.
5. Sexuality is but one aspect of human development and should be considered in the whole context of physical, psychological, spiritual and social growth, as well as in the context of the wider cultural milieu.
6. All persons need basic information about sexuality, as well as formal opportunities to examine their own and others' values regarding love and sexuality. They need to build skills in making decisions, solving problems, and communicating with others about sexuality and reproductive health.
7. Adequate self-esteem is the key to making healthy, ethical and effective sexual and fertility-related decisions.
8. Each sexual decision has an effect or consequence.
9. Sexual decisions should support the dignity, equality and worth of each individual, and should take into account the medical, psychological and social effects of sexual activity.
10. Sexual and reproductive decisions should be based on self-esteem and respect for others; knowledge of one's own values; appreciation of one's family, cultural and religious heritage; and respect for democratic principles.
11. It is wrong to exploit or force someone into an unwanted sexual experience or to knowingly spread disease. It is undesirable to bring a child into the world that one cannot adequately care for.
12. Young adolescents usually are not ready for sexual intercourse because of its medical, psychological and social ramifications.
13. Parenthood involves many responsibilities that adolescents are usually unable to assume, and capabilities they usually do not possess.
14. Parents are the primary sexuality educators of their children, although not the sole educators, nor necessarily the best transmitters of information. Social institutions such as schools, churches and family planning centers

should supplement, not supplant parents in this role.

15. Everyone benefits when children, of their own free will, can discuss issues related to sexual and reproductive health with their parents and other valued adults.
16. While formal programs of sexuality education can have a significant effect upon sexual values and behavior, they are just one of many influencing factors, and their impact should not be expected to be immediate, direct and dramatic.
17. Parents, as well as other people in the community, should be involved in planning formal sexuality education programs.
18. Participation in sexuality education programs and activities should be voluntary.
19. Education staff should be highly trained, participate in regular continuing education programs, and abide by accepted standards of professional ethics.
20. In a democratic society, a wide range of values and beliefs about sexuality is to be expected and respected.

Contributors

Nancy Abbey is a family life and sexuality educator with many years of experience working with youth from diverse ethnic groups. As a teacher of a program for school-age mothers and fathers and as a community health educator, she has spent much of her professional life in direct contact with young people and their struggle for individuality and connection. As a project coordinator at ETR Associates, she has been closely involved with the development of curriculum and classroom materials that help students to be seen both as individuals and as members of various cultures. She worked with Manuel Casas and Claire Brindis, in collaboration with an expert panel of educators, to establish guidelines and materials for multiculturally relevant and appropriate family life and sexuality education. She is coauthor of *Family Life Education in Multicultural Classrooms* (ETR Associates, 1990) and *Entering Adulthood: Coping with Sexual Pressures* (ETR Associates, 1989).

Warren J. Blumenfeld, MEd, is the editor of *Homophobia: How We All Pay the Price* (Beacon Press, 1992). He wrote *AIDS and Your Religious Community: A Hands-On Guide for Local Programs* (1992) for the Unitarian Universalist Association and is coauthor, with Diane Raymond, of *Looking at Gay and Lesbian Life* (Beacon Press, 1988; Second Edition, 1993). He is a multicultural/ diversity workshop facilitator for educational, business, religious, community and government organizations; a longtime steering committee member and trainer for the Gay, Lesbian and Bisexual Speakers Bureau of Boston; a former outreach educator for the Public Broadcasting Service series "The AIDS Quarterly"; a former classroom teacher and peripatologist at Perkins School for the Blind, where he coauthored the school's *Sex Education and Family Life Curriculum;* and the founder of the National Gay Student Center of the National Student Association in Washington, D.C.

Peggy Brick, MEd, is Director of Education for Planned Parenthood of Greater Northern New Jersey. Formerly a high school teacher of human behavior, she now trains professionals throughout the nation in positive approaches to teaching about sexuality. The current president of the Sex Information and Education Council of the United States (SIECUS), she is coauthor of a number of teaching manuals, including *Positive Images: A New Approach to Contraceptive Education; Teaching Safer Sex; Bodies, Birth and Babies: Sexuality Education in Early Childhood Programs;* and *Healthy Foundations: Developing Policies and Programs Regarding Children's Learning about Sexuality.*

Claire Brindis, DrPH, is Director, Center for Reproductive Health Policy Research, Institute for Health Policy Studies and Associate Adjunct Professor in the Department of Pediatrics, Division of Adolescent Medicine, at the University of California, San Francisco. She has had a longstanding interest in the field of adolescent pregnancy prevention, and has conducted policy analyses and written several publications on the subject, including *Adolescent Pregnancy and Parenting in California: A Strategic Plan for Action* (University of California, San Francisco) and *Adolescent Pregnancy Prevention: A Guidebook for Communities* (Stanford University Health Promotion Center). She has conducted a number of evaluation studies including evaluations of a comprehensive program for pregnant and parenting adolescents, nine school-based health centers, and programs related to the use of case management services as a strategy for the reduction of adolescent pregnancy.

Karen Cancino, LCSW, has worked in the area of adolescent pregnancy and parenting for over 15 years. She developed the Information, Referral and Service Center for Pregnant Girls in San Mateo County, California, during the 1970s. She has also been a counselor in the teen parent program for the Oakland Unified School District and served as a supervisor of case managers in Family Service Agency of San Francisco's Teenage Pregnancy and Parenting Project (TAPP). She is currently a program coordinator for the School Health Programs Department, San Francisco Unified School District, where she is responsible for health-related counseling and support services as well as parent and community involvement. She has also worked extensively in the fields of child and adolescent sexual abuse and foster parenting.

Chwee Lye Chng, PhD, is a professor at the University of North Texas. He has published extensively in the areas of human sexuality and HIV/AIDS education with a special focus on sexual behaviors of young adults. At the university he teaches an undergraduate and a graduate sexuality education course. He has been involved in teacher preparation for the past 14 years.

Kay Clark is an editor with ETR Associates, Santa Cruz, California. She has worked in the area of health education since 1984 and has edited numerous ETR publications, including books, pamphlets and the national journal *Family Life Educator.*

Elma Phillipson Cole recently completed over seventeen years with The Salvation Army Eastern Territory where her primary task was to develop and encourage the use of programs for young people. Included were *Bridging the Gap Between Youth and Community Services,* a lifeskills education program partially supported by a Federal grant; *Getting to Know You* on personal relationships with the opposite sex; *Can I Protect Myself from AIDS?* and others on prevention of child sexual abuse and substance use by youth; and a series on education for parenthood with Federal support. She currently serves on the board of directors for SIECUS. She completed her undergraduate degree at Berea College, Kentucky, and her masters at the University of Chicago School of Social Service Administration. She is an accredited member of the National Association of Social Workers and of the Public Relations Society of America.

Karin Coyle, PhD, is currently the associate director of research at ETR Associates. Her background includes training in health science as well as social science research methodology and evaluation. She has been involved in the evaluation of health promotion programs for over ten years. Currently, she is co-directing a five-year, federally funded HIV, STD and pregnancy prevention project for high school youth. She is also conducting several local-level evaluations of comprehensive substance use and HIV/AIDS prevention programs.

Betsy Crane, MA, is executive director of Planned Parenthood of Tompkins County in Ithaca, New York. She has worked in the area of mental health and sexuality education since 1972, including work as a teen outreach worker/educator for a rural family planning program, as a leader of mother/daughter and mother/son retreats for parents and puberty-age youth, as a trainer for human services workers, and as a curriculum consultant on elementary sexuality education for public schools. Her special interests have been in the area of using marketing concepts in human services and ending oppression, including heterosexism.

Daniel Daley is Public Policy Associate at the Alan Guttmacher Institute in Washington, D.C., where he concentrates on federal policy concerning youth sexuality and reproductive behavior-related issues, including sexuality education, adolescent pregnancy and HIV/AIDS prevention. In addition, he has recently conducted research on public funding of contraceptive, sterilization and abortion services; the coverage of reproductive health services in private-sector insurance; and the extent to which women are served and family planning organizations are involved in the Ryan White CARE Act HIV/AIDS early intervention program.

Judy C. Drolet, PhD, CHES, FASHA, received her secondary teaching credential and master's degree in health science from San Francisco State University and her doctorate in health education from the University of Oregon. She is a Certified Health Education Specialist and Fellow of the American School Health Association. She began teaching human sexuality and health education courses in 1975. Recent course emphases include sexuality education methods and issues, professional preparation, mental health and foundations of health education. She has been elected to the national boards of directors of the Association for the Advancement of Health Education and the American School Health Association and national vice-president of Eta Sigma Gamma. She received national distinguished service awards from the American School Health Association and Eta Sigma Gamma and has served on the advisory board of the *Family Life Educator* since 1986. She is coauthor of *Are You Sad Too? Helping Children Deal with Loss and Death* (ETR Associates, 1993), and *Sexuality Education Curricula: The Consumer's Guide* (ETR Associates, 1994).

Joyce V. Fetro, PhD, CHES, is Acting Supervisor of School Health Programs for the San Francisco Unified School District. In that role, she is responsible for planning and implementing the district's comprehensive school health program. She received her doctoral degree in health education from Southern Illinois University, with an emphasis on evaluation, instrument development and research methods. Her experience in health education spans more than twenty years, including three years as a curriculum specialist, thirteen years as a middle school teacher, two years as a university instructor, and three years conducting research and evaluation studies about the effectiveness of substance use, pregnancy and HIV/AIDS prevention programs. She is author of *Step by Step to Substance Use prevention: The Planning Guide for School-Based Programs* (ETR Associates, 1991) and *Personal and Social Skills: Understanding and Integrating Competencies Across Health Content* (ETR Associates, 1992) and is coauthor of *Are You Sad Too? Helping Children Deal with Loss and Death* (ETR Associates, 1993).

Jodie B. Rieger Fischer, MS, LCSW, is a clinical social worker, currently working at the University of California, San Francisco Medical Center. Previously, she was a case manager at Family Service Agency of San Francisco's Teenage Pregnancy and Parenting Project (TAPP), where she provided comprehensive case management services—counseling pregnant and parenting adolescents and helping them to receive health, educational and social services. While at TAPP, she was part of a team that developed and implemented a pilot citywide Teen GAIN program, the liaison from TAPP to the Medical Center's Young Women's Clinic. She served on the Board of Directors of the San Francisco Chapter of the National Association of Social Workers for three years.

Susan Giarratano, EdD, CHES, is a professor in the Health Science Department of California State University, Long Beach. She is the minority health consultant for *KCET-PBS*, Public Television for Southern and Central California. She has television credits for her work on substance use prevention, nutrition, sexuality, Alzheimer's disease, and smoking cessation and prevention. She is the principal investigator and projector director for two federally funded research demonstration programs in comprehensive school health education. She is the author of *Entering Adulthood: Looking at Body Image and Eating Disorders* (ETR Associates, 1991) and coauthor of *Entering Adulthood: Examining Drugs and Risks* (ETR Associates, 1990) and *Into Adolescence: Avoiding Drugs* (ETR Associates, 1990.)

Lenora E. Johnson, MPH, CHES, is currently serving as director of the Professional Health Education Network for the Association for the Advancement of Health Education. She has worked as a health education specialist for such organizations as the American Cancer Society and the American Public Health Association. Along with classroom teaching experience, she has served as a community health education trainer and has worked in Atlanta with the

Emory AIDS Training Network and the Carter Presidential Center. She also serves as the project director for "Cultural Sensitivity and Awareness: A Crucial Component to the Success of Comprehensive School Health Education," a project funded by the U.S. Department of Education.

Douglas Kirby, PhD, director of research at ETR Associates, has directed nationwide studies of adolescent sexual behavior, sexuality education programs, school-based clinics, and direct mailings of STD/AIDS pamphlets to adolescent males. He coauthored research on the *Reducing the Risk* curriculum which substantially reduced unprotected intercourse, both by delaying the onset of intercourse and increasing the use of contraception. In a recent review of the literature, he assessed the characteristics of school-based programs which effectively reduce adolescent sexual risk-taking behavior. Over the years, he has also authored or coauthored numerous volumes, articles and chapters both on these programs and on methods of evaluating them. Currently he is principal investigator or co-principal investigator for several studies of school-based programs designed to reduce unprotected intercourse.

Lynn Leight, RN, PhD, is founder/director of 17 national private, not-for-profit, freedom of choice, Sex Health Education (SHE) Centers providing complete gynecological and counseling care. As a Certified Sexuality Educator/Counselor (AASECT) and initiator of the mandated Dade County Schools sexuality education curriculum, she lectures, trains and consults on issues related to sexuality education and women's health care. She is an assistant professor at the University of Miami, School of Family Medicine and School of Nursing. She is also an advisory board member to the Jackson Memorial Hospital Rape Treatment Center and serves on a wide variety of boards concerned with adolescence and sexuality education. In addition to contributing to many professional journals and popular magazines, she is the author of *Raising Sexually Healthy Children* (New York: Rawson Associates, 1988).

David K. Lohrmann, PhD, CHES, is presently project director for the Academy for Educational Development in Washington, D.C., and is involved in evaluating HIV/AIDS prevention programs. Most recently he was director of curriculum for the Troy School District in Troy, Michigan, and project director for the Troy Community Coalition to Prevent Alcohol and Drug Abuse. He was responsible for supervising the development of the school health promotion program in Troy beginning in 1987. Earlier in his career he developed and taught sexuality education at the high school level and supervised implementation of a middle school program for the West Bloomfield

Schools in Orchard Lake, Michigan. He has taught related professional preparation courses at Syracuse University, the University of Georgia and Wayne State University, and recently sat on a committee for the Michigan Department of Education to revise the guidelines to statutes governing the teaching of sexuality education. He has given numerous presentations on sexuality and HIV/AIDS education and has published articles on these topics.

Robert J. McDermott, PhD, is professor and chairman of the Department of Community and Family Health, University of South Florida College of Public Health. He has authored or coauthored more than one hundred papers in health education, and has written extensively in the areas of human sexuality education and substance use prevention. He has designed and delivered workshops in school and community health education for national and international audiences. He is active in the American Public Health Association, the American School Health Association, the Association for the Advancement of Health Education, the American Psychological Association and other professional societies. He is the coauthor of two widely used collegiate texts: *Connections for Health* and *Health Education Evaluation and Measurement: A Practitioner's Perspective.*

Warren L. McNab, PhD, FASHA, is a professor of health education at the University of Nevada at Las Vegas. He has served on the boards of directors of the Association for the Advancement of Health Education and the American School Health Association and has received several excellence in teaching awards at UNLV. He teaches university-level teacher preparation courses on human sexuality and has written extensively in the area of adolescent sexuality and health.

Deborah A. Miller, PhD, CHES, is the health coordinator and an associate professor at the College of Charleston in Charleston, South Carolina. She received the SCAHPERD Founder's Award of the Teaching Excellence at the college level and was also named the Outstanding Health Educator in South Carolina in 1992. She is on the advisory board of the *Family Life Educator* and has spent the past ten years teaching, conducting workshops and doing research in the field of sexuality education. In addition, she is the author of three books that are targeted toward meeting the special needs of adolescents: *Coping with Your Sexual Orientation* (Rosen Publishing, 1990), *Coping with Incest* (1992), which was selected by the New York Public Library as one of the best books for the Teen Age in 1993, and *Coping When a Parent Is Gay* (1993).

Lynne Muccigrosso is a private educational consultant in sexuality education with Stiggall and Associates of Los Gatos, California. She entered the field of sexuality education in the early 1970s as a social worker for a rehabilitation workshop serving persons with disabilities. She served as Disability Project Coordinator at Planned Parenthood of Santa Clara County in San Jose, California, for over eight years. She has been in private practice since 1985 and divides her time between teaching a community college course in human sexuality for mildly disabled young adults, facilitating training courses for teachers and other staff in how to teach sexuality education, offering one-to-one and group sexuality education through the California Department of Developmental Services, writing, coproducing films, and politically advocating for the rights of persons with disabilities to receive appropriate sexuality education and counseling.

James J. Neutens, PhD, CHES, FASHA, is director of the Division of Education in the Department of Obstetrics and Gynecology at the University of Tennessee Graduate School of Medicine in Knoxville, Tennessee. He is the health education editor for the *Journal of School Health* and is the author of *Healthy Sexual Development,* a set of two sexuality education books, one for middle school and one for senior high school students. He is a certified sexuality educator and counselor and is a Diplomate of the American Board of Sexology.

Kenneth M. Newbury, PhD, is a national speaker and trainer for school systems and organizations. He is coauthor of *Discover Skills for Life,* a junior high curriculum, and the *Discover Life Skills* workbooks. He directs the award-winning student assistance program in Toledo, Ohio, which was named "The Outstanding Student Assistance Program" in the country in 1986. He is a past Ohio district PTA educator of the year. He is a board member for the National Association of Leadership for Student Assistance Programs and president of the Ohio Association of Student Assistance. He is also the codirector of an America's Pride group that has presented workshops and performed for the White House and U.S. Department of Education. He received his doctorate in community psychology from the University of Michigan.

Roberta J. Ogletree, HSD, CHES, is an assistant professor in the Department of Health Education and Recreation at Southern Illinois University at Carbondale. Her 16 years of experience as a sexuality educator have been at the high school, junior college and university levels. A graduate of Indiana University, she is an active member of the American School Health Association

Council on Sexuality Education. Her research has focused on sexual coercion and sexuality education curriculum evaluation.

Laura B. Pfefferkorn, MAT, is a graduate research assistant in the Department of Health Promotion and Education, School of Public Health, University of South Carolina. She specializes in school-based sexuality education curriculum development and instructional techniques.

Charles E. W. Regin, PhD, is an assistant professor of health education at the University of Nevada at Las Vegas. He has been a coordinator of K-12 comprehensive health education programs at five different school districts. He served as Elementary Health Education Specialist at San Francisco State University and at the University of Wisconsin at Whitewater and is currently responsible for preparing elementary education majors to teach comprehensive health education issues. He has conducted numerous workshops and given presentations on elementary health education methods at local, state and national meetings and has authored articles on health methods.

Cory L. Richards is Vice President for Public Policy and director of the Washington office of the Alan Guttmacher Institute, where he has been a policy analyst since 1975. A 1970 graduate of Yale, he was an appointed Public Member of the Reproductive Freedom Task Force, National Commission on the Observance of International Women's Year in 1976 and has served on the boards of directors of the National Abortion Rights Action League, National Family Planning and Reproductive Health Association, National Abortion Federation and Sex Information and Education Council of the United States (SIECUS).

Barbara A. Rienzo, PhD, CHES, FASHA, is an associate professor in the Department of Health Science Education, University of Florida. She has taught human sexuality education to undergraduate and graduate students and provided training for teachers in Florida and throughout the southeast for the past 17 years. Her publications focus on establishment and implementation of sexuality education and school-based primary care, and program development and training. She recently was appointed to Florida Governor Lawton Chiles' 11-member Red-Ribbon Panel on AIDS to consider ways the state could facilitate prevention of and improve treatment of persons with HIV/AIDS. In 1993, she was appointed to the Florida Department of Education Task Force on Minimum Guidelines for HIV Prevention and Human Sexuality Education by Commissioner Betty Castor.

Martha R. Roper, MA, holds a masters degree in family and community relations from Columbia University Teachers College in New York. She is a high school health teacher in the St. Louis, Missouri, metropolitan area and a teacher educator at Webster University. A regular guest on KMOX radio, she is also a speaker nationwide. She is featured in the video series "Family Life Education: Understanding Sexuality with Martha Roper" for grades 2 through 4 and for middle school students. She was named National Health Education Professional of the Year by the Association for the Advancement of Health Education in 1992.

Peter C. Scales, PhD, is the St. Louis-based Director of National Initiatives for the Center for Early Adolescence, School of Medicine, University of North Carolina at Chapel Hill and a research associate professor of social work at the University of North Carolina at Chapel Hill. Prior to these positions, he directed the Anchorage Center for Families and chaired the Alaska Governor's Commission on Children and Youth, for which he received the 1988 U.S. Administration for Children, Youth, and Families Commissioner Award. He has published more than 125 articles, books, chapters and other publications, including *The Sexual Adolescent* (with Sol Gordon and Kathleen Everly), *The Front Lines of Sexuality Education: A Guide to Building and Maintaining Community Support, An Analysis of U.S. Sex Education Programs and Evaluation Methods* (with Douglas Kirby and Judith Alter), *A Portrait of Young Adolescents in the 1990s* and *Windows of Opportunity: Improving Middle Grades Teacher Preparation.*

Selene D. Skonie-Hardin, MPH, CHES, is a middle school health teacher at Liberty Bell Middle School in Johnson City, Tennessee. She was a member of the state curriculum development task force on HIV/AIDS education in Tennessee and helped develop the human sexuality curriculum in the Johnson City School System. The curriculum was chosen as a Tennessee State Model Program for three consecutive years (1990–1992) and was part of a collaborative effort with the Johnson City Medical Center Hospital and Science Hill High School which was distinguished with the 1992 Outstanding Achievement Award by the National Organization for Pregnancy and Parenting, Inc.

Murray L. Vincent, EdD, CHES, is a professor of health promotion and education in the School of Public Health at the University of South Carolina, Columbia. He has taught sexuality education to groups ranging from preadolescents to the elderly, and has authored numerous articles and book chapters on health education topics with particular emphasis on sexuality behaviors. He is known nationally as the principal investigator and originator of the South Carolina School/Community Sexual Risk Reduction Model which documented the efficacy of education in reducing teen pregnancies.

Ellen Wahl, MA, is Director of Program at Girls Incorporated (formerly Girls Clubs of America). An applied anthropologist and health educator by training, she has worked for twenty years in program development, applied research, fundraising and policy analysis, trying to effect change in the health care and educational systems and to fight discrimination, particularly in the areas of gender and disability. She is a research associate of the Center for Policy Research, where she conducted research in the 1970s on innovative schools, vocational education and nursing home reform, and has worked over the years with such organizations as the Educational Priorities Panel, the National Commission on Resources for Youth, the National Center for Service Learning, the New York Academy of Medicine's Growing Healthy project, the Young Adult Institute, Xerox Learning Systems and the Horace Mann-Lincoln Institute of Teachers College.

Pamela M. Wilson, MSW, is a nationally known sexuality education consultant and trainer. She has led sexuality education programs with youth of all ages and with parents. As a consultant, she assists organizations around the country in the development of sexuality and life-planning programs for children, adolescents and parents. She trains educators, counselors and youth development professionals in the areas of sexuality, adolescent pregnancy prevention and managing diversity. A social worker by training, she is certified as a sexuality educator by the American Association of Sex Educators, Counselors and Therapists (AASECT) and is a member of the board of directors of the Sex Information and Education Council of the United States (SIECUS). She is the author of several sexuality education publications, including *When Sex Is the Subject: Attitudes and Answers for Young Children* (ETR Associates, 1991).

Susan N. Wilson, MS, is the executive coordinator of the New Jersey Network for Family Life Education, a program of the Rutgers University's School of Social Work. Since 1985, she has managed the activities of a statewide resource, advocacy and technical assistance organization whose mission is to enhance comprehensive family life, sexuality and HIV/AIDS education in the public schools. As a member and vice-president of the New Jersey State Board of Education in the 1980s, she headed the effort for mandatory family life education in the public schools. As a result of these efforts, New Jersey became the second state in the nation to adopt such a public policy. In recent years, she has provided technical assistance on policy and curriculum development and teacher training to Idaho, Utah and Wisconsin.

William L. Yarber, HSD, CHES, FASHA, is professor of health education and graduate program coordinator in the Department of Applied Health Science, Indiana University, Bloomington. He is a former public school sexuality and health science teacher and has taught at the University of Minnesota and Purdue University. In 1991 he received the President's Award for Distinguished Teaching at Indiana University, and was named the Scholar of the Association for the Advancement of Health Education. He has published numerous sexuality-related research and pedagogical articles in professional journals and is the author of four school curricula on HIV/AIDS and STD. He chaired the National Guidelines Task Force that produced the *Guidelines for Comprehensive Sexuality Education, K-12.* He is the 1993/94 President of the Society for the Scientific Study of Sex and a former member of the Board of Directors of SIECUS.

Susan A. Yeres, EdD, is the director of MacCormick Center, a residential treatment facility for juvenile offenders. She has worked for over 18 years in the field of juvenile justice with young men and women, both in the community and in treatment programs. As a trainer, she has consulted with the National Center for Juvenile Justice and the National Council of Juvenile and Family Court Judges in such areas as adolescent development, sex offender treatment and case management. She is currently on the board of directors for Planned Parenthood of Tompkins County and chairs the Education Committee.

Michael Young, PhD, is a professor in the program in health sciences at the University of Arkansas at Fayetteville, Arkansas. He has authored more than 180 publications, most in the areas of drug education and sexuality education. Since 1988, he has directed the "Be A Winner" program, which involves law enforcement officers in drug education; three other drug education projects; and a major project in sexuality education. The nationally known *Living Smart* curriculum series, which promotes sexual abstinence as a positive choice for young people, originated with this project. The project has received five national awards from the U.S. Department of Health and Human Services for "Outstanding Work in Community Health Promotion," citations from then-governor Bill Clinton, and two awards from the State Department of Health.

Index